Growth Factors: Structure and Function

Growth Factors: Structure and Function

Proceedings of the
British Society for Cell Biology – The Company of Biologists Limited Symposium
Glasgow, April 1985

Organized and edited by

Colin R. Hopkins

(Department of Medical Cell Biology, University of Liverpool)

and

R. Colin Hughes

(National Institute for Medical Research, London)

SUPPLEMENT 3   1985
JOURNAL OF CELL SCIENCE
Published by THE COMPANY OF BIOLOGISTS LIMITED, Cambridge

Typeset, Printed and Published by
THE COMPANY OF BIOLOGISTS LIMITED
Department of Zoology, University of Cambridge, Downing Street,
Cambridge CB2 3EJ

© The Company of Biologists Limited 1985

JOURNAL OF CELL SCIENCE SUPPLEMENTS

All supplements are available free to subscribers to *Journal of Cell Science* or may be purchased separately from The Biochemical Society Book Depot, P.O. Box 32, Commerce Way, Colchester CO2 8HP, UK

GROWTH FACTORS: STRUCTURE AND FUNCTION

CONTENTS

Continued overleaf

Contents

TRANSDUCTION OF GROWTH FACTOR SIGNALS

J. Cell Sci. Suppl. 3, 1–9 (1985)
Printed in Great Britain © The Company of Biologists Limited 1985

EPIDERMAL GROWTH FACTOR: BIOLOGY AND RECEPTOR METABOLISM

GRAHAM CARPENTER

Department of Biochemistry and Division of Dermatology, Vanderbilt University School of Medicine, Nashville, Tennessee 37212, U.S.A.

SUMMARY

Epidermal growth factor (EGF) is a small (M_r 6045) protein that stimulates cell proliferation in cell culture systems and in intact animals. This growth factor has been isolated from rodents and human material and probably exists in nearly all animal species. In humans EGF has been detected in many body fluids and receptors for the growth factor are also ubiquitous. While the mitogenic activity of EGF has been most frequently reported, it clearly has other functions, such as the inhibition of gastric acid secretion, that are unrelated to mitogenic responses. Correspondingly, receptors for EGF have been localized on cells that are rapidly proliferating and cells that are essentially non-proliferating. Nevertheless, it has not been possible to define experimentally the biological function(s) of the endogenous EGF present in the intact animal.

Studies of the mechanism of action of EGF have concentrated, to date, on the plasma membrane receptor that specifically binds this ligand. The receptor is undoubtedly the first cellular component that mediates the eventual biological response(s) of the cell to this extracellular signal. Studies of the EGF receptor have shown that this molecule, which has no subunit structure, functions not only in ligand recognition, but also may produce an intracellular 'second message'. The receptor contains a protein kinase activity that is activated by the binding of EGF and it is this enzymic function that may yield the critical 'second messenger', by phosphorylation of an intracellular protein. Although intracellular targets of this EGF-sensitive protein kinase have been identified, it has not been possible to demonstrate their relevance as regulatory mediators of EGF activity.

INTRODUCTION

The metabolism of the EGF receptor has been studied in some detail. The 'turnover' rate or half-life of the receptor has been determined in the presence and absence of EGF. Interestingly, EGF rapidly produces a nearly 10-fold increase in the rate of degradation of the receptor. This result suggests that internalized EGF–receptor complexes are probably co-ordinately degraded within lysosomal compartments. In most cell types there does not appear to be substantial recycling of the EGF receptor. While EGF has a dramatic effect on the rate of degradation of the EGF receptor, it does not influence the biosynthesis of receptor molecules. The receptor is synthesized as a 160 000 M_r immature glycoprotein that is eventually processed, on the oligosaccharide moieties, to yield a mature 170 000 M_r receptor species. Studies using inhibitors of glycosylation, i.e. tunicamycin, show that the non-glycosylated form of the receptor (M_r 130 000) does not exhibit significant capacity for [125I]EGF binding and also does not seem to have an active protein kinase.

EGF STRUCTURE AND OCCURRENCE

Epidermal growth factor was originally isolated from the male mouse submaxillary gland by Cohen (1962). The molecule was later sequenced (Savage, Inagami & Cohen, 1972) and location of three intramolecular disulphide bonds was determined (Savage, Hash & Cohen, 1973). The mouse EGF contains 53 amino acid residues and disulphide bonds between residues 5 and 20, 14 and 31, and 33 and 42 produce three disulphide loops in the secondary structure of the molecule. In the mid-1970s EGF was detected (Starkey, Cohen & Orth, 1975) and isolated from human urine (Cohen & Carpenter, 1975). Work from Gregory's (1975) laboratory demonstrated the equivalence of human EGF and urogastrone, a hormone capable of inhibiting gastric acid secretion, and also provided the primary amino acid sequence of the human form of this growth factor. During the mid-1980s the structure of other EGF-like molecules has been produced. Transforming growth factors (TGF), type α or I have been isolated from rat and human material (Marquardt *et al.* 1983; Marquardt, Hunkapiller, Hood & Todaro, 1984; Derynck *et al.* 1984) and their sequences determined. These proteins are structurally analogous to the EGF sequence, compete with [^{125}I]EGF in radioreceptor assays, and produce EGF-like biological responses in sensitive cells. Transforming growth factors, type α or I, seem to be produced, unlike EGF, as a result of cell transformation, but are also found in foetal fluids. Also, the TGFs are antigenetically distinct from EGF. Recently, the deduced sequence of a protein encoded by the vaccinia virus genome has been demonstrated to be related to the sequence of EGF (Blomquist, Hunt & Barker, 1984; Reisner, 1985; Brown, Twardzik, Marquardt & Todaro, 1985). While the function of this viral protein is unknown, it is secreted into the media by infected cells.

In all these members of the EGF family of polypeptides, the positioning of cysteine residues is strictly conserved. This suggests that the relative positioning and size of the three disulphide loops are the most conserved aspect of the structure found in this group of related growth factors.

In humans, EGF has been detected by radioimmunoassay in nearly all body fluids. These results are summarized in Table 1. The site(s) of synthesis of EGF in humans is not clear. While there is evidence to indicate synthesis in Brunner's glands and the submandibular glands (Heitz *et al.* 1978), it is unlikely that the hormone is produced at one primary site. In the mouse, EGF is made predominantly in the submaxillary glands (Cohen, 1962), but secondary sites of synthesis are evident when the submaxillary glands are removed (Byyny, Orth, Cohen & Doyne, 1974).

With the exception of the circulating cells of the haemopoietic system, receptors for [^{125}I]EGF seem to be present on a great many different cell types (Carpenter & Cohen, 1979). In some cases receptors are present on both proliferating and non-proliferating cells. In the skin, for example, the proliferating stem cells of the epidermis, the basal cells, are enriched for EGF receptors. Abundant receptor levels also seem to be present on the non-proliferating smooth muscle cells of the arrector pilorum and the modified epithelial cells of the eccrine sweat gland (Nanney, Magid, Stoschek & King, 1984).

MECHANISM OF EGF ACTION

At the cellular level, EGF stimulates the proliferation of quiescent cells of many cell types (Carpenter & Cohen, 1979). The studies that have been carried out in cell culture systems suggest that the biochemical mechanism that alters or regulates the proliferative state of cells is complex. Clearly, the first step in this mechanism involves the formation of EGF–receptor complexes on the cell surface. Under physiological conditions, the plasma membrane receptors for EGF are rapidly saturated (within 30–60 min) when the growth factor is added to quiescent cells (Carpenter & Cohen, 1976a). During this period of time two events occur in regard to EGF–receptor complexes and either or both may be involved in intracellular signalling.

First, binding of EGF to the receptor activates the protein kinase activity that is intrinsic to the receptor (Carpenter, King & Cohen, 1979). The EGF receptor, as deduced from the cDNA sequence (Ullrich *et al.* 1984), is a transmembrane protein that crosses the membrane once. Therefore, the receptor can be depicted as having two domains. One part of the molecule protrudes from the membrane to form a domain on the cell surface that contains the binding site for EGF and EGF-like ligands. The other portion of the receptor is located on the cytoplasmic side of the plasma membrane facing the intracellular environment. This cytoplasmic domain contains the tyrosine-specific protein kinase activity of the EGF receptor. The receptor is thought to be a complex example of an enzyme (protein kinase) subject to allosteric regulation (growth factor binding). How this regulation of kinase activity is transmitted from one side of the membrane to the other is not known. Likewise, it remains unclear, despite searches in many laboratories, which substrates of receptor-kinase activity are important to the process of mitogenesis.

Table 1. *Presence of EGF in human fluids*

Source	Approximate concentration (ng ml^{-1})	Reference
Colostrum	130–800	Beardmore *et al.* (1983)
	300	Read *et al.* (1984)
Milk	80	Starkey & Orth (1977)
	69	Moran *et al.* (1983)
	30	Read *et al.* (1984)
	20–111	Beardmore *et al.* (1983)
Urine	88	Starkey & Orth (1977)
	30	Gregory *et al.* (1977)
Seminal fluid	36	Elson *et al.* (1984)
Saliva	9	Starkey & Orth (1977)
Pancreatic juice	2	Hirata *et al.* (1982a)
Cerebrospinal fluid	0·2	Hirata *et al.* (1982b)
Amniotic fluid	0·3	Barka *et al.* (1978)
Plasma (platelet-rich)	0·3	Oka & Orth (1983)
(platelet-poor)	N.D.	

Co-ordinate with activation of protein kinase activity, EGF–receptor complexes are subject to a complex series of events that involve the formation of clusters on the cell surface and endocytic internalization of ligand and receptor (Carpenter & Cohen, 1976a; Haigler, McKanna & Cohen, 1979). While it has been clear for some time that internalized EGF is subject to rapid degradation within lysosomes, the mechanism and pathway directing the internalized material to lysosomes has been unclear. Also, until recently it has not been determined whether internalized receptors for EGF are degraded. Since the internalized receptors for ligands such as transferrin and low density lipoproteins are known to recycle to the cell surface, it is possible that growth factor receptors might also be subject to recycling.

To examine the fate of internalized EGF receptors, we have determined the rates of degradation, or metabolic turnover, of EGF receptors in the presence and absence of EGF (Stoscheck & Carpenter, 1984a,b). In these experiments, the half-life of the receptor is not determined by measurements of $[^{125}I]$EGF binding activity or protein kinase activity. Instead, the cells are metabolically labelled with $[^{35}S]$methionine and then a 'chase' is performed to allow the prelabelled protein to 'turnover'. Immunoprecipitations, sodium dodecyl sulphate (SDS)/polyacrylamide gels, fluorography, and densitometric scanning are used to determine quantitatively the levels of labelled EGF receptor present at various times during the chase period. The half-life values, therefore, reflect the physical turnover rate of the receptor molecule. The results of these experiments demonstrate that EGF has a marked effect on the rate of degradation of its receptor. In experiments performed with diploid human fibroblasts, the half-life of the receptor was determined to be approximately 10 h when the medium did not contain EGF. If EGF was added to medium, however, the half-life of the receptor was decreased to approximately 1 h. The same experiment was performed with A-431 cells, which contain an exaggerated (<20-fold) level of EGF receptors and inefficiently internalize occupied EGF receptors, and the results indicate half-lives of 20 h and 7 h, for cells cultured in the absence and presence of EGF, respectively. The EGF-induced accelerated degradation of its receptor was specific for EGF, began rapidly (within 15 min) after the addition of EGF, and could be blocked by reagents that interfere with lysosome function. The studies, therefore, are consistent with a process in which both EGF and its receptor are delivered to lysosomal compartments and degraded. Although prelysosomal processing of the internalized peptide is possible, no evidence for this was obtained during these studies.

Of course, the key question that remains to be solved is how does the EGF–receptor complex 'communicate' with the nucleus to alter transcriptional processes and stimulate DNA synthesis. Unfortunately, there has been little progress in the last six years in understanding the role of either EGF-stimulated protein phosphory-lation or endocytic internalization and degradation of EGF–receptor complexes in relationship to the mechanism(s) of nuclear activation.

RECEPTOR BIOGENESIS

Studies in which cells are exposed to EGF for varying lengths of time and the ensuing level of commitment to DNA synthesis is measured, have shown that cells need a relatively long period of interaction with the growth factor before DNA synthesis is stimulated. In most studies this period of time is approximately 6–8 h (Carpenter & Cohen, 1976*b*; Haigler & Carpenter, 1980; Shechter, Hernaez & Cuatrecasas, 1978). Since EGF binding and the internalization and degradation of growth factor–receptor complexes occurs much more rapidly, cells must maintain constant synthesis of new receptor molecules. Otherwise, the cell surface would be depleted of receptors within 2–3 h, and EGF–receptor interactions at the surface would not be possible for the required 6–8 h period of time. Therefore, receptor biosynthesis may be a critical or required element during growth stimulation by EGF.

The following studies were undertaken to gain additional information on various aspects of EGF receptor biosynthesis. When cells are pulse-labelled for brief periods of time (5–30 min) with [^{35}S]methionine and EGF receptor-related proteins are isolated and analysed by immunoprecipitation and SDS/PAGE, a precursor form of the mature receptor molecule is detected (Soderquist & Carpenter, 1984; Mayes & Waterfield, 1984; Decker, 1984; Stoscheck, Soderquist & Carpenter, 1985). This precursor is slightly smaller in apparent mass than the mature receptor as it migrates at 160 000 M_r on SDS/PAGE gels, while the mature molecule migrates at 170 000 M_r. The radioactivity in this precursor form of the receptor can be quantitatively 'chased' into the mature receptor species. The precursor is an immature glycoprotein as judged by its sensitivity to endoglycosidase H. Treatment of the 160 000 M_r precursor with endoglycosidase H lowers its mass to 130 000 M_r by the removal of high-mannose N-linked oligosaccharide chains. In contrast, exposure of the mature 170 000 M_r receptor to endoglycosidase H does not significantly affect its mass.

When cells are labelled in the presence of an inhibitor, such as tunicamycin, that prevents the addition of any N-linked oligosaccharides, a receptor species of 130 000 M_r is immunoprecipitated. This is the size of the protein portion of the EGF receptor. Since the 130 000 M_r non-glycosylated receptor is not detected in pulse-labelling experiments carried out in the absence of tunicamycin, it would seem that the 160 000 M_r precursor is formed by the co-translational addition of oligosaccharides to the nascent protein chain. This would occur as the nascent peptide enters the lumen of the rough endoplasmic reticulum.

One can, with inhibitors such as tunicamycin, determine whether glycosylation of the protein is necessary for the receptor to exhibit [^{125}I]EGF binding or protein kinase activity (Soderquist & Carpenter, 1984). The results of these studies indicate that the 130 000 M_r non-glycosylated form of the EGF receptor does not possess either [^{125}I]EGF binding activity or protein kinase activity. Therefore, either glycosylation or a glycosylation-dependent event is required for EGF receptor to assume a conformation that favours the expression of these biochemical properties, i.e. ligand binding and protein kinase activity. It is also clear from these studies that the non-glycosylated form of the receptor is not processed to the cell surface. Recent studies by Slieker & Lane (1985) have shown that this activation of the receptor probably occurs after the addition of immature N-linked oligosaccharide chains. These authors report that the 160 000 M_r receptor precursor labelled in a brief 5–10 min pulse is not able to bind efficiently to EGF–agarose. If, however, the labelling time is increased to about 30 min, then the 160 000 M_r precursor has acquired an increased capacity to bind to EGF–agarose. This suggests that post-translational events are involved in the formation of active EGF receptor molecules. Whether these steps in post-translational activation occur in the endoplasmic reticulum or are associated with transfer of the receptor precursor to the Golgi apparatus is not known.

Final processing of the receptor occurs in the Golgi apparatus with the removal of mannosyl residues from the oligosaccharide precursor core and the addition of terminal sugar residues, such as fucose, sialic acid, galactose and N-acetyl-glucosamine. Swainsonine is a fungal alkaloid that inhibits one of the Golgi mannosidases involved in processing. In the presence of swainsonine, an immature 160 000 M_r form of the EGF receptor is produced (Soderquist & Carpenter, 1984). This inhibitor-derived receptor species can be digested with endoglycosidase H to yield a 130 000 M_r aglyco form of the receptor. It is not, however, likely to be identical to the 160 000 M_r receptor precursor that is seen in pulse-labelled cells not exposed to inhibitor. In the presence of swainsonine an immature glycoprotein is formed, but it is not maintained within an intracellular compartment, such as the Golgi apparatus. Rather, this immature form of the EGF receptor is processed to the cell surface and functions, both in [^{125}I]EGF binding and EGF-stimulated DNA synthesis, as efficiently as the mature 170 000 M_r form of the receptor. Therefore, it is difficult to assign a clear functional role to the final steps in the processing of the EGF receptor.

Complete biosynthesis of the EGF receptor requires a period of 2–3 h (Stoscheck, Soderquist & Carpenter, 1985). This is the time required for receptor protein labelled in a 15 min pulse to appear on the cell surface. This time frame is somewhat long for the biosynthesis of membrane proteins, which are usually processed to the cell surface within 30–90 min. However, both the insulin receptor (Ronnett *et al.* 1984) and the acetylcholine receptor (Devreotes, Gardner & Fambrough, 1977) also require approximately 2–3 h for complete biogenesis.

OLIGOSACCHARIDE STRUCTURE

The deduced amino acid sequence of the EGF receptor protein contains 15 possible sites for the addition of N-linked oligosaccharide chains. Three of these sites are within the cytoplasmic domain and undoubtedly are not glycosylated. Evidence from both endoglycosidase H intermediates (Mayes & Waterfield, 1984) and sequential lectin chromatography (Cummings, Soderquist & Carpenter, 1985) indicates that 11 of the possible 12 glycosylation sites on the extracellular domain of EGF receptor are, in fact, used. Data from lectin chromatography indicate that seven of these oligosaccharide chains in the mature $170\,000\,M_r$ receptor are complex type and four are high-mannose type. Several lines of evidence indicate that the EGF receptor contains no O-linked oligosaccharides.

The author is a recipient of an Established Investigator Award from the American Heart Association. Research support from the National Cancer Institute, grant CA24071, and American Cancer Society, grant BC294, is gratefully acknowledged.

REFERENCES

BARKA, T., VAN DER NOEN, H., GRESIK, E. W. & KERENYI, T. (1978). Immunoreactive epidermal growth factor in human amniotic fluid. *Mt Sinai J. Med.* **45**, 679–684.

BEARDMORE, J. M., LEWIS-JONES, D. I. & RICHARDS, R. C. (1983). Urogastrone and lactose concentrations in precolostrum, colostrum, and milk. *Pediatr. Res.* **17**, 825–828.

BLOMQUIST, M. C., HUNT, L. & BARKER, W. C. (1984). Vaccinia virus 19-kilodalton protein: relationship to several mammalian proteins, including two growth factors. *Proc. natn. Acad. Sci. U.S.A.* **81**, 7363–7367.

BROWN, J. P., TWARDZIK, D. R., MARQUARDT, H. & TODARO, G. J. (1985). Vaccinia virus encodes a polypeptide homologous to epidermal growth factor and transforming growth factor. *Nature, Lond.* **313**, 491–492.

BYYNY, R. L., ORTH, D. N., COHEN, S. & DOYNE, E. S. (1974). Epidermal growth factor: effects of androgens and adrenergic agents. *Endocrinology* **95**, 776–782.

CARPENTER, G. & COHEN, S. (1976a). ^{125}I-labeled human epidermal growth factor (hEGF): binding, internalization, and degradation in human fibroblasts. *J. Cell Biol.* **71**, 159–171.

CARPENTER, G. & COHEN, S. (1976b). Human epidermal growth factor and the proliferation of human fibroblasts. *J. cell. Physiol.* **88**, 227–237.

CARPENTER, G. & COHEN, S. (1979). Epidermal growth factor. *A. Rev. Biochem.* **48**, 193–216.

CARPENTER, G., KING, L. & COHEN, S. (1979). Rapid enhancement of protein phosphorylation in A-431 cell membrane preparations by epidermal growth factor. *J. biol. Chem.* **254**, 4884–4891.

COHEN, S. (1962). Isolation of a mouse submaxillary gland protein accelerating incisor eruption and eyelid opening in the new-born animal. *J. biol. Chem.* **237**, 1555–1562.

COHEN, S. & CARPENTER, G. (1975). Human epidermal growth factor: isolation and chemical and biological properties. *Proc. natn. Acad. Sci. U.S.A.* **72**, 1317–1321.

CUMMINGS, R. D., SODERQUIST, A. M. & CARPENTER, G. (1985). The oligosaccharide moieties of the epidermal growth factor receptor in A-431 cells: presence of both high mannose N-linked chains and complex chains that contain terminal *N*-acetylgalactosamine residues. *J. biol. Chem.* (in press).

DECKER, S. J. (1984). Aspects of the metabolism of the epidermal growth factor receptor in A431 human epidermoid carcinoma cells. *Molec. cell. Biol.* **4**, 571–575.

DERYNCK, R., ROBERTS, A. B., WINKLER, M. E., CHEN, E. Y. & GOEDDEL, D. V. (1984). Human transforming growth factor-α: precursor structure and expression in *E. coli*. *Cell* **38**, 287–297.

DEVREOTES, P. N., GARDNER, J. M. & FAMBROUGH, D. M. (1977). Kinetics of biosynthesis of acetylcholine receptor and subsequent incorporation into plasma membrane of cultured chick skeletal muscle. *Cell* **10**, 365–373.

ELSON, S. D., BROWNE, C. A. & THORBURN, G. D. (1984). Identification of epidermal growth factor-like activity in human male reproductive tissues and fluids. *J. clin. Endocr. Metab.* **58**, 589–594.

GREGORY, H. (1975). Isolation and structure of urogastrone and its relationship to epidermal growth factor. *Nature, Lond.* **257**, 325–327.

GREGORY, H., HOLMES, J. E. & WILLSHIRE, I. R. (1977). Urogastrone levels in the urine of normal adult humans. *J. clin. Endocr. Metab.* **45**, 668–672.

HAIGLER, H. T. & CARPENTER, G. (1980). Production and partial characterization of antibody blocking epidermal growth factor: receptor interactions. *Biochim. biophys. Acta* **598**, 314–325.

HAIGLER, H. T., McKANNA, J. A. & COHEN, S. (1979). Direct visualization of the binding and internalization of a ferritin conjugate of epidermal growth factor in human carcinoma cells A-431. *J. Cell Biol.* **81**, 382–395.

HEITZ, P. U., KASPAR, M., VAN NOORDEN, S., POLAK, J. M., GREGORY, H. & PEARSE, A. G. E. (1978). Immunohistochemical localization of urogastrone in human duodenal and sub-mandibular glands. *Gut* **19**, 408–413.

HIRATA, Y., UCHIHASHI, M., NAKAJIMA, M., FUJITA, T. & MATSUKURA, S. (1982a). Immunoreactive human epidermal growth factor in human pancreatic juice. *J. clin. Endocr. Metab.* **54**, 1242–1245.

HIRATA, Y., UCHIHASHI, M., NAKAJIMA, H., FUJITA, T. & MATSUKURA, S. (1982b). Presence of human epidermal growth factor in human cerebrospinal fluid. *J. clin. Endocr. Metab.* **55**, 1174–1177.

MARQUARDT, H., HUNKAPILLER, M. W., HOOD, L. E. & TODARO, G. J. (1984). Rat transforming growth factor type 1: structure and relation to epidermal growth factor. *Science* **223**, 1079–1082.

MARQUARDT, H., HUNKAPILLER, M. W., HOOD, L. E., TWARDZIK, D. R., DELARCO, J. E., STEPHENSON, J. R. & TODARO, G. J. (1983). Transforming growth factors produced by retrovirus-transformed rodent fibroblasts and human melanoma cells: amino acid sequence homology with epidermal growth factor. *Proc. natn. Acad. Sci. U.S.A.* **80**, 4684–4688.

MAYES, E. L. V. & WATERFIELD, M. D. (1984). Biosynthesis of the epidermal growth factor receptor in A-431 cells. *EMBO J.* **3**, 351–537.

MORAN, J. R., COURTNEY, M. E., ORTH, D. N., VAUGHAN, R., COY, S., MOUNT, C. D., SHERRELL, B. J. & GREENE, H. L. (1983). Epidermal growth factor in human milk: daily production and diurnal variation during early lactation in mothers delivering at term and at premature gestation. *J. Pediat.* **103**, 402–405.

NANNEY, L. B., MAGID, M., STOSCHECK, C. M. & KING, L. E. (1984). Comparison of epidermal growth factor binding and receptor distribution in normal human epidermis and epidermal appendages. *J. invest. Derm.* **83**, 385–393.

OKA, Y. & ORTH, D. N. (1983). Human plasma epidermal growth factor/β-urogastrone is associated with blood platelets. *J. clin. Invest.* **72**, 249–259.

READ, L. C., UPTON, F. M., FRANCIS, G. L., WALLACE, J. C., DAHLENBERG, G. W. & BALLARD, F. J. (1984). Changes in the growth-promoting activity of human milk during lactation. *Pediatr. Res.* **18**, 133–139.

REISNER, A. H. (1985). Similarity between the vaccinia virus 19K early protein and epidermal growth factor. *Nature, Lond.* **313**, 801–803.

RONNET, G. V., KNUTSON, V. P., KOHANSKI, R. A., SIMPSON, T. L. & LANE, M. D. (1984). Role of glycosylation in the processing of newly translated insulin proreceptor in 373-L1 adipocytes. *J. biol. Chem.* **259**, 4566–4575.

SAVAGE, C. R. JR, HASH, J. H. & COHEN, S. (1973). Epidermal growth factor: location of disulfide bonds. *J. biol. Chem.* **248**, 7669–7672.

SAVAGE, C. R. JR, INAGAMI, T. & COHEN, S. (1972). The primary structure of epidermal growth factor. *J. biol. Chem.* **247**, 7612–7621.

SHECHTER, Y., HERNAEZ, L. & CUATRECASAS, P. (1978). Epidermal growth factor: biological activity requires persistent occupation of high-affinity cell surface receptors. *Proc. natn. Acad. Sci. U.S.A.* **75**, 5788–5791.

SLIEKER, L. J. & LANE, M. D. (1985). Post-translational processing of the epidermal growth factor receptor. Glycosylation-dependent acquisition of ligand-binding capacity. *J. biol. Chem.* **260**, 687–690.

SODERQUIST, A. M. & CARPENTER, G. (1984). Glycosylation of the epidermal growth factor receptor in A-431 cells. The contribution of carbohydrate to receptor function. *J. biol. Chem.* **259**, 12 586–12 594.

STARKEY, R. H., COHEN, S. & ORTH, D. N. (1975). Epidermal growth factor: identification of a new hormone in human urine. *Science* **189**, 800–802.

STARKEY, R. H. & ORTH, D. N. (1977). Radioimmunoassay of human epidermal growth factor (urogastrone). *J. clin. Endocr. Metab.* **45**, 1144–1153.

STOSCHECK, C. M. & CARPENTER, G. (1984a). Down regulation of epidermal growth factor receptors: direct demonstration of receptor degradation in human fibroblasts. *J. Cell Biol.* **98**, 1048–1053.

STOSCHECK, C. M. & CARPENTER, G. (1984*b*). Characterization of the metabolic turnover of epidermal growth factor receptor protein in A-431 cells. *J. cell. Physiol.* **120**, 296–302.

STOSCHECK, C. M., SODERQUIST, A. M. & CARPENTER, G. (1985). Biosynthesis of the epidermal growth factor receptor in cultured human cells. *Endocrinology* **116**, 528–535.

ULLRICH, A., COUSSENS, L., HAYFLICK, J. S., DULL, T. J., GRAY, A., TAM, A. W., LEE, J., YARDEN, Y., LIBERMANN, T., SCHLESSINGER, J., DOWNWARD, J., MAYES, E. L. V., WHITTLE, N., WATERFIELD, M. D. & SEEBURG, P. H. (1984). Human epidermal growth factor receptor cDNA sequence and aberrant expression of the amplified gene in A431 epidermoid carcinoma cells. *Nature, Lond.* **309**, 418–425.

J. Cell Sci. Suppl. 3, 11–17 (1985)
Printed in Great Britain © The Company of Biologists Limited 1985

IN VIVO ASPECTS OF UROGASTRONE-EPIDERMAL GROWTH FACTOR

H. GREGORY

Imperial Chemical Industries PLC, Pharmaceuticals Division, Mereside, Alderley Park, Macclesfield, Cheshire SK10 4TG, U.K.

SUMMARY

Recent evidence indicates that human urogastrone-epidermal growth factor originates in submandibular and Brunner's glands and that serum levels are low ($< 1 \, \text{ng ml}^{-1}$). It occurs in many secreted fluids to a much greater extent and many tissues are thus exposed to concentrations greater than $100 \, \text{ng ml}^{-1}$. Rapid actions *in vivo* of URO-EGF include the ability to inhibit gastric acid secretion at low doses ($250 \, \text{ng kg h}^{-1}$ in humans) and to provide cytoprotective effects against ulcerogenic agents ($250 \, \text{ng kg h}^{-1}$ in cats). More prolonged exposure of tissues shows increases in parameters related to wound healing, beneficial effects upon ulceration and also the ability to accelerate crypt cell production rate along the gastrointestinal tract. Synthetic material has been prepared with an identical structure to the natural URO-EGF thus enabling detailed studies of the biological effects to be pursued.

INTRODUCTION

The early literature on urogastrone contains several allusions to its ability to cause tissue proliferation as well as to inhibit acid secretion (Sandweiss, 1943), but because the latter property lent itself to clear definition the purification and characterization of urogastrone was as an inhibitor of gastric acid secretion (Gregory, 1975). Comparison of the structure of urogastrone derived from human urine with the growth factor from the mouse submaxillary gland (Gregory, 1975; Savage, Inagami & Cohen, 1972) immediately indicated that they were most probably equivalent molecules from the different species. Subsequent studies have reinforced this belief and as both names, urogastrone and epidermal growth factor, are well-established in the literature it is justified to refer to URO-EGF as the functional agent. Although it has been found in many secretions, and presumably has a function in the many tissues with receptors for URO-EGF, the physiological role of URO-EGF has not been defined. The rapidly expanding literature on URO-EGF is dominated by studies on *in vitro* cell systems, which are exploring the mechanisms of action of the growth factor, but these need to be seen in relation to the concentrations found *in vivo* and the biological effects seen at physiological levels. The objective here, therefore, is to present in summary some of the relevant physiological data.

SOURCES AND CONCENTRATIONS OF URO-EGF IN MAN

Human URO-EGF was readily immunogenic in rabbits and mice, and antisera could be selected with high specificity for the human molecule, e.g. where cross-reaction with the mouse molecule with 70% homology was less than 1 in 10000.

These antisera have been used in immunofluorescence and immunoperoxidase localization studies, which showed strongly positive staining in human submandibular glands and Brunner's glands (Elder, Williams, Lacey & Gregory, 1978; Heitz *et al.* 1978). In particular, the heavy staining of the duct cells in the latter gland in the duct lumen suggested an exocrine secretion. No other tissue gave definable positive results.

The specific antibodies were used also to provide an accurate radioimmunoassay, enabling fluid concentrations to be readily measured. Urine levels of URO-EGF vary widely in the normal population (Gregory, Holmes & Willshire, 1977) and we have not found any significant variation in daily output in relation to body weight in a number of disease states. Thus patients with duodenal ulcer, Sjorgren's Syndrome or psoriasis did not show abnormal excretion of growth factor, nor did we find altered amounts in patients with different types of malignant growth. Raised levels have been reported in a number of patients with tumours when expressed in relation to the daily creatinine output (Uchihashi *et al.* 1983), whereas we related output to body weight. However, it is probable that urine output will not show small fluctuations in body content that may be physiologically important.

The amounts of URO-EGF in serum were also measured together with a number of secretions, saliva, gastric juice, etc. (Gregory, Walsh & Hopkins, 1979), and it was clear that many secretions had concentrations far in excess of that found in serum. Furthermore, whilst the URO-EGF in saliva and gastric juice had the same size and biological activity as the characterized peptide, that in serum had predominantly a much higher molecular size and lower potency. This was not due to a simple association with serum proteins, but treatment with the highly specific proteolytic enzyme trypsin gave rise to the smaller biologically active agent. Thus the blood contains URO-EGF in precursor form, perhaps to be available on demand at some point in the body. When pure submandibular and parotid salivas were collected they had similar amounts of URO-EGF present in both resting and stimulated secretions. Immunohistochemical studies had shown submandibular but not parotid cells to be rich in growth factor and, presumably, therefore, the parotid secretion was supplied from the general circulation. As the total immunoactivity in serum is rarely greater than $1 \, \mathrm{ng \, ml^{-1}}$ and in saliva $> 10 \, \mathrm{ng \, ml^{-1}}$ then some concentration must occur. The amounts in milk, urine and prostatic fluid can reach $> 100 \, \mathrm{ng \, ml^{-1}}$. Once again no evidence of synthesis was observed in mammary tissue yet large amounts appeared in milk; presumably it is actively transported from serum. Normal mouse mammary epithelial cells do have functional receptors (Taketani & Oka, 1983). Whereas breast tissue is oestrogen-responsive the prostate gland is androgen-responsive, and secretions from the latter do have very high concentrations of URO-EGF. The mean concentration in human prostatic fluid of $280 \, \mathrm{ng \, ml^{-1}}$ was the highest observed, apart from precolostrum, and it was predominantly the normal growth factor as characterized from urine and accounted for the entire content of URO-EGF in seminal fluid (Gregory *et al.* 1985). Because of the observation that benign prostatic hypertrophy was uncommon in certain groups, e.g. native Chinese and Japanese, it is possible that it may be related to diet. As production of URO-EGF from the duodenum may be influenced by diet, measurements were also made of concentrations in BPH patients to see if any relationship was apparent. In fact the amounts of URO-EGF in prostatic fluid from BPH patients was approximately half that found in normal controls. No evidence of synthesis within prostatic tissue could be observed, implying that the growth factor in the secretions was a transported phenomenon, but the physiological relevance of reduced amounts in BPH was not clear.

In summary, therefore, two sites of origin are proposed in the human with low levels in serum but many tissues are exposed to URO-EGF at concentrations $> 100 \, \text{ng ml}^{-1}$. Also many cells have specific receptors for the growth factor to promote activities, which may be divided arbitrarily into short- and long-term events.

RAPID ACTIONS 1

Human urogastrone was isolated using inhibition of gastric acid secretion as bioassay and the potency was clearly established in dogs in particular. URO-EGF will inhibit secretion stimulated by histamine, pentagastrin or cholinergic stimulation at doses of $0 \cdot 1 - 1 \cdot 0 \, \mu\text{g kg}^{-1}$. The effect is very rapid, in that 15 min after parenteral administration to dogs with Heidenhain pouches the secretion from the pouches has stopped completely (Gregory, Bower & Willshire, 1977). This may be entirely consistent in speed with the observed *in vitro* effect of URO-EGF in inducing rapid phosphorylation at cell membranes upon binding to receptors. Clearance from blood of the injected factor is also very rapid, and following intravenous administration it is no longer detectable in blood by radioimmunoassay at 5 min. Also this clearance is reflected by rapid transfer into the urine in dogs, which reached completion by ~20 min, although this represents less than 10 % of the intravenous dose (Elder, Kiff & Gregory, 1978). Other secretions such as pancreatic, biliary and salivary were not inhibited by similar doses of URO-EGF. In other species gastric secretion was invariably inhibited, although with different potency; the rat was much less sensitive, but the human was more sensitive. If gastric secretion was evoked by histamine, pentagastrin, insulin, or the autonomous drive of gastrin in patients with Zollinger Ellison syndrome, or indeed by the basal tone of duodenal ulcer patients, inhibition occurred at ~$0 \cdot 25 \, \mu\text{g kg}^{-1}$ (Koffman *et al.* 1982).

Inhibition of acid secretion could be demonstrated using isolated mucosal preparations, indicating that the URO-EGF was acting in the stomach and that inhibition was not a consequence of some distant phenomenon, although it was not due to direct action at either histamine 1 or 2 receptor (Gregory *et al.* 1977). However, it has been shown to act directly at the parietal cell in a highly purified cell preparation. It has been shown (Chen, Amirian & Soll, 1984) that mouse URO-EGF at 10^{-7} to 10^{-9} M blocked the histamine-stimulated amino pyrene uptake in these cells but did not have an effect upon post-membrane receptor stages. The direct effect of gastrin or cholinergic stimuli on these cells was not blocked. Thus inhibition of acid secretion *in vivo* is reflected as a specific *in vitro* action in isolated cells.

RAPID ACTIONS 2

The inhibition of gastric secretion is a rapid observable effect of URO-EGF on parietal cells, but other cells are affected equally rapidly by becoming unresponsive to insult. Guinea pigs treated with reserpine over a short time developed gastric erosions; a concomitant infusion of URO-EGF completely abolished this effect (Gregory et al. 1977). This cytoprotective effect was also demonstrated in rats and cats against gastric ulceration produced by acid and aspirin. The time scale of the experiment was 3 h and during that period URO-EGF at doses below that necessary to inhibit acid secretion ($0.25 \mu g \, kg^{-1} h^{-1}$ in cats) prevented the formation of erosions (Konturek et al. 1981a). This was achievable even though mucosal prostaglandin synthesis was much reduced by the aspirin, whereas the aspirin-associated decrease in mucosal DNA synthesis was prevented by URO-EGF. Infusion of the growth factor into the lumen of the stomach at somewhat higher doses (1, 10 and $100 \mu g \, kg^{-1} h^{-1}$) also gave a protective effect (Konturek et al. 1981b), and the amounts contained in salivary and duodenal secretions suggested a physiological role in the maintenance of gut integrity.

Whatever process is involved in cytoprotection it clearly is not dependent upon the full mitogenic response, which takes several hours in vitro, but rather on the very early membrane events, which occur immediately upon exposure of the cell to URO-EGF.

LONG-TERM ACTIONS

The consequence of treatment with URO-EGF are to induce mitogenesis and in some cases differentiation, the indication being that it will enhance whatever function particular cells are programmed to perform. This has been shown in neonatal gut using the mouse peptide (Malo & Menard, 1982), whereby some brush border enzymes are enhanced by single treatments whereas several applications are necessary for a mitogenic response. The longer-term actions can be explored by healing of wounds rather than preventing their formation as in cytoprotective studies. Relatively slowly healing duodenal ulcers can be produced in rats using acetic acid and the healing process can be accelerated by parenteral treatment with human URO-EGF at $5 \mu g \, kg^{-1}$ once daily (Gregory et al. 1977). Impressive data on the effects that URO-EGF can have on the gastrointestinal tract have been obtained from experiments with rats maintained on total parenteral nutrition (Goodlad et al. 1985). Under these conditions crypt cell production rate (CCPR) fell to $\sim 20\%$ of orally fed controls, as determined by counting the cells arrested in metaphase following vincristine treatment. URO-EGF added to the parenteral food at $60 \mu g \, kg^{-1} day^{-1}$ prevented the fall in CCPR and also restored the production rate in animals allowed to settle at the 20% level. Thus the peptide alone will stimulate cell production along the length of the gastrointestinal tract. Given intragastrically at a higher dose ($1.5 \, mg \, rat^{-1} \, day^{-1}$), it failed to have any effect in an intact gut in contrast to those reported in the presence of damaging agents such as aspirin or cysteamine. The latter agent will produce chronic duodenal ulcers in rats, which largely remain unhealed at 50 days. Application of URO-EGF continuously in the drinking water at $30\,\mu g\,kg^{-1}\,day^{-1}$ caused a significant increase in healing: 13 out of 29 compared to a control value of 2 out of a total of 28 animals (Olsen, Poulsen, Therkelsen & Nexo, 1985). This was comparable to the healing rate produced by an antisecretory agent, cimetidine, at $500\,mg\,kg^{-1}\,day^{-1}$ and the two agents together produced a greater effect: 19 out of 28 animals were healed. The test system is complex and time-consuming but these results support the view that URO-EGF that is normally in secretions may have a role in the maintenance and repair of gut epithelium.

The implications are that URO-EGF has effects in the gastrointestinal tract at doses below those influencing acid secretion and are most probably due to the mitogenic effects that were apparent in cell systems *in vitro* at similar concentrations. Further confirmation of beneficial effects upon damaged tissue was provided by studies in rats in which small steel-mesh cylinders were placed in groups of four, subcutaneously, into rats (Hunt *et al.* 1985). Test samples were placed in the cylinders and 14 days later the uptake of tissue and the hydroxyproline content of the cylinders were noted. Injections of $0.25\,\mu g$ URO-EGF into the cylinders produced a significant increase in wet and dry weights, and in hydroxyproline in the test cylinders. These observations were relevant to the tissue proliferation occurring in the healing of wounds. Whilst these studies did show that, *in vivo*, beneficial effects are seen with administration of URO-EGF in the 'physiological' range, they do not necessarily define a physiological role. As mentioned earlier, URO-EGF has clear effects upon the gut of neonatal mice, but there were also effects *in utero*; administration of mouse URO-EGF *in utero* to rabbits or sheep caused maturation of pulmonary epithelium and increased the weight of several organs: thyroid, liver, kidney, adrenals. A further study of urine output in newborn human infants was carried out on normal and premature infants. When expressed as the ratio to creatinine output, URO-EGF rose steadily following birth from well below adult levels and appeared to be related to time of conception rather than time of delivery. There was no apparent inflexion enabling conclusions to be drawn about whether URO-EGF plays a role in the maturation of gut or epidermis in the newborn (Evans, Rutter & Gregory, unpublished data).

SYNTHETIC URO-EGF

The natural molecule has good stability not only under extremes of solution pH conditions but also against mammalian enzymes such as pepsin and trypsin. As mentioned above, the biologically active peptide can be derived from a blood-borne precursor by tryptic-like action. Thus a synthetic gene prepared by G. D. Searle in a collaboration with ICI contained part of the *Escherichia coli trp*E gene linked via the gene coding for two lysine residues to the gene coding for human URO-EGF (Smith *et al.* 1982). The expressed protein from *E. coli* was partially purified, treated with trypsin and then purified by ion-exchange and gel chromatography to give a product indistiguishable from natural URO-EGF. The physical data for both were the same and biologically the potency was indistinguishable, as both mitogen and inhibitor of gastric secretion.

It has been known for some time that mouse and human URO-EGF have the same action in inducing eye opening in neonatal mice, which is a function of increased keratinization of the epidermis. Recently, the transforming growth factor, TGFα, has been synthesized by Genentech and its activity compared precisely with synthetic human and natural mouse URO-EGF (Smith *et al*. 1985). Dose-response curves with doses of $0.25-4.0 \mu g^{-1} kg^{-1} day^{-1}$ show that all three have precisely the same potency in inducing this biological effect. Previously it had been noted that the human material lacking the C-terminal five amino acids and the similar mouse molecule both retained full secretory activity but reduced mitogenic potency. Surprisingly, therefore, the TGFα, which lacks this C-terminal sequence naturally, is fully active in the *in vivo* system.

In addition to the studies described above conducted with human URO-EGF, many others conducted with the mouse peptide confirm the useful mitogenic effects upon damaged tissues and support the hypothesis that its role may be that of wound hormone available on demand from a blood-borne reservoir. The ready availability of these peptides by biosynthesis should enable more detailed experiments to be carried out in the immediate future to clarify further the physiological relevance.

REFERENCES

CHEN, M. C., AMIRIAN, D. A. & SOLL, A. H. (1984). Epidermal growth factor binding and inhibitory effect on acid secretion on isolated canine paretal cells. *Fedn Proc. Fedn Am. Socs exp. Biol.* **43**, A4607.

ELDER, J. B., KIFF, E. S. & GREGORY, H. (1978). Half-life of urogastrone in conscious dogs. *Gut* **19**, A435.

ELDER, J. B., WILLIAMS, G., LACEY, E. & GREGORY, H. (1978). Cellular localisation of human urogastrone/epidermal growth factor. *Nature, Lond.* **271**, 466–467.

GOODLAD, R. A., WILSON, T. J. G., LENTON, W., GREGORY, H., MCCULLOGH, K. G. & WRIGHT, N. A. (1985). Urogastrone-epidermal growth factor is trophic to the intestinal epithelium of parenterally fed rats. *Experientia* (in press).

GREGORY, H. (1975). Isolation and structure of urogastrone and its relationship to epidermal growth factor. *Nature, Lond.* **257**, 325–327.

GREGORY, H., BOWER, J. M. & WILLSHIRE, I. R. (1977). Urogastrone and epidermal growth factor. In *Growth Factors* (ed. K. W. Kastrup & J. H. Nielsen), pp. 75–84. Oxford: Pergamon Press.

GREGORY, H., HOLMES, J. E. & WILLSHIRE, I. R. (1977). Urogastrone levels in the urine of normal adult humans. *J. clin. Endocr. Metab.* **45**, 668–672.

GREGORY, H., WALSH, S. & HOPKINS, C. R. (1979). The idenification of urogastrone in serum, saliva and gastric juice. *Gastroenterology* **77**, 313–318.

GREGORY, H., WILLSHIRE, I. R., KAVANAGH, J., BLACKLOCK, N. J. & CHOWDURY, S. (1985). Urogastrone-epidermal growth factor concentrations in prostatic fluid of normal individuals and patients with benign prostatic hypertrophy.

HEITZ, PH. U., KASPER, M., VAN NOORDEN, S., POLAK, J. M., GREGORY, H. & PEARSE, A. G. E. (1978). Immunohistochemical localisation of urogastrone to human duodenal and submandibular glands. *Gut* **19**, 408–413.

HUNT, T. K., KNIGHTON, D. R., ELDER, J. B., THRAKAL, K. K., ANDREWS, W. S. & GREGORY, H. (1985). The effect of urogastrone on collagen synthesis, angiogenesis, fibroplasia and epithelialization in wound models.

KOFFMAN, C. G., ELDER, J. B., GANGULI, P. C., GREGORY, H. & GEARY, C. G. (1982). Effect of urogastrone on gastric secretion and serum gastrin in patients with duodenal ulceration. *Gut* **23**, 951–956.

KONTUREK, S. J., BRZOZOWSKI, T., PIASTUCKI, I., DEMBINSKI, A., RADECKI, T., DEMBINSKA-KIEC, A., ZMUDA, A. & GREGORY, H. (1981*b*). Role of mucosal prostaglandins and DNA synthesis in gastric cytoprotection by lumenal epidermal growth factor. *Gut* **22**, 927–932.

KONTUREK, S. J., RADECKI, T., BRZOZOWSKI, T., PIASTUCKI, I., DEMBINSKI, A., DEMBINSKI-KIEC, A., ZMUDA, A., GRYGLEWSKI, R. & GREGORY, H. (1981*a*). Gastric cytoprotection by epidermal growth factor. *Gastroenterology* **81**, 438–443.

MALO, C. & MENARD, D. (1982). Influence of epidermal growth factor on the development of suckling mice intestinal mucosa. *Gastroenterology* **83**, 28–35.

OLSEN, P. S., POULSEN, S. S. THERKELSEN, K. & NEXO, E. (1985). Oral administration of synthetic human urogastrone promotes healing of chronic duodenal ulcers in rats. *Gastroenterology* (in press).

SANDWEISS, D. J. (1943). The immunising effect of the antiulcer factor in normal human urine against the experimental gastrojejunal ulcers in dogs. *Gastroenterology* **1**, 965–969.

SAVAGE, C. R. JR, INAGAMI, T. & COHEN, S. (1972). The primary structure of epidermal growth factor. *J. biol. Chem.* **247**, 7612–7621.

SMITH, J., COOK, E., FOTHERINGHAM, I., PHEBY, S., DERBYSHIRE, R., EATON, M. A. W., DOEL, M., LILLEY, D. M. J., PARDON, J. F., PATEL, T., LEWIS, H. & BELL, L. D. (1982). Chemical synthesis and cloning of a gene for human beta urogastrone. *Nucl. Acids Res.* **10**, 4477–4482.

SMITH, J. M., SPORN, M. B., ROBERTS, A. B., DERYNCK, R., WINKLER, M. E. & GREGORY, H. (1985). Human transforming growth factor-alpha causes precocious eyelid opening in newborn mice.

TAKETANI, Y. & OKA, T. (1983). Biological action of epidermal growth factor and its functional receptors in normal mammary epithelial cells. *Proc. natn. Acad. Sci. U.S.A.* **80**, 2647–2650.

UCHIHASHI, M., HIRATA, Y., NAKAJIMA, H., FUJITA, T. & MATSUBARA, S. (1983). Urinary excretion of human epidermal growth factor (hEGF) in patients with malignant tumours. *Horm. Metab. Red.* **15**, 261–262.

J. Cell Sci. Suppl. 3, 19–28 (1985)
Printed in Great Britain © The Company of Biologists Limited 1985

THE STRUCTURE AND BIOSYNTHESIS OF
EPIDERMAL GROWTH FACTOR PRECURSOR

J. SCOTT, S. PATTERSON

MRC, Clinical Research Centre, Harrow, U.K.

L. RALL, G. I. BELL

Chiron Corporation, 4560 Horton Street, Emeryville, California 94608, U.S.A.

R. CRAWFORD, J. PENSCHOW, H. NIALL AND J. COGHLAN

Howard Florey Institute of Experimental Physiology and Medicine, University of Melbourne, Parkville, Victoria 3052, Australia

SUMMARY

The structure of mouse submaxillary gland epidermal growth factor (EGF) precursor has been deduced from complementary DNAs. The mRNA is approximately 4800 bases and predicts prepro EGF to be a protein of 1217 amino acid residues ($133 \times 10 M_r$). EGF (53 amino acid residues) is flanked by polypeptides of 188 and 976 residues at its carboxy and amino termini, respectively. The amino terminus of the precursor contains seven cysteine-rich peptides that resemble EGF. Towards the carboxy terminus is a 20-residue hydrophobic membrane spanning domain. The mid portion of the EGF precursor shares a 33% homology with the low density lipoprotein receptor, which extends over 400 amino acid residues. These features suggest that EGF precursor could function as a membrane-bound receptor.

RNA dot-blot analysis and *in situ* hybridization show EGF mRNA to be abundant in the submaxillary gland, kidney and incisor tooth buds. Lower EGF mRNA levels were found in the lactating breast, pancreas, small intestine, ovary, spleen, lung, pituitary and liver. In the kidney EGF mRNA was most abundant in the distal convoluted tubules. Analysis of EGF precursor biosynthesis in organ culture of the submaxillary gland and kidney showed differential processing of the precursor in the two tissues. In the submaxillary gland immunoreactive low molecular weight EGF was produced, but in the kidney the high molecular weight precursor was not processed. In the distal convoluted tubule of the kidney EGF precursor may act as a receptor that is involved in ion transport.

INTRODUCTION

The androgen-regulated products of the mouse submaxillary gland represent an important source of material for the experimental biologist (Carpenter, 1979; Hollenberg, 1979; Barka, 1980). Among the secretory products are the kallikrein family of arginyl-esteropeptidases, which are responsible for processing enzyme and growth factor precursors, the hormone renin and the growth factors nerve and epidermal growth factor (EGF). Apart from the secretory products of the gland the cytoplasmic enzyme glucose-6-phosphate dehydrogenase, the first enzyme of the pentose phosphate shunt, and a variety of lysosomal glycosidases are also regulated by androgens.

Histologically, the gland consists of two cellular components; these are the acinar cells and the cells of the granular convoluted tubules. It is the latter cells that respond

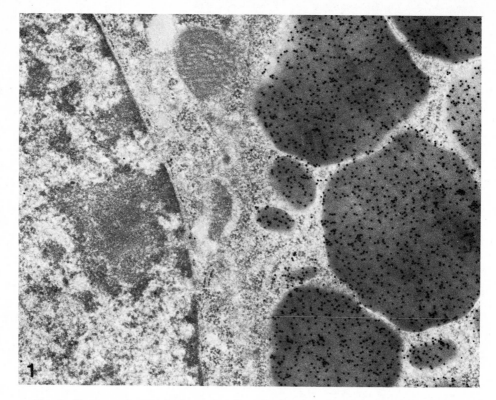

Fig. 1. Electron micrograph of a section through a serous cell in the mouse submaxillary gland showing granules after immunogold labelling to detect EGF. Tissue was fixed for 1 h at 20 °C in 1 % glutaraldehyde in 0·1 M-cacodylate buffer (pH 7·3) containing 5 % sucrose. After treating with 0·5 M-ammonium chloride for 4 h at 20 °C, the tissue was dehydrated and embedded in Lowicryl K4M resin as described by Bendayan & Orstavik (1982). Ultrathin sections were labelled by incubating for 2 h with a rabbit anti-EGF reagent and after washing, the distribution of bound antibody was shown by incubating with 18–20 nm colloidal gold coupled to protein A. Labelled sections were stained with uranyl acetate and lead citrate before examination. ×30 000.

to androgens and that are responsible for the production of EGF. Immune electron microscopy of the submaxillary gland tissue indicates that EGF is secreted by all the cells of the granular convoluted tubules and that EGF is uniformly distributed within the secretory granules (Fig. 1). Antibody raised against EGF does not, however, recognize the EGF precursor in the Golgi apparatus or in the endoplasmic reticulum.

The physiology of EGF has already been discussed at length by Dr Carpenter and Dr Gregory (this symposium) and will not be discussed here. The primary structure of EGF as determined by Savage, Inagami & Cohen (1972) was essential for the synthesis of oligodeoxynucleotides and for the cloning of cDNAs corresponding to EGF precursor. These experiments have been described elsewhere (Scott *et al.* 1983). By Northern hybridization, EGF was determined to be encoded by an mRNA of 4800 bases.

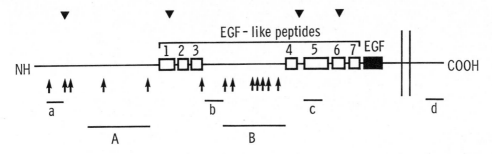

Fig. 2. Prepro EGF inserted into cell membrane. Triangles represent N-glycosylation sites. Arrows show dibasic residues. Regions of homology in the precursor are shown (a, b, c, d; *A* and *B*).

Fig. 3. EGF-like peptides 1 (residues 357–399), 2(400–440), 3(441–480), 4(745–784), 5(803–885), 6(886–925), 7(926–976) and EGF(977–1029). The peptides are aligned on the motif Cys-X-Cys. Cys residues and residues in four or more of the peptides are shaded. Computer-predicted turns are underlined. Black squares are Cys residues outside the EGF-like peptides. The one-letter code for amino acids has been used.

The precursor was deduced to be of 1217 amino acids, including an amino-terminal signal peptide of 25 residues (Fig. 2) (Gray, Dull & Ullrich, 1983; Scott *et al.* 1983; Pfeffer & Ullrich, 1985). EGF was demonstrated to reside towards the carboxy terminal of the precursor (residues 976–1029). The most remarkable feature of the precursor was the presence of at least seven EGF-like peptides. The presence of these peptides was established by aligning the motif Cys-X-Cys throughout the precursor.

The EGF-like peptides are situated in two blocks (Fig. 3). These are situated in a group of four immediately after the amino terminus of EGF itself and in a group of three further towards the amino terminus of the precursor. The homology of these peptides with EGF varies from 20 to 40 %. Each of the EGF peptides is flanked by a basic amino acid residue, which could facilitate cleavage of the peptide from the precursor, although some of these residues are lysine, an unlikely cleavage site. However, a computer prediction of the turns made by the EGF moiety itself indicates that, if these turns are made, the three disulphide bonds made in EGF would occur normally and that the EGF-like peptides would preferentially make exactly the same turns as EGF itself (Doolittle, Fong & Johnson, 1984). Under these circumstances each of the EGF peptides would make the three disulphide bonds and lock the EGF moiety tightly into the precursor.

A number of other features of interest are present in the EGF precursor: five potential N-glycosylation sites are found. There are a large number of dibasic amino acid residues, which would be classical sites for intracellular cleavage of the precursor into peptides of potential function. These dibasic sites occur exclusively outside the domains of the EGF-like peptides. Apart from the group of EGF peptides at the carboxy and amino termini, there are other elements of homology repeating within the molecule (Fig. 2). These segments of homology suggest that the EGF precursor has evolved by duplication of an ancestral gene. A further feature of particular interest is found at the carboxy terminus of the EGF precursor. This is a region of some 20 hydrophobic amino acid residues, which could form a membrane-spanning domain and cross the plasma membrane in six alpha-helical turns. This domain would be locked in the plasma membrane by the basic amino acids at its carboxy terminus.

There is considerable circumstantial evidence that EGF precursor may indeed be a membrane glycoprotein and possibly a receptor molecule. Recently, the structure of rat and human α-transforming growth factors has been determined and in addition a vaccinia virus protein has been shown to be homologous to EGF (Reisner, 1985). Not only is each of these molecules capable of making the same disulphide bonds as EGF, but they are equipotent as mitogens. In addition each molecule has a membrane-spanning domain towards the carboxy terminus of the ligand in exactly the same position as EGF precursor. Thus, EGF precursor contains two cysteine-rich regions formed by the EGF-like peptides and a membrane-spanning domain.

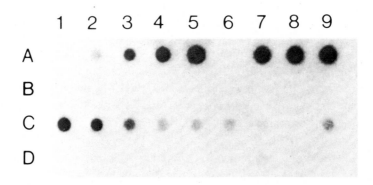

Fig. 4. Dot-blot analysis of total RNA isolated from tissues. A, 1–5: 0·005, 0·01, 0·025, 0·05 and 0·1 μg of male submaxillary gland RNA, respectively; 7, 1·0 μg of female submaxillary gland RNA; 8, 9, 0·2 μg each of male and female kidney RNA. B. The samples described for A but treated with NaOH. C. 1–9: 10 μg each of mammary gland, pancreas, small intestine (duodenum), ovary, spleen, lung, liver, L cell and pituitary RNAs. D. The samples described for C, but treated with NaOH. (Except for mammary gland and ovary, these RNA samples were prepared from male mice.)

This structure is analogous to the plasma membrane receptors for low density lipoprotein and EGF itself. With the characterization of the structure of the low density lipoprotein receptor an additional intriguing story has emerged. In the mid portion of both the EGF precursor and the low density lipoprotein receptor there is a region of homology spanning some 400 amino acid residues (Goldstein & Brown, 1985). The strength of this homology ranges from some 27 to 40 %. This homology is reflected in the intron structure of the gene.

The tissue distribution of EGF mRNA has been assessed by RNA dot-blot analysis (Rall *et al.* 1985). The differences in EGF produced at the protein level in the male and female submaxillary glands was demonstrated to be due to transcription (Fig. 4A). The difference in the amount of the male and female submaxillary gland mRNA for EGF being approximately 10:1. The kidney was surprisingly high in EGF mRNA. It contained half the amount of EGF mRNA found in the submaxillary gland, but the kidney showed no sexual dimorphism. Other tissues found to produce EGF were, in descending order of abundance: the lactating mammary gland, the pancreas, small intestine, ovary, spleen, lung, pituitary and liver. Mouse L cell RNA contained no EGF mRNA (Fig. 4). *In situ* hybridization of a cDNA against a longitudinal section of a whole mouse EGF confirmed the distribution of EGF mRNA in the kidney and submaxillary glands of the male mouse (Fig. 5A,B). In addition EGF was shown to be abundant in the buds of the incisor teeth. In the rodent these teeth grow throughout life. Analysis of kidney tissue sections by *in situ* hybridization showed that EGF mRNA was localized predominantly in the cortex with a much smaller amount being present in the medulla (Fig. 5C,D). The particular region of the kidney in which EGF mRNA was most abundant was the distal convoluted tubules (Fig. 5C,D).

It was surprising to find so much EGF mRNA in kidney tissue because little EGF protein had been previously demonstrated in this organ. The ratio of EGF protein between the submaxillary gland and kidney was 2000:1, compared to the 2:1 at the messenger RNA level (Table 1). Analysis of EGF messenger RNA size in the kidney and submaxillary gland showed a message of the same size (4800 bases) (Fig. 6). Thus, the differences in protein levels in these two tissues were unlikely to be due to differential splicing of the EGF gene.

To examine the possibility that these differences might be due to differential processing of the EGF precursor, antibodies were raised against a portion of the EGF molecule that does not encode EGF but encodes the first three of the EGF-like peptides. Organ culture of the mouse submaxillary gland and kidney was performed in the presence of [^{35}S]methionine. After 6 h the proteins of each tissue were extracted in the presence of deoxycholate and sodium dodecyl sulphate (SDS) and subjected to immunoprecipitation with antibodies against EGF itself and against the precursor. This was followed by polyacrylamide gel electrophoresis in the presence of SDS (Fig. 7). For the submaxillary gland, the antibody against EGF precipitated EGF itself and this could be inhibited with unlabelled EGF. Antibody against the precursor precipitated a number of higher molecular weight components. The situation in the kidney tissue was quite different. Both antibodies precipitated a

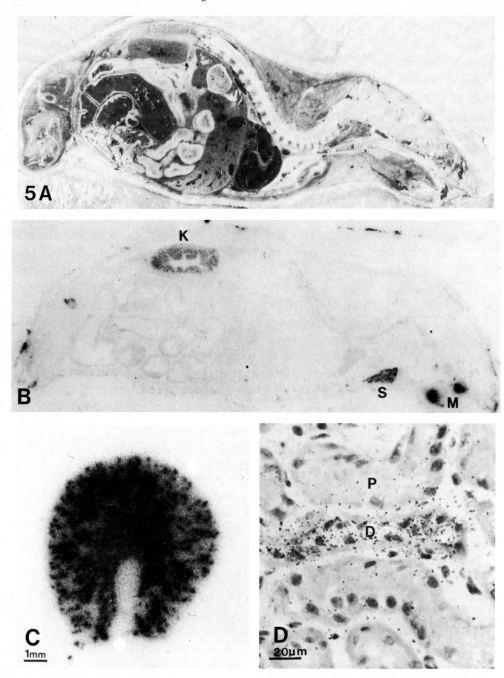

Fig. 5. A–C. *In situ* hybridization of prepro EGF cDNA to mouse tissues. A. Sagittal
section of an adult male Swiss-Webster mouse; B. Autoradiographs of sections of a whole
male mouse; C, transverse section of kidney; and D, male kidney cortex. S, submaxillary
gland; K, kidney; M, mouth region; D, distal tubule; P, proximal tubule. The distal
tubules can be distinguished from the proximal kidney tubules by their wider lumen and
thinner walls. C, bar, 1 mm; D, bar, 20 μm.

protein of some $130\,000\,M_r$ but there were no major degradation products and there was no evidence of EGF production in the kidney.

It is evident that EGF itself is a potent mitogen, but the demonstration of the huge EGF precursor suggests the possibility of other functions for this molecule. The precursor models as a membrane glycoprotein. The presence of a membrane-spanning domain in the other EGF-like molecules such as α-transforming growth factor and vaccinia virus protein, together with the strong homology to the low density lipoprotein receptor, suggests that EGF precursor itself could be a membrane protein and probably a receptor. The demonstration of unprocessed EGF precursor in the kidney further suggests that such a receptor function could be operative in the distal convoluted tubule of this tissue. The function of this region of the kidney tissue is the transport of sodium and hydrogen ions. One of the earliest actions on cells of EGF, PDGF and indeed of the hormone vasopressin is to activate a sodium/hydrogen ion antiporter, which moves sodium into the cell and hydrogen ions out of the cell (Rozengurt, 1983). Such a function occurs in the distal convoluted tubule of the kidney. Furthermore, the sodium/hydrogen antiporter in the distal convoluted tubule and in cell lines that respond to growth factors is

Table 1. *Relative abundances of prepro EGF mRNA and EGF protein in various mouse tissues*

Tissue	Relative prepro EGF mRNA abundance	Relative EGF abundance*
Submaxillary gland (male)	2 (1/200)	2000
Kidney (male, female)	1 (1/400)	1
Submaxillary gland (female)	0·2 (1/2000)	140
Mammary gland (lactating)	0·01 (1/40 000)	—
Pancreas	0·008 (1/50 000)	0·43
Small intestine (duodenum)	0·004 (1/100 000)	0·33
Pituitary	0·003 (1/150 000)	0·02
Lung	0·002 (1/200 000)	<0·02
Spleen	0·002 (1/200 000)	—
Brain	0·002 (1/200 000)	<0·02
Ovary	0·002 (1/200 000)	—
Liver	(<1/200 000)	0·33
Eye	(<1/200 000)	—
L cell	(<1/200 000)	—

The relative prepro EGF mRNA levels were determined by averaging laser densitometry scans of three dot-blot matrices (e.g., see Fig. 4). Values were normalized to that of the kidney and the numbers in parentheses are the predicted frequency of prepro EGF mRNA in poly(A)-containing RNA isolated from the tissues of 8-week-old Balb/c male mice, unless otherwise indicated. Analysis of a cDNA library prepared from male submaxillary RNA indicated that at least 0·5 % of the colonies hybridized to a probe encoding the 3′-untranslated region of prepro EGF mRNA (J. Scott & G. I. Bell, unpublished). The male submaxillary gland contains approximately 1 µg of EGF per mg or tissue (wet weight); no values for the EGF content of lactating mammary gland, ovary, spleen, eye or L cells are available. The amount of EGF found in each tissue has been normalized to that determined for the kidney.

*See Byyny *et al.* (1972).

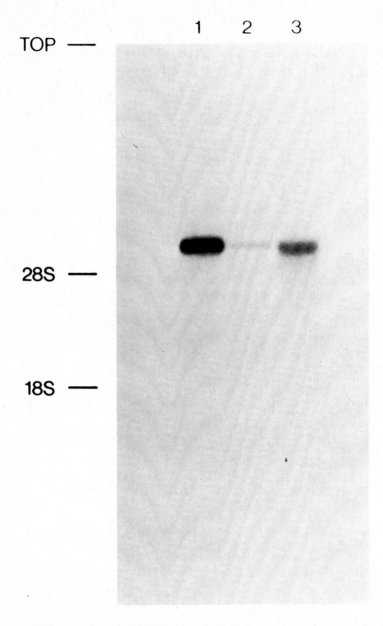

Fig. 6. Northern analysis of prepro EGF mRNA in the kidney and submaxillary gland. Lane 1, 0·1 μg poly(A)-containing RNA from a male submaxillary gland; lane 2, 5 μg total RNA from a female submaxillary gland; lane 3, 5 μg total RNA from a male kidney. The positions of 18 S and 28 S ribosomal RNAs are shown. The size of prepro EGF mRNA was estimated using denatured fragments of a *Hin*dIII digest of phage λ DNA.

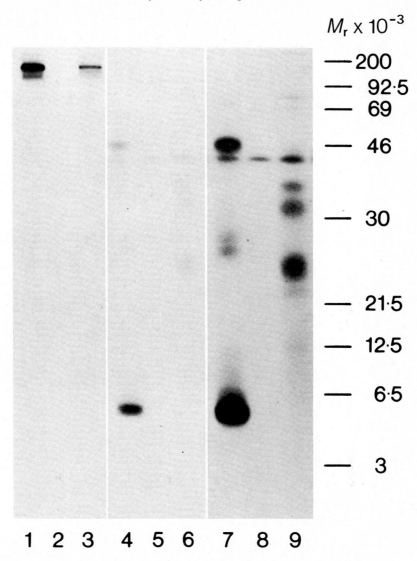

$M_r \times 10^{-3}$

—200

— 92·5
— 69

— 46

— 30

— 21·5

— 12·5

— 6·5

— 3

1 2 3 4 5 6 7 8 9

Fig. 7. Synthesis of prepro EGF-related proteins in the kidney and submaxillary gland. The proteins immunoprecipitated *in vitro* labelled kidney slices (lanes 1–3) and submaxillary gland lobules (lanes 4–9) by control rabbit serum (lanes 2,5,8), anti-mouse EGF antibody (lanes 1,4,7) and anti-prepro EGF II (lanes 3,6,9) were analysed by SDS/polyacrylamide gel electrophoresis. Sizes of molecular weight standards are indicated. The gel was exposed for 24 h for lanes 1–6 and for 4 days in the case of lanes 7–9.

amiloride-sensitive. We speculate that the large EGF precursor may be involved in the regulation of salt and water movement. In other tissues such as the submaxillary gland it is evident that EGF the mitogen is produced and secreted in its low molecular weight form.

Mrs A. Smith and Mrs T. Barrett are thanked for typing this manuscript.

REFERENCES

BARKA, T. (1980). Biologically active peptides in submandibular glands. *J. Histochem. Cytochem.* **28**, 836–859.

BENDAYAN, M. & ORSTAVIK, T. B. (1982). Immunocytochemical localization of Kallitrein in rat exocrine pancreas. *J. Histochem. Cytochem.* **30**, 58–66.

BYYNY, R. C., ORTIS, D. N. & COHEN, S. (1972). Radioimmunoassay of epidermal growth factor. *Endocrinology* **90**, 1261–1266.

CARPENTER, G. (1979). Epidermal growth factor. *A. Rev. Biochem.* **48**, 193–216.

DOOLITTLE, R. F., FONG, D. F. & JOHNSON, M. S. (1984). Computer-based characterization of epidermal growth factor precursor. *Nature, Lond.* **307**, 558–560.

GRAY, A., DULL, T. J. & ULLRICH, A. (1983). Nucleotide sequence of epidermal growth factor cDNA predicts a 128,000-molecular weight protein precursor. *Nature, Lond.* **303**, 722–725.

GOLDSTEIN, J. L. & BROWN, M. S. (1985). The LDL receptor and the regulation of cellular chololesterol metabolism. *J. Cell Sci. Suppl. 3*, 00–00.

HOLLENBERG, M. D. (1979). Epidermal growth factor-urogastrone, a polypeptide acquiring normal status. *Vitamins Hormones* **37**, 69–110.

PFEFFER, S. & ULLRICH, A. (1985). Epidermal growth factor: Is the precursor a receptor? *Nature, Lond.* **313**, 184.

RALL, L. B., SCOTT, J., BELL, G. I., CRAWFORD, R. J., PENSCHOW, J. D., NIALL, H. D. & COGHLAN, J. P. (1985). Mouse prepro-epidermal growth factor synthesis by the kidney and other tissues. *Nature, Lond.* **313**, 228–231.

REISNER, A. H. (1985). Similarity between the vaccinia virus 19K early protein and epidermal growth factor. *Nature, Lond.* **313**, 801–803.

ROZENGURT, E. (1983). Growth factors, cell proliferation and cancer: an overview. *Molec. Biol. Med.* **1**, 169–181.

SAVAGE, C. R. JR, INAGAMI, T. & COHEN, S. (1972). The primary structure of epidermal growth factor. *J. biol. Chem.* **247**, 7612–7621.

SCOTT, J., URDEA, M., QUIROGA, M., SANCHEZ-PESCADOR, R., FONG, N., SELBY, M., RUTTER, W. J. & BELL, G. I. (1983). Structure of mouse submaxillary messenger RNA encoding epidermal growth factor and seven related proteins. *Science* **221**, 238–240.

J. Cell Sci. Suppl. 3, 29–38 (1985)
Printed in Great Britain © *The Company of Biologists Limited 1985*

PRODUCTION OF EPIDERMAL GROWTH FACTOR IN *ESCHERICHIA COLI* FROM A SYNTHETIC GENE

GEOFFREY ALLEN, CORA A. PAYNTER AND
MICHAEL D. WINTHER

Department of Molecular Biology, Wellcome Biotechnology Limited, Langley Court, Beckenham, Kent BR3 3BS, U.K.

SUMMARY

Mouse epidermal growth factor (EGF) is under investigation as a defleecing agent for sheep. Substantial quantities of the pure protein are required for these studies and to supply this need a gene for the protein was synthesized and inserted into plasmid vectors to direct the expression of EGF polypeptide, or fusion proteins containing the EGF peptide sequence, in transformed *Escherichia coli*. Mature EGF was released by lysine specific proteolysis of a fusion protein consisting of part of the *E. coli* TrpE protein, a lysine linker and EGF polypeptide. The EGF was purified and characterized and was found to be biologically active.

INTRODUCTION

Epidermal growth factor (EGF), a 53-residue polypeptide of known primary structure (Savage, Inagami & Cohen, 1972), can be extracted from adult male mouse submaxillary glands and rapidly purified (Savage & Cohen, 1972). EGF was shown to cause defleecing of sheep (Moore, Panaretto & Robertson, 1981) but substantial quantities (several grams) of the growth factor are required for extensive testing of the agent, at a dose of 3–5 mg per sheep. Gene synthesis and expression in microorganisms is a recent but established technology, having been applied to somatostatin (Itakura *et al.* 1977), insulin A and B chains (Crea, Kraszewski, Hirose & Itakura, 1978; Goeddel *et al.* 1979), interferon α (De Maeyer *et al.* 1982; Edge *et al.* 1981, 1983) and human EGF (urogastrone) (Smith *et al.* 1982; Urdea *et al.* 1983) among other polypeptides.

It is generally observed that expression of small polypeptides, such as insulin chains, directly in *Escherichia coli* is extremely inefficient, primarily because proteolysis by intracellular proteases is rapid, but also because of the necessity to construct an efficient ribosome binding site and surrounding sequences within the gene that are compatible with the desired amino terminal sequence. The rules governing the efficiency of translation initiation are not completely understood. In addition, an initiator methionine codon is required and the N-terminal methionine may not be efficiently removed by the host protein synthetic machinery, as, for example, is the case with human growth hormone (Ikehara *et al.* 1984), particularly at high levels of expression.

As an alternative to expression of a mature polypeptide, the synthetic gene may be fused to part of a gene for a host protein that can itself be expressed at high levels in a controllable manner. The resultant fusion protein may well be stabilized against proteolysis. The polypeptide of interest may then be released by specific chemical or enzymic cleavage. The application of this technology to the production of murine EGF in *E. coli* is described here. A fusion protein containing a lysine link to EGF was expressed and cleaved by lysine-specific proteolysis. EGF lacks lysine, and is thus resistant to the specific protease.

OLIGODEOXYNUCLEOTIDE SYNTHESIS

Sixteen oligodeoxynucleotides of 16–25 nucleotide residues for the initial gene construction were synthesized by a manual solid-phase method similar to that described by Sproat & Bannwarth (1983). Protected intermediates, generally dimers, were assembled on controlled-pore glass. All intermediates were prepared from commercially available deoxynucleosides and all reagents were prepared or further treated to ensure purity. After deprotection, the oligodeoxynucleotides were purified by anion-exchange chromatography (Fig. 1) and desalted on a Sephadex G25 column. Each of the oligodeoxynucleotides was pure as revealed by auto-radiography of radiolabelled kinased material separated by electrophoresis in 15 % acrylamide gels in 8 M-urea.

EGF GENE CONSTRUCTION

Each oligodeoxynucleotide except those yielding the 5′-OH ends of the assembled gene was fully kinased with an excess of $[\gamma\text{-}^{32}P]ATP$ and polynucleotide kinase. Several ligation experiments were conducted using different subsets of oligo-deoxynucleotides, polyacrylamide gel electrophoretic purification of intermediates and final ligation of these intermediates, using methods similar to those previously described (Smith *et al.* 1982; Edge *et al.* 1981). The final ligation product was ligated into the *Bam*HI–*Eco*RI fragment of pAT153. *E. coli* HB101 was transformed with the ligation product and ampicillin-resistant colonies were selected by restriction enzyme digestion of plasmids and polyacrylamide gel electrophoretic analysis. Plasmid pEGF6 was further characterized by restriction analysis and the EGF genes from two colonies were completely sequenced by the Maxam–Gilbert procedure (Maxam & Gilbert, 1980). One isolate had the correct sequence (Fig. 2).

CONSTRUCTION OF EXPRESSION VECTORS FOR EGF

For proposed expression of mature EGF, a 167 base-pair *Eco*RI fragment of pEGF6 was purified and ligated into the *Eco*RI site of pXY611, a pAT153-based vector containing the *tac* promoter (Amann, Brosius & Ptashne, 1983), to yield pWRL510 that contained the gene for Met-EGF under the control of the *tac* promoter. The correct product was identified by restriction analysis of plasmids from transformed *E. coli* JM105.

For expression of a fusion protein, the complete EGF gene and downstream sequences were excised from pEGF6 using a *Bam*HI–*Pst*I digest. Plasmid pTrpE, that contained the genes for part of the *trp* operon, was digested with *Eco*RI and *Bgl*II and the fragment containing the *trp* promoter, attenuator and part of the *trpE* gene was isolated. These two fragments were ligated into the *Eco*RI–*Pst*I large

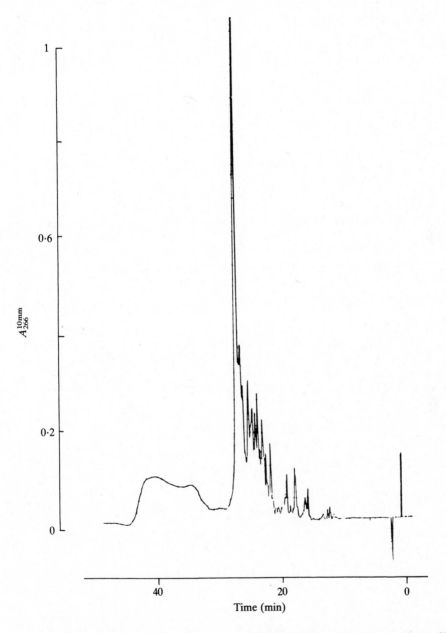

Fig. 1. Purification of oligodeoxynucleotide EGF-3 (25-mer) by anion-exchange HPLC. The crude, deprotected and desalted synthetic product was chromatographed on a Whatman Partisil SAX column in a linear gradient of 25 mM to 700 mM-KH_2PO_4 in 30 % (v/v) formamide at 50 °C over 40 min, with a flow rate of 2 ml min^{-1}. The final peak contained pure TAT CCG GGT TGT CCG TCT TCT TAC G.

fragment of pAT153 to yield pWRL500 (Fig. 3) that contained a gene for a TrpE-EGF fusion protein under the control of the *trp* promoter–operator.

Linker   →EGF

Ile - Leu - Lys - Asn - Ser - Tyr - Pro - Gly - Cys - Pro - Ser - Ser -
G ATC CTT AAG AAT TCT TAT CCG GGT TGT CCG TCT TCT

*Bam*HI   *Eco*RI

   10   20
Tyr - Asp - Gly - Tyr - Cys - Leu - Asn - Gly - Gly - Val - Cys
TAC GAC GGT TAC TGC CTG AAC GGT GGT GTT TGC

                                     30
Met - His - Ile - Glu - Ser - Leu - Asp - Ser - Tyr - Thr - Cys
ATG CAC ATC GAA TCT CTG GAC TCT TAC ACT TGC

                                  40
Asn - Cys - Val - Ile - Gly - Tyr - Ser - Gly - Asp - Arg - Cys - Gln
AAC TGC GTT ATC GGT TAC TCT GGT GAC CGT TGC CAG

                       50
Thr - Arg - Asp - Leu - Arg - Trp - Trp - Glu - Leu - Arg -STOP
ACT CGT GAC CTG CGT TGG TGG GAA CTG CGT TAA GG

Fig. 2. Sequence of synthetic gene for EGF, coding strand.   *Eco*RI

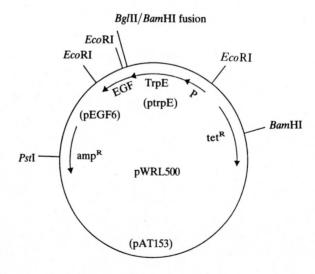

Fig. 3. Structure of plasmid pWRL500.

EXPRESSION OF EGF *IN E. COLI*

To detect expression of EGF polypeptide in *E. coli* radioimunoassay (Byyny, Orth & Cohen, 1972) and immunoblotting ('Western blotting') were used. No EGF was detected in expression experiments with pWRL510 and it was assumed that intracellular proteolysis was rapid. The *E. coli* bearing pWRL500 could be induced to produce high levels, estimated about 10% of total cell protein by inspection of Coomassie Blue-stained polyacrylamide gel electrophoretograms (Fig. 4), of the fusion protein (M_r 42 085) following starvation for tryptophan and addition of indole acrylic acid. The bulk of the fusion protein was present as inclusion bodies as seen by immunocytochemical analysis.

PURIFICATION OF EGF FROM *E. COLI*

Harvested cells containing the fusion protein were disrupted by lysozyme/EDTA and freeze–thawing, followed by treatment with DNase. Most of the fusion protein was in the pellet fraction after centrifugation at 40 000 g for 1 h at 20°C. The pellet was extracted with 8 M-urea and diluted fivefold. The fusion protein was present in the supernatant. The supernatant was digested with endoproteinase LysC for 24 h at 37°C. The digest was dialysed against 50 mM-HCl, 0·1 M-NaCl and the supernatant, after centrifugation, was concentrated in an Amicon ultrafiltration cell with a UM2 membrane. The solution was chromatographed on a column of Bio Gel P-10 as described by Savage & Cohen (1972) and the EGF peak, eluting after the total column volume, was collected. After neutralization and reduction in volume the crude EGF was chromatographed on DEAE-cellulose in ammonium acetate at pH 5·6 (Savage & Cohen, 1972). Following these procedures, the EGF was 80–90% pure as judged by high performance liquid chromatography (HPLC), gave a single band on sodium dodecyl sulphate/polyacrylamide gel electrophoresis (SDS/PAGE) (Fig. 4) and had very low endotoxin contamination. Peptide mapping of thermolysin-digested performic acid-oxidized material on thin layers revealed the expected peptides as shown by N-terminal and amino acid analysis. The EGF was biologically active.

ALTERNATIVE FUSION PROTEIN CONSTRUCTIONS

It was observed that some batches of endoproteinase LysC were ineffective at specifically cleaving the fusion protein. Inspection of the properties of different batches of the enzyme from Boehringer (Mannheim) revealed gross differences in relative catalytic rates for different substrates. Other proteases, including trypsin and plasmin in trace amounts were tested but found to be ineffective at concentrations that already gave partial cleavage at one or more arginyl peptide bonds near the C terminus of EGF. Alternative potential cleavage points were therefore introduced into the fusion protein gene by replacement of the 5'-terminal linking region by other oligodeoxynucleotide pairs, as shown in Table 1.

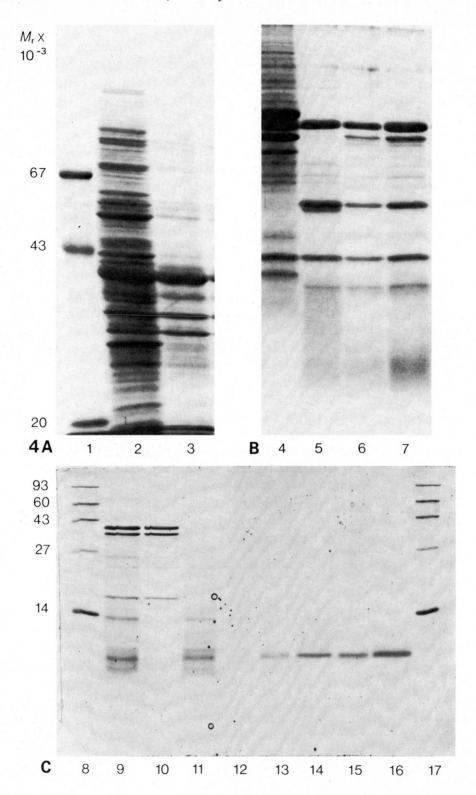

Since EGF is relatively stable to acid, it was conceivable that an acid-sensitive bond, Asp–Pro, would be cleaved under conditions that allowed retention of EGF activity. However, the fusion protein, treated under a range of conditions in formic, acetic or hydrochloric acid could not be cleaved to give more than a trace amount of EGF-like protein as determined by Bio-Gel P-10 chromatography, and the conditions required to cleave the polypeptide chain were sufficiently harsh to cause extensive amide hydrolysis and other non-specific peptide bond cleavage.

Blood-clotting factor Xa was reported to cleave a fusion protein with an Ile-Glu-Gly-Arg link to globin chain (Nagai & Thøgersen, 1984). A fusion protein containing this link between the TrpE fragment and EGF was produced but was hardly cleaved by factor Xa even at a weight ratio of one part enzyme to ten parts of substrate. An arginine-specific protease from mouse submaxillary glands was also ineffective, possibly due to inhibition of the protease by EGF, with which it, or a closely related protease, forms a complex *in vivo* (Schenkein, Levy, Franklin & Frangione, 1977). Thrombin was also ineffective.

Collagenase has been used to cleave a fusion protein (Germino & Bastia, 1984), but the linking polypeptide contained an extensive region (60 residues) of collagen structure. Short peptide substrates are cleavable, however, and a fusion protein with a linking Gly-Pro-Leu-Gly-Pro sequence was produced in *E. coli* following further genetic manipulation and verification by DNA sequencing. However, neither *Achromobacter iophagus* nor *Clostridium histolyticum* collagenases cleaved the resulting fusion protein. The calcium ions required for collagenase activity caused precipitation of the fusion protein and physical chemical factors might have been partly responsible for the lack of proteolysis.

INCREASING LEVELS OF PRODUCTION OF EGF

Several approaches have been made to increase levels of production of EGF in *E. coli*, including increasing the copy number of the plasmid using temperature-sensitive runaway-copy-number plasmids and using different promoter systems. Development of extraction and purification procedures suitable for larger-scale operation has also been done. It is apparent from this work that the methods available for gene synthesis are relatively straightforward compared with those for expressing and recovering pure material in good yields from genetically engineered *E. coli*.

Fig. 4. Polyacrylamide gel electrophoresis of *E. coli* extracts and purified EGF. SDS/PAGE under reducing conditions (Laemmli, 1971) was followed by staining with Coomassie Blue R250. A. 10% acrylamide; B,C, 15% acrylamide. Tracks: 1, marker proteins, bovine serum albumin ($67 \times 10^3 M_r$), ovalbumin (43×10^3), soybean trypsin inhibitor (20×10^3); 2, total cell extract of *E. coli* transformed with pWRL500 and induced; 3, cell pellet; 4, cell pellet incubated in 1·6 M-urea at pH 8 for 3 h at 37°C; 5, as track 4, but with 1/100 (w/w) trypsin; 6, as track 4 but with 1/100 (w/w) endoproteinase Lys-C and at 20°C; 7, as track 6 but at 37°C; 8, 17, marker proteins; 9, as track 7 but from a separate preparation; 10, pellet fraction after centrifugation of the digest shown in track 9; 11, supernatant fraction from digest; 12, pellet fraction after dialysis at pH 1·5 of material shown in track 11; 13, 14, purified bacterial EGF, 1 μg and 2 μg, respectively; 15, 16, authentic mEGF (BRL), 1 μg and 2 μg, respectively.

Table 1. *Structure of linking regions in genes and fusion proteins designed for specific cleavage*

(1) TrpE-Lys-EGF (pWRL500, pWRL505, pEGF *tac trp* 1)

```
                        Endoproteinase Lys-C cleavage ┌─→ EGF
                                          ↓           │
TrpE(1–320) -  Ile - Glu - Ile - Leu - Lys - Asn - Ser - Tyr
               ATT GAG ATC CTT AAG AAT TCT TAT
               TAA CTC TAG GAA TTC TTA AGA ATA

                   BglII/BamHI              EcoRI
                   fusion
```

(2) TrpE-Asp-Pro-EGF (pWRL507, pWRL515)

```
                     Acid-sensitive bond ──────┐      ┌→ EGF
                                               ↓      │
TrpE(1–320) -  Ile - Glu - Ile - Tyr - Asp - Pro - Asn - Ser - Tyr
               ATT GAG ATC TAC GAC CCG AAT TCT TAT
               TAA CTC TAG ATG CTG GGC TTA AGA ATA

                    BglII                         EcoRI
```

(3) TrpE-Ile-Glu-Gly-Arg-EGF (pWRL516, pWRL530)

```
                     Factor Xa-specific site ─────────┐ ┌→ EGF
                                                      ↓ │
TrpE(1–320) -  Ile - Glu - Ile - Tyr - Ile - Glu - Gly - Arg - Asn - Ser
               ATT GAG ATC TAC ATC GAA GGT CGG AAT TCT
               TAA CTC TAG ATG TAG CTT CCA GCC TTA AGA

                    BglII                              EcoRI
```

(4) Collagen sequence linker (pWRL535)

```
                  Potential collagenase site───┐          ┌→ EGF
                                              ↓          │
TrpE(1–320) -  Ile - Glu - Ile - Gly - Pro - Leu - Gly - Pro - Asn - Ser
               ATT GAG ATC GGT CCG CTG GGC CCG AAT TCT
               TAA CTC TAG CCA GGC GAC CCG GGC TTA AGA
               BglII fusion        AvaII       ApaI     EcoRI
               (MboI)
```

We thank Katrina Green for technical assistance in part of the gene cloning work, Hugh Spence for some of the oligonucleotide synthesis, Dave Brown for fermentation, J. Beesley for immuno-electron microscopy and Ros Ellis for typing the manuscript.

REFERENCES

AMANN, E., BROSIUS, J. & PTASHNE, M. (1983). Vectors bearing a hybrid *trp-lac* promoter useful for regulated expression of cloned genes in *Escherichia coli. Gene* **25**, 167–178.

BYYNY, R. L., ORTH, D. N. & COHEN, S. (1972). Radioimmunoassay of epidermal growth factor. *Endocrinology* **90**, 1261–1266.

CREA, R., KRASZEWSKI, A., HIROSE, T. & ITAKURA, K. (1978). Chemical synthesis of genes for human insulin. *Proc. natn. Acad. U.S.A.* **75**, 5765–5769.

DE MAEYER, E., SKUP, D., PRASAD, K. S. N., DE MAEYER-GUIGNARD, J., WILLIAMS, B., MEACOCK, O., SHARPE, G., PIOLI, D., HENNAM, J., SCHUCH, W. & ATHERTON, K. (1982). Expression of a chemically synthesized human αl interferon gene. *Proc. natn. Acad. Sci. U.S.A.* **79**, 4256–4259.

EDGE, M. D., GREENE, A. R., HEATHCLIFFE, G. R., MEACOCK, P. A., SCHUCH, W., SCANLON, D. B., ATKINSON, T. C., NEWTON, C. R. & MARKHAM, A. F. (1981). Total synthesis of a human leukocyte interferon gene. *Nature, Lond.* **292**, 756–762.

EDGE, M. D., GREENE, A. R., HEATHCLIFFE, G. R., MOORE, V. E., FAULKNER, N. J., CAMBLE, R., PETTER, N. N., TRUEMAN, P., SCHUCH, W., HENNAM, J., ATKINSON, T. C., NEWTON, C. R. & MARKHAM, A. F. (1983). Chemical synthesis of a human interferon-α_2 gene and its expression in *Escherichia coli. Nucl. Acids Res.* **11**, 6419–6434.

GERMINO, J. & BASTIA, D. (1984). Rapid purification of a cloned gene product by genetic fusion and site-specific proteolysis. *Proc. natn. Acad. Sci. U.S.A.* **81**, 4692–4696.

GOEDDEL, D. V., KLEID, D. G., BOLIVAR, F., HEYNEKER, H. L., YANSURA, D. G., CREA, R., HIROSE, T., KRASZEWSKI, A., ITAKURA, K. & RIGGS, A. D. (1979). Expression in *Escherichia coli* of chemically synthesized genes for human insulin. *Proc. natn. Acad. Sci. U.S.A.* **76**, 106–110.

IKEHARA, M., OHTSUKA, E., TOKUNAGA, T., TANIYAMA, Y., IWAI, S., KITANO, K., MIYAMOTO, S., OHGI, T., SAKURAGAWA, Y., FUJIYAMA, K., IKARI, T., KOBAYASHI, M., MIYAKE, T., SHIBAHARA, S., ONO, A., UEDA, T., TANAKA, T., BABA, H., MIKI, T., SAKURAI, A., OISHI, T., CHISAKA, O. & MATSUBARA, K. (1984). Synthesis of a gene for human growth hormone and its expression in *Escherichia coli. Proc. natn. Acad. Sci. U.S.A.* **81**, 5956–5960.

ITAKURA, K., HIROSE, T., CREA, R., RIGGS, A. P., HEYNEKER, H. L., BOLIVAR, F. & BOYER, H. W. (1977). Expression in *Escherichia coli* of a chemically synthesized gene for the hormone somatostatin. *Science* **198**, 1056–1063.

LAEMMLI, U. K. (1970). Cleavage of structural proteins during the assembly of the head of bacteriophage T4. *Nature, Lond.* **227**, 680–685.

MAXAM, A. & GILBERT, W. (1980). Sequencing end-labeled DNA with base-specific chemical cleavages. *Meth. Enzym.* **65**, 499–560.

MOORE, G. P. M., PANARETTO, B. A. & ROBERTSON, D. (1981). Epidermal growth factor causes shedding of the fleece of Merino sheep. *Search* **12**, 128–129.

NAGAI, K. & THØGERSEN, H. C. (1984). Generation of β-globin by sequence-specific proteolysis of a hybrid protein produced in *Escherichia coli. Nature, Lond.* **309**, 810–812.

SAVAGE, C. R. JR. & COHEN, S. (1972). Epidermal growth factor and a new derivative. *J. biol. Chem.* **247**, 7609–7611.

SAVAGE, C. R. JR, INAGAMI, T. & COHEN, S. (1972). The primary structure of epidermal growth factor. *J. biol. Chem.* **247**, 7612–7621.

SCHENKEIN, I., LEVY, M., FRANKLIN, E. C. & FRANGIONE, B. (1977). Proteolytic enzymes from the mouse submaxillary gland. *Archs Biochem. Biophys.* **182**, 64–70.

SMITH, J., COOK, E., FOTHERINGHAM, I., PHEBY, S., DERBYSHIRE, R., EATON, M. A. W., DOEL, M., LILLEY, D. M. J., PARDON, J. F., PATEL, T., LEWIS, H. & BELL, L. D. (1982). Chemical synthesis and cloning of a gene for human β-urogastrone. *Nucl. Acids Res.* **10**, 4467–4482.

SPROAT, B. S. & BANNWARTH, W. (1983). Improved synthesis of oligodeoxynucleotides on controlled pore glass using phosphotriester chemistry and a flow system. *Tetrahedron Lett.* **24**, 5771–5774.

URDEA, M. A., MERRYWEATHER, J. P., MULLENBACH, G. T., COIT, D., HEBERLEIN, U., VALENZUELA, P. & BARR, P. J. (1983). Chemical synthesis of a gene for human epidermal growth factor urogastrone and its expression in yeast. *Proc. natn. Acad. Sci. U.S.A.* **80**, 7461–7465.

J. Cell Sci. Suppl. 3, 39–51 (1985)
Printed in Great Britain © The Company of Biologists Limited 1985

INSULIN-LIKE GROWTH FACTOR RECEPTORS

S. PETER NISSLEY, JOYCE F. HASKELL

Metabolism Branch, National Cancer Institute, National Institutes of Health, Bethesda, MD 20205, U.S.A.

NORIO SASAKI, MONIQUE A. De VROEDE AND MATTHEW M. RECHLER

Molecular, Cellular and Nutritional Endocrinology Branch, National Institute of Arthritis, Diabetes, and Digestive and Kidney Diseases, National Institutes of Health, Bethesda, MD 20205, U.S.A.

SUMMARY

There are two types of insulin-like growth factor (IGF) receptors. The type I receptor generally binds IGF-I more tightly than IGF-II and also interacts weakly with insulin. The type II receptor prefers IGF-II over IGF-I and does not recognize insulin. The type I receptor is made up of an alpha binding subunit (M_r 130 000) and a beta subunit (M_r 95 000) probably organized as a heterotetramer ($\alpha_2\beta_2$). The type II receptor consists of a single binding unit (M_r 250 000). IGF stimulates phosphorylation of the beta subunit of the type I receptor in whole cells and solubilized receptor preparations. Tyrosine kinase activity is associated with the type I receptor, resulting in autophosphorylation of the beta subunit and phosphorylation of exogenous substrates. In contrast, phosphorylation of the type II receptor in whole cells is less IGF-dependent, solubilized receptor preparations are not phosphorylated, and purified type II receptors do not exhibit tyrosine kinase activity toward the artificial substrate poly(Glu,Tyr)4:1. There are many similarities between the type I IGF receptor and the insulin receptor; however, different ligand-binding properties, subtle differences in the size of alpha and beta subunits, and immunoreactivity toward anti-receptor antibodies allow us to distinguish between these two receptors. The presence of both IGF receptors as well as insulin receptors on most cells and cross-reactivity of ligands for binding to these receptors present difficulties in assigning a particular biological response to a specific receptor. The type I receptor is down-regulated by ligand while in several cell types the type II receptor is rapidly up-regulated by insulin; the mechanism of up-regulation appears to be a translocation of type II receptors to the cell surface. There are two classes of serum binding proteins for IGF, a M_r 150 000 species found in adult blood and a M_r 40 000 species, which predominates in foetal blood. Like the type II receptor, IGF binding proteins do not bind insulin. The binding site on the type II receptor can be distinguished from the binding protein sites by a hybrid molecule $A_{insulin}$-B_{IGF-I}, which recognizes the binding protein but not the type II receptor. Binding proteins produced by cells in culture may cause confusion in the interpretation of experiments that are designed to study the binding of radiolabelled IGF to cell surface receptors in monolayer culture.

INTRODUCTION

The insulin-like growth factors (IGF) and insulin are closely related as shown originally by amino acid sequence data (Rinderknecht & Humbel, 1978*a,b*) and more recently by cDNA cloning and sequencing results (Jansen *et al.* 1983; Dull, Gray, Hayflick & Ullrich, 1984; Bell *et al.* 1984; Whitfield *et al.* 1984). Insulin, IGF-I and IGF-II are capable of eliciting the same biological responses including cell multiplication in tissue culture, suggesting that they have similar or identical effector pathways. On the cell surface there are two types of IGF receptors in addition to the well-described insulin receptor. Interestingly, one of the IGF receptors (type I) closely resembles the insulin receptor. In this paper we will briefly review the present state of knowledge of the IGF receptors, including receptor structure, phosphorylation, function and regulation.

EARLY COMPETITIVE BINDING DATA; EVIDENCE FOR RECEPTOR HETEROGENEITY

Before it was recognized that somatomedin A, somatomedin C and IGF-I were different names for the same polypeptide, and that multiplication stimulating activity (MSA) was the rat homologue of human IGF-II, data generated from binding of these various radioligands to intact cells and membrane preparations in competitive binding experiments showed two distinct patterns of reactivity with insulin.

In the case of the binding of $[^{125}I]$SM-C to human placental membranes (Marshall *et al.* 1974), insulin completely inhibited IGF tracer binding whereas insulin competed only partially for binding of a radiolabelled preparation of non-suppressible insulin-like activity (mixture of IGF-I and IGF-II) to purified rat liver membranes (Megyesi *et al.* 1974). More subtle evidence for receptor heterogeneity emerged from a comparison of the potencies of IGF-I and IGF-II for competition for the binding of these radioligands to the same cell line (BRL 3A2) (Rechler *et al.* 1980). When IGF-I was the radioligand, IGF-I competed more potently than IGF-II whereas when binding of $[^{125}I]$IGF-II was examined, IGF-II competed more potently than IGF-I. Interestingly, competition by insulin was associated with the binding site that preferred IGF-I and insulin insensitivity was characteristic of the binding site that preferred IGF-II (Table 1).

STRUCTURE

The structural basis of the different binding patterns was provided by chemical cross-linking studies in which radiolabelled IGF-I and IGF-II were allowed to bind

Table 1. *Comparison of type I and type II IGF receptors*

	Type I	Type II
Relative binding potency	IGF-I > IGF-II	IGF-II > IGF-I
Binds insulin	+	−
M_r (without reduction)	300 000	220 000
M_r (with reduction)	130 000	260 000
Down-regulation by ligand	+	−
Phosphorylation		
Whole cell	+	+
IGF-dependent	+	+
Cell-free	+	−
Tyrosine kinase activity	+	−

IGF RECEPTORS

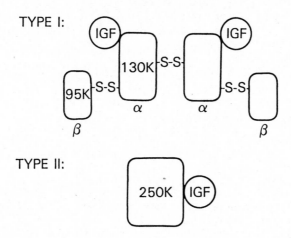

Fig. 1. Structure of the type I and type II IGF receptors. 95 K etc., 95 000 M_r.

to receptors on membranes or cells and the radioligands were chemically cross-linked to binding sites with bifunctional reagents such as disuccinimidyl suberate. The radioligand–receptor complexes were solubilized from the cells or membranes and analysed by sodium dodecyl sulphate/polyacrylamide gel electrophoresis (SDS/PAGE) and autoradiography. Analysis was performed with or without reduction of disulphide bonds to define the subunit composition of the receptor. For the receptor that preferred IGF-I over IGF-II and recognized insulin (type I), [^{125}I]IGF-I was cross-linked to an M_r 130000 binding subunit following reduction of disulphide bonds (Kasuga, Van Obberghen, Nissley & Rechler, 1981; Bhaumick, Bala & Hollenberg, 1981); the size of the receptor with disulphide bonds intact was > 300000 (Chernausek, Jacobs & Van Wyk, 1981; Massague & Czech, 1982). In contrast, the size of the receptor that preferred IGF-II over IGF-I and did not recognize insulin (type II) was 220000 M_r without reduction and 260000 M_r with reduction (Table 1; Fig. 1) (Massague, Guillette & Czech, 1981; Kasuga *et al.* 1981; Massague & Czech, 1982).

The sizes of the IGF receptors have been determined independently by other methods. Perdue *et al.* (1983) calculated an M_r of 290000 on the basis of hydro-dynamic measurements made on a solubilized type II receptor preparation from rat placental membranes. Thibault, Chan, Perdue & Daughaday (1984) used quantitative PAGE under non-denaturing conditions to determine the size of the detergent solubilized type II receptor from rat placental membranes. By determining the mobilities of the radiolabelled IGF-II–receptor complexes and standard proteins with different gel concentrations, a molecular radius $\bar{R}$ of 4·13 nm could be estimated from which an M_r of 250000 was calculated. These results suggest that the type II receptor as solubilized from membranes by detergent does not consist of subunits in addition to the binding subunit defined by cross-linking and analysis on SDS/PAGE under reducing conditions (M_r 260 000).

The type II receptor has been purified to homogeneity from rat chondrosarcoma cells (August et al. 1983) and rat placental membranes (Oppenheimer & Czech, 1983). When analysed on SDS/PAGE with silver staining for protein, the M_r of the receptor preparation (250 000 with reduction, 210 000 without reduction) agrees with the cross-linking data. Thus a purification scheme, which relied on [^{125}I]IGF binding activity, yielded a receptor with the same size as the receptor identified by cross-linking radioligand to intact cells.

Bhaumick et al. (1981) calculated an M_r of 402 000 for the type I receptor on the basis of a series of hydrodynamic measurements made on a detergent-solubilized preparation from human placenta. This value is in rough agreement with the M_r of > 300 000 from cross-linking studies. Although chemical cross-linking experiments with the type I receptor showed weak labelling of an M_r 90 000–98 000 species in addition to the more heavily labelled M_r 130 000 alpha subunit (Chernausek et al. 1981; Massague & Czech, 1982), the strongest support for the existence of a beta subunit in the type I receptor came from biosynthetic and cell surface labelling experiments. Jacobs, Kull & Cuatrecasas (1983a) immunoprecipitated biosynthetically labelled or cell surface labelled receptor using monoclonal antibodies specific for the type I receptor. In addition to the alpha subunit, a 92 000–98 000 M_r species was identified (beta subunit).

PHOSPHORYLATION

Given the structural similarities between the insulin receptor and the type I IGF receptor it was of obvious interest to determine whether the type I IGF receptor was phosphorylated as had been shown for the insulin receptor. Jacobs et al. (1983b) used a specific monoclonal antibody to the type I receptor to demonstrate phosphorylation of the type I receptor. The ATP pool of IM-9 lymphocytes was labelled with $H_3{}^{32}PO_4$ before the cells were incubated with IGF-I. The cells were solubilized and glycoproteins isolated on a wheat-germ lectin Sepharose column. Type I receptors were immunoprecipitated with the specific monoclonal antibody and the immunoprecipitate analysed by SDS/PAGE and autoradiography. IGF-I stimulated the phosphorylation of the beta subunit of the type I receptor. Cell-free phosphorylation of the beta subunit of the type I receptor was demonstrated using a solubilized glycoprotein fraction from unlabelled IM-9 lymphocytes. The solubilized receptor preparation was incubated with IGF-I and then [^{32}P]ATP was added. A monoclonal antibody specific for the type I receptor was used for immunoprecipitation and the immunoprecipitate was analysed by SDS/PAGE. Upon addition of as little as 2·5 ng ml^{-1} of IGF-I, phosphorylation of the type I receptor was increased. Phosphoamino acid analysis indicated that phosphorylation was occurring on tyrosine residues. Rubin, Shia & Pilch (1983) also demonstrated IGF-I-dependent phosphorylation of the type I receptor using a solubilized receptor preparation from human placenta that contained both type I IGF receptors and insulin receptors. The concentration of IGF-I (3 nM) required for half-maximal stimulation of beta subunit phosphorylation coincided with the concentration of IGF-I required for half-maximal inhibition of [^{125}I]IGF-I binding. Also, monoclonal antibody specific for the type I receptor immunoprecipitated the 90 000 M_r species. These results suggest that IGF-I-stimulated phosphorylation of the beta subunit of the type I receptor by binding to the type I receptor rather than by interacting with the insulin receptor.

Zick *et al.* (1984) and Sasaki *et al.* (1985) have studied the phosphorylation of an artificial tyrosine containing substrate poly(Glu,Tyr)4:1 by a solubilized receptor preparation containing type I and type II IGF receptors. The receptors were prepared from BRL 3A2 rat liver cells, a cell line that has type I and type II receptors but few insulin receptors, by solubilization of a 100 000 *g* membrane fraction and wheat-germ lectin affinity chromatography. IGF-I produced half-maximal stimulation of phosphorylation of poly(Glu,Tyr)4:1 and the beta subunit at 3 nM; insulin was several-fold less potent. These results are consistent with intrinsic tyrosine kinase activity of the type I receptor resulting in IGF-I stimulated autophosphorylation of the beta subunit and phosphorylation of tyrosine-containing substrates. Sasaki *et al.* (1985) showed that phosphorylation of the type I receptor resulted in activation of tyrosine-kinase activity as had been shown previously for the insulin receptor (Rosen *et al.* 1983). In addition, cation requirements and substrate specificities were very similar for the two receptor-associated kinase activities.

We have recently demonstrated that the type II receptor is also phosphorylated in intact cells (Haskell *et al.* 1985). The ATP pools of monolayer cultures of H-35 rat hepatoma cells, BRL 3A2 rat liver cells, Swarm rat chondrosarcoma cells and rat embryo fibroblasts were labelled with $H_3^{32}PO_4$. Cell monolayers were solubilized with detergent, glycoproteins purified by wheat-germ lectin Sepharose affinity chromatography and the type II receptor isolated by IGF-II affinity chromatography. Analysis by SDS/PAGE and autoradiography revealed a phosphorylated species with the M_r expected for the type II receptor. We examined the IGF dependence of the phosphorylation of the type II receptor in rat embryo fibroblasts and BRL 3A2 cells. In rat embryo fibroblasts phosphorylation of the type II receptor was not increased by addition of IGF-II to the cultures. However, rat embryo fibroblasts produce IGF-II, which could potentially autostimulate phosphorylation of the type II receptor. In BRL 3A2 cells that do not produce IGF-II, addition of IGF-II resulted in increased phosphorylation of the type II receptor. Lability of the phosphate–receptor bonds at alkaline pH suggested that phosphorylation was occurring primarily on serine residues. The level of basal phosphorylation of the type II receptors in BRL 3A2 cells was variable, however, suggesting that other factors in addition to IGF control type II receptor phosphorylation.

It has not been possible to demonstrate phosphorylation of the type II receptor in cell-free preparations. Thus when a solubilized glycoprotein preparation containing both type I and type II receptors was incubated with IGF and [^{32}P]ATP only the type I receptor was phosphorylated (Zick *et al.* 1984; Sasaki *et al.* 1985). Similarly, we were unable to demonstrate phosphorylation of poly(Glu,Tyr)4:1 using a purified type II receptor preparation from chondrosarcoma cells together with

[^{32}P]ATP and IGF-I; in the same experiment a solubilized type I receptor preparation exhibited tyrosine kinase activity toward the tyrosine-containing substrate (Sasaki & Haskell, unpublished results). Thus in contrast to insulin and type I IGF receptors the type II IGF receptor appears not to possess intrinsic tyrosine kinase activity. It will be of interest to determine whether type II receptor phosphorylation observed in intact cells plays a role in receptor function or regulation.

SIMILARITY OF THE TYPE I IGF RECEPTOR AND THE INSULIN RECEPTOR

Table 2 outlines the many similarities between the type I IGF receptor and the insulin receptor, some of which have been described earlier in this paper. Although both receptors contain alpha and beta subunits there is evidence for small differences in the size of these common subunits when comparing type I receptors and insulin receptors. Stuart, Pietrzyk, Siu & Furlanetto (1984) used simultaneous double-label affinity cross-linking of human placental type I IGF receptors (labelled with [^{125}I]IGF-I) and insulin receptors (labelled with [^{131}I]insulin) to demonstrate that the type I receptor alpha subunit was 8000 in M_r smaller than the alpha subunit of the insulin receptor. Experiments in which biosynthetically labelled and surface-labelled insulin and IGF receptors were immunoprecipitated with specific monoclonal antibodies and analysed by SDS/PAGE, showed that the beta subunit of the type I receptor was larger than the beta subunit of the insulin receptor (Jacobs *et al.* 1983*a*). The relative contributions of protein and carbohydrate moieties to these size differences are not known.

Biosynthetic labelling experiments in IM-9 lymphocytes in which processing was blocked with monensin revealed a similar-sized M_r 180 000 precursor for the type I IGF receptor and the insulin receptor (Jacobs *et al.* 1983*a*). Analagous to the insulin receptor, the M_r 180 000 type I IGF receptor precursor is presumed to be made up of contiguous alpha and beta subunits.

Experiments with polyclonal and monoclonal antibodies to type I IGF receptors and insulin receptors point to similar antigenic determinants on the two receptors. Using a panel of sera from patients with autoantibodies to the insulin receptor, Kasuga *et al.* (1983) showed that each of seven sera also recognized the type I IGF

Table 2. *Type I IGF receptors and insulin receptors*

	Type I	Insulin
Binds IGF-I > insulin	+	
Binds insulin > IGF-I		+
M_r > 300 000 (native)	+	+
Alpha subunit (M_r 130 000–135 000)	+	+
Beta subunit (M_r 90 000–98 000)	+	+
M_r 180 000 precursor	+	+
Beta subunit phosphorylation	+	+
Tyrosine kinase activity	+	+
Cross-reactivity with heterologous receptor antibody	+	+

receptor but with less reactivity. Similarly, monoclonal antibodies that preferentially immunoprecipitate type I IGF receptors on the one hand or insulin receptors on the other will also immunoprecipitate the heterologous receptor at higher concentrations (Kull *et al.* 1983; Roth *et al.* 1983).

Ullrich *et al.* (1985) have deduced the primary structure of the insulin receptor by cloning and sequencing the cDNA for the insulin receptor. There is one transmembrane region that is in the beta subunit; the alpha subunit appears to be entirely extracellular. There is sequence homology between regions of the cytoplasmic domain of the beta subunit and members of the *src* family of tyrosine-specific protein kinases and even more extensive homology with the avian sarcoma virus UR2 oncogene v-*ros*. Given all the similarities between the insulin receptor and the type I IGF receptor listed in Table 2, it is expected that the type I IGF receptor primary structure will resemble the insulin receptor in its essential features.

RECEPTOR FUNCTION

Most cells have both types of IGF receptors as well as insulin receptors (Rechler & Nissley, 1985). IGF-I, IGF-II and insulin can interact with both insulin receptors and type I IGF receptors; only IGF-I and IGF-II interact with the type II receptor. Because of this extensive cross-reactivity of ligands with these three receptor types it is difficult to assign particular biological responses to specific receptors. Comparison of dose-response curves for eliciting a biological response with competitive binding curves have been helpful but in most cases not conclusive. In chick embryo fibroblasts the dose-response curves of rat IGF-II, insulin and proinsulin for stimulation of DNA synthesis were superimposable on binding curves for inhibition of IGF-II tracer binding (Nissley *et al.* 1977). These data together with the failure to demonstrate a type II receptor on these cells lead to the conclusion that stimulation of DNA synthesis by IGF and insulin in chick embryo fibroblasts proceeds via the type I receptor. Indeed the requirements for high concentrations of insulin for the growth of many cells in defined media suggest that the type I IGF receptor rather than the insulin receptor may be involved in the growth response. Exceptions to this generalization are found in H-35 rat hepatoma (Koontz & Iwahashi, 1981; Koontz, 1984) and F9 mouse teratocarcinoma cells (Nagarajan & Anderson, 1982) where physiological rather than pharmacological concentrations of insulin stimulate DNA synthesis. By doing appropriate experiments using antisera directed against the insulin receptor it has been demonstrated that insulin is acting as a mitogen through the insulin receptor in these cells.

Insulin receptor antisera were also used to demonstrate that IGF-II stimulates glucose oxidation in rat adipocytes by acting through the insulin receptor rather than via the type II receptor, which is also present on these cells (King, Kahn, Rechler & Nissley, 1980).

Recently, Mottola & Czech (1984) used a polyclonal antiserum directed against the type II receptor to provide evidence that IGF-II does not use the type II receptor to stimulate DNA synthesis in H-35 rat hepatoma cells. IGF-II binding could be inhibited by 75 % without affecting the stimulation of DNA synthesis by maximal or submaximal concentrations of rat IGF-II. Since H-35 cells do not appear to have a type I receptor, presumably IGF-II was acting through the insulin receptor. Indeed, to date there are no biological functions that have been shown conclusively to be mediated by the type II receptor. Further studies with anti-receptor antibodies in a variety of systems will be required to define the roles of the type I and type II receptors and the insulin receptors.

RECEPTOR REGULATION

The type I IGF receptor is down-regulated following prolonged incubation with ligand in IM-9 lymphocytes (Rosenfeld, Hintz & Dollar, 1982), human fibroblasts (Rosenfeld & Dollar, 1982) and BC_3H-1 mouse muscle cells (De Vroede *et al.* 1984). In contrast, the type II receptor is not down-regulated in rat chondrosarcoma cells (Stevens, Austen & Nissley, 1983), BC_3H-1 mouse muscle cells (De Vroede *et al.* 1984) and HTC rat hepatoma cells (Heaton *et al.* 1984).

Brief incubation of rat adipocytes or H-35 rat hepatoma cells with insulin leads to a rapid increase in IGF-II binding to the type II receptor (Schoenle, Zapf & Froesch, 1976; King, Rechler & Kahn, 1982; Oppenheimer *et al.* 1983). Agonistic auto-antibodies to the insulin receptor duplicated this effect and Fab fragments of these autoantibodies blocked insulin-stimulated increase in IGF-II binding in rat ad-ipocytes (King *et al.* 1982). Thus the up-regulation of the type II receptor by insulin appears to occur by interaction with the insulin receptor. Two types of experimental approach have led to the conclusion that this up-regulation of the type II receptor by insulin results from cycling of type II receptors from an intracellular compartment to the cell surface. Thus insulin treatment of rat adipocytes resulted in increased binding of a type II receptor polyclonal antibody to the cell surface (Oka, Mottola, Oppenheimer & Czech, 1984). In a second approach, following exposure of the adipocytes to insulin, receptor endocytosis was blocked with KCN and IGF-II binding was analysed according to the method of Scatchard (Wardzala, Simpson, Rechler & Cushman, 1984). Insulin caused a fivefold stimulation in type II receptor number with no change in binding affinity.

IGF BINDING PROTEINS AND IGF RECEPTORS

Unlike insulin, IGF-I and IGF-II are found complexed to larger binding proteins in serum and other extracellular fluids (Hintz, 1984; Nissley & Rechler, 1985). The association of IGF with binding proteins extends to tissue culture systems; although there are examples of cells producing binding protein without producing IGF, the reverse situation has not been described.

There appear to be two classes of IGF binding proteins in serum. A small (M_r 40 000) binding protein is the predominant binding protein in foetal blood (D'Ercole, Willson & Underwood, 1980; White *et al.* 1982), whereas in adult blood the major carrier of IGF is an M_r 150 000 species, which is partially under the control of pituitary growth hormone (White *et al.* 1981). The 150 000 M_r species is made up of subunits. One model for 150 000 M_r binding protein structure proposes that a 40 000 M_r acid-stable binding subunit is complexed to a larger acid-labile component, which does not bind IGF (Furlanetto, 1980). A more recent model describes the 150 000 M_r species as simply being an oligomer of a binding subunit of 24 000–28 000 M_r (Wilkins & D'Ercole, 1985). Binoux, Hardouin, Lassarre & Hossenlopp (1982) have provided competitive binding data that suggest that within the 150 000 and 40 000 M_r classes of IGF binding proteins there may be species which prefer IGF-I over IGF-II and *vice versa*.

The role of the binding proteins has not been defined. The binding proteins appear to prolong the half-life of circulating IGF and thus may constitute both a reservoir and a system for delivery and release of IGF to tissues. Although, on the basis of experiments in which acid-treated binding proteins (free of IGF) were shown to inhibit bioactivity of IGF in systems *in vitro* (Zapf *et al.* 1979; Drop *et al.* 1979; Knauer & Smith, 1980) it has been assumed that the bound forms of IGF are biologically inactive, a purified native IGF binding protein complex has not been available for testing.

What is the relation, if any, between IGF binding proteins and cell surface receptors? On the basis of binding properties the type I IGF receptor is distinct from binding proteins. Whereas insulin binds to the type I receptor, insulin has consistently not competed for IGF tracer binding to binding proteins. The type II receptor also does not recognize insulin. Recently, a hybrid molecule containing the B domain of IGF-I and the A domain of insulin ($A_{insulin}$-B_{IGF-I}) has been shown to recognize binding proteins from a variety of sources but not to interact with the type II receptor, indicating that the binding site of the type II receptor and the binding site of certain binding proteins are different (De Vroede *et al.* 1985*a*).

For *in vitro* studies of the binding of IGF tracer to receptors on cells and membranes, binding proteins present a potential problem in the interpretation of data. For example, Grizzard *et al.* (1984) showed that human placental membranes prepared by differential centrifugation contained a small molecular weight binding protein that could only be removed by extensive washing. Presumably this binding protein represented a contaminant from amniotic fluid and, or, plasma. In monolayer cultures of human skin fibroblasts binding protein released to the media during the binding incubation may produce complex competitive binding curves. Cell-associated binding protein may potentially account for some binding of IGF tracer to the monolayer (De Vroede, Katsoyannis & Rechler, 1985*b*).

CONCLUSIONS

Major differences between type I and type II IGF receptors raise the possibility that these receptors will be found to be coupled to different post-receptor events. In contrast, the similarities between the insulin receptor and the type I IGF receptor are striking, and suggest that, like insulin and IGFs, these two receptors may have evolved from a common ancestral gene.

REFERENCES

AUGUST, G. P., NISSLEY, S. P., KASUGA, M., LEE, L., GREENSTEIN, L. A. & RECHLER, M. M. (1983). Purification of an insulin-like growth factor II receptor from rat chondrosarcoma cells. *J. biol. Chem.* **258**, 9033–9036.

BELL, G.I., MERRYWEATHER, J. P., SANCHEZ-PESCADOR, R., STEMPIEN, M. M., PREISTLY, L., SCOTT, J. & RALL, L. B. (1984). Sequence of a cDNA clone encoding human preproinsulin-like growth factor II. *Nature, Lond.* **310**, 775–777.

BHAUMICK, B., BALA, R. M. & HOLLENBERG, M. D. (1981). Somatomedin receptor of human placenta: solubilization, photolabeling, partial purification, and comparison with insulin receptor. *Proc. natn. Acad. Sci U.S.A.* **78**, 4279–4283.

BINOUX, M., HARDOUIN, S., LASSARRE, C. & HOSSENLOPP, P. (1982). Evidence for production by the liver of two IGF binding proteins with similar molecular weights but different affinities for IGF I and IGF II. Their relations with serum and cerebrospinal fluid IGF binding proteins. *J. clin. Endocr. Metab.* **55**, 600–602.

CHERNAUSEK, S. D., JACOBS, S. & VAN WYK, J. J. (1981). Structural similarities between human receptors for somatomedin C and insulin; analysis by affinity labeling. *Biochemistry* **20**, 7345–7350.

D'ERCOLE, J. A., WILLSON, D. F. & UNDERWOOD, L. E. (1980). Changes in the circulating form of serum somatomedin-C during fetal life. *J. clin. Endocr. Metab.* **51**, 674–676.

DE VROEDE, M. A., KATSOYANNIS, P. G. & RECHLER, M. M. (1985*b*). Insulin-like growth factor I (IGF-I) binding to type I and type II IGF receptors and to IGF-carrier proteins in human fibroblast monolayer cultures is distinguished using insulin-IGF-I hybrid molecules. *Program of the 67th Annual Meet. Endocrine Soc., U.S.A.*, abstract 808.

DE VROEDE, M. A., RECHLER, M. M., NISSLEY, S. P., JOSHI, S., BURKE, G. T. & KATSOYANNIS, P. G. (1985*a*). Hybrid molecules containing the B-domain of insulin-like growth factor (IGF-I) are recognized by IGF carrier proteins. *Proc. natn. Acad. Sci. U.S.A.* **82**, 3010–3014.

DE VROEDE, M. A., ROMANUS, J. A., STANDAERT, M. L., POLLET, R. J., NISSLEY, S. P. & RECHLER, M. M. (1984). Interaction of insulin-like growth factors with a nonfusing mouse muscle cell line: binding, action, and receptor down-regulation. *Endocrinology* **114**, 1917–1929.

DROP, S. L. S., VALIQUETTE, G., GUYDA, H. J., CORVOL, M. T. & POSNER, B.I. (1979). Partial purification and characterization of a binding protein for insulin-like activity (ILAs) in human amniotic fluid: a possible inhibitor of insulin-like activity. *Acta endocr., Copenh.* **90**, 505–518.

DULL, T. J., GRAY, A., HAYFLICK, J. S. & ULLRICH, A. (1984). Insulin-like growth factor II precursor gene organization in relation to insulin gene family. *Nature, Lond.* **310**, 777–781.

FURLANETTO, R. W. (1980). The somatomedin-C binding protein: evidence for a heterologous subunit structure. *J. clin. Endocr. Metab.* **51**, 12–19.

GRIZZARD, J. D., D'ERCOLE, A. J., WILKINS, J. R., MOATS-STAATS, B. M. & WILLIAMS, R. W. (1984). Affinity-labeled somatomedin-C receptors and binding proteins from the human fetus. *J. clin. Endocr. Metab.* **58**, 535–542.

HASKELL, J. F., NISSLEY, S. P., RECHLER, M. M., SASAKI, N., GREENSTEIN, L. A. & LEE, L. (1985). Evidence for phosphorylation of the type II insulin-like growth factor (IGF) receptor in cultured cells. *Biochem. biophys. Res. Commun.* **130**, 793–799.

HEATON, J. H., KRETT, N. L., ALVAREZ, J. M., GELEHRTER, T. D., ROMANUS, J. A. & RECHLER, M. M. (1984). Insulin regulation of insulin-like growth factor action in rat hepatoma cells. *J. biol. Chem.* **259**, 2396–2402.

HINTZ, R. L. (1984). Plasma forms of somatomedin and the binding protein phenomenon. *J. clin. Endocr. Metab.* **31**, 41–42.

JACOBS, S., KULL, F. C. & CUATRECASAS, P. (1983*a*). Monensin blocks the maturation of receptors for insulin and somatomedin C: identification of receptor precursors. *Proc. natn. Acad. Sci. U.S.A.* **80**, 1128–1131.

JACOBS, S., KULL, F. C., EARP, H. S., SVOBODA, M., VAN WYK, J. J., CUATRECASAS, P. (1983*b*). Somatomedin-C stimulates the phosphorylation of the β-subunit of its own receptor. *J. biol. Chem.* **258**, 9581–9584.

JANSEN, M., VAN SCHAIK, F. M. A., RICKER, A. T., BULLOCK, B., WOODS, D. E., GABBAY, K. H., NUSSBAUM, A. L., SUSSENBACH, J. S. & VAN DEN BRANDE, J. L. (1983). Sequence of cDNA encoding human insulin-like growth factor I precursor. *Nature, Lond.* **306**, 609–611.

KASUGA, M., SASAKI, N., KAHN, C. R., NISSLEY, S. P. & RECHLER, M. M. (1983). Antireceptor antibodies as probes of insulin-like growth factor receptor structure. *J. clin. Invest.* **72**, 1459–1469.

KASUGA, M., VAN OBBERGHEN, E., NISSLEY, S. P. & RECHLER, M. M. (1981). Demonstration of two subtypes of insulin-growth factor receptors by affinity cross-linking. *J. biol. Chem.* **256**, 5305–5308.

KING, G. L., KAHN, C. R., RECHLER, M. M. & NISSLEY, S. P. (1980). Direct demonstration of separate receptors for growth and metabolic activities of insulin and multiplication stimulating activity (an insulin-like growth factor) using antibodies to the insulin receptor. *J. clin. Invest.* **66**, 130–140.

KING, G. L., RECHLER, M. M. & KAHN, C. R. (1982). Interactions between receptors for insulin and the insulin-like growth factors on adipocytes. *J. biol. Chem.* **257**, 10001–10006.

KNAUER, D. J. & SMITH, G. L. (1980). Inhibition of biological activity of multiplication-stimulating activity by binding to its carrier protein. *Proc. natn. Acad. Sci. USA* **7**, 7252–7256.

KOONTZ, J. W. (1984). The role of insulin receptor in mediating the insulin-stimulated growth response in Reuber H-35 Cells. *Mol. cell. Biochem.* **58**, 139–146.

KOONTZ, J. W. & IWAHASHI, M. (1981). Insulin as a potent, specific growth factor in a rat hepatoma cell line. *Science* **211**, 947–949.

KULL, F. C., JACOBS, S., SU, Y-F., SVOBODA, M. E., VAN WYK, J. J. & CUATRECASAS, P. (1983). Monoclonal antibodies to receptors for insulin and somatomedin-C. *J. biol. Chem.* **258**, 6561–6566.

MARSHALL, R. M., UNDERWOOD, L. E., VOINA, S. J., FOUSHEE, D. B. & VAN WYK, J. J. (1974). Characterization of the insulin and somatomedin-C receptors in human placental cell membranes. *J. clin. Endocr. Metab.* **39**, 283–292.

MASSAGUE, J. & CZECH, M. P. (1982). The subunit structures of two distinct receptors for insulin-like growth factor I and II and their relationship to the insulin receptor. *J. biol. Chem.* **257**, 5038–5041.

MASSAGUE, J., GUILLETTE, B. J. & CZECH, M. P. (1981). Affinity labeling of multiplication-stimulating activity receptors in membranes from rat and human tissues. *J. biol. Chem.* **256**, 2122–2125.

MEGYESI, K., KAHN, C. R., ROTH, J., FROESCH, E. R., HUMBEL, R. E., ZAPF, J. & NEVILLE, D. M. (1974). Insulin and nonsuppressible insulin-like activity (NSILA-s): evidence for separate plasma membrane receptor sites. *Biochem. biophys. Res. Commun.* **57**, 307–315.

MOTTOLA, C. & CZECH, M. P. (1984). The type II insulin-like growth factor receptor does not mediate increased DNA synthesis in H-35 hepatoma cells. *J. biol. Chem.* **259**, 12705–12713.

NAGARAJAN, L. & ANDERSON, W. B. (1982). Insulin promotes the growth of F9 embryonal carcinoma cells apparently by acting through its own receptor. *Biochem. biophys. Res. Commun.* **106**, 974–980.

NISSLEY, S. P. & RECHLER, M. M. (1985). Insulin-like growth factors: biosynthesis, receptors and carrier proteins. In *Hormonal Proteins and Peptides* (ed. C. H. Li), pp. 127–203. New York: Academic Press.

NISSLEY, S. P., RECHLER, M. M., MOSES, A. C., SHORT, P. A. & PODSKALNY, J. M. (1977). Proinsulin binds to a growth peptide receptor and stimulates DNA synthesis into chick embryo fibroblasts. *Endocrinology* **101**, 708–716.

OKA, Y., MOTTOLA, C., OPPENHEIMER, C. L. & CZECH, M. P. (1984). Insulin activates the appearance of insulin-like growth factor II receptors on the adipocyte cell surface. *Proc. natn. Acad. Sci. U.S.A.* **81**, 4028–4032.

OPPENHEIMER, C. L. & CZECH, M. P. (1983). Purification of the type II insulin-like growth factor receptor from rat placenta. *J. biol. Chem.* **258**, 8539–8542.

OPPENHEIMER, C. L., PESSIN, J. E., MASSAGUE, J., GITOMER W. & CZECH, M. P. (1983). Insulin action rapidly modulates the apparent affinity of the insulin-like growth factor II receptor. *J. biol. Chem.* **258**, 4824–4830.

PERDUE, J. F., CHAN, J. K., THIBAULT, C., RADAJ, P., MILLS, B. & DAUGHADAY, W. H. (1983). The biochemical characterization of detergent-solubilized insulin-like growth factor II receptors from rat placenta. *J. biol. Chem.* **258**, 7800–7811.

RECHLER, M. M. & NISSLEY, S. P. (1985). Receptors for insulin-like growth factors. In *Receptors for Polypeptide Hormones* (ed. B. I. Posner), pp. 227–297. New York: Dekker.

RECHLER, M. M., ZAPF, J., NISSLEY, S. P., FROESCH, E. R., MOSES, A. C., PODSKALNY, J. M., SCHILLING, E. E. & HUMBEL, R. E. (1980). Interactions of insulin-like growth factors I and II and multiplication stimulating activity with receptors and serum carrier proteins. *Endocrinology* **107**, 1451–1459.

RINDERKNECHT, E. & HUMBEL, R. E. (1978a). The amino acid sequence of human insulin-like growth factor I and its structure homology with proinsulin. *J. biol. Chem.* **253**, 2769–2776.

RINDERKNECHT, E. & HUMBEL, R. E. (1978b). Primary structure of human insulin-like growth factor II. *FEBS Lett.* **89**, 283–286.

ROSEN, O. M., HERRERA, R., OLOWE, Y., PETRUZZELLI, L. M. & COBB, M. H. (1983). Phosphorylation activates the insulin receptor tyrosine protein kinase. *Proc. natn. Acad. Sci. U.S.A.* **80**, 3237–3240.

ROSENFELD, R. G. & DOLLAR, L. A. (1982). Characterization of the somatomedin-C/insulin-like growth factor I (SM-C/IGF-I) receptor on cultured human fibroblast monolayers: regulation of receptor concentrations by SM-C/IGF-I and insulin. *J. clin. Endocr. Metab.* **55**, 434–440.

ROSENFELD, R. G., HINTZ, R. L. & DOLLAR, L. A. (1982). Insulin-induced loss of an insulin-like growth factor-I receptor on IM-9 lymphocytes. *Diabetes* **31**, 375–381.

ROTH, R. A., MADDUX, B., WONG, K. Y., STYNE, D. M., VAN VLIET, G., HUMBEL, R. E. & GOLDFINE, I. D. (1983). Interactions of a monoclonal antibody to the insulin receptor with receptors for insulin-like growth factors. *Endocrinology* **112**, 1865–1867.

RUBIN, J. B., SHIA, M. A. & PILCH, P. F. (1983). Stimulation of tyrosine specific phosphorylation *in vitro* by insulin-like growth factor I. *Nature, Lond.* **305**, 438–440.

SASAKI, N., REES-JONES, R. W., ZICK, Y., NISSLEY, S. P. & RECHLER, M. M. (1985). Characterization of insulin-like growth factor I (IGF-I)-stimulated tyrosine kinase activity associated with the β-subunit of type I IGF receptors of rat liver cells. *J. biol. Chem.* **260**, 9793–9804.

SCHOENLE, E., ZAPF, J. & FROESCH, E. R. (1976). Binding of non-suppressible insulin-like activity (NSILA) to isolated fat cells: evidence for two separate membrane acceptor sites. *FEBS Lett.* **67**, 175–179.

STEVENS, R. L., AUSTEN, K. F. & NISSLEY, S. P. (1983). Insulin induced increase in insulin binding to cultured chondrosarcoma chondrocytes. *J. biol. Chem.* **258**, 2940–2944.

STUART, C. A., PIETRZYK, R., SIU, A. K. Q. & FURLANETTO, R. W. (1984). Size discrepancy between somatomedin-C and insulin receptors. *J. clin. Endocr. Metab.* **58**, 1–5.

THIBAULT, C., CHAN. J. K., PERDUE, J. F. & DAUGHADAY, W. H. (1984). Insulin-like growth factor II receptors: molecular radius and molecular weight determination using quantitative polyacrylamide gel electrophoresis. *J. biol. Chem.* **259**, 3361–3367.

ULLRICH, A., BELL, J. R., CHEN, E. Y., HERRERA, R., PETRUZZELLI, L. M., DULL, T. J., GRAY, A., COUSSENS, L., LIAO, Y., TSUBOKAWA, M., JASON, A., SEEBURG, P. H., GRUNFELD, C., ROSEN, O. M. & RAMACHANDRAN, J. (1985). Human insulin receptor and its relationship to the tyrosine kinase family of oncogenes. *Nature, Lond.* **313**, 756–761.

WARDZALA, L. J., SIMPSON, I. A., RECHLER, M. M. & CUSHMAN, S. W. (1984). Potential mechanism of the stimulatory action of insulin on insulin-like growth factor II binding to the isolated rat adipose cell: apparent redistribution of receptors recycling between a large intracellular pool and the plasma membrane. *J. biol. Chem.* **259**, 8378–8383.

WHITE, R. M., NISSLEY, S. P., MOSES, A. C., RECHLER, M. M. & JOHNSONBAUGH, R. E. (1981). The growth hormone dependence of a somatomedin-binding protein in human serum. *J. clin. Endocr. Metab.* **53**, 49–57.

WHITE, R. M., NISSLEY, S. P., SHORT, P. A., RECHLER, M. M. & FENNOY, I. (1982). Developmental pattern of a serum binding protein for multiplication stimulating activity in the rat. *J. clin. Invest.* **69**, 1239–1252.

WHITFIELD, H. J., BRUNI, C. B., RUNZIO, R., TERRELL, J. E., NISSLEY, S. P. & RECHLER, M. M. (1984). Isolation of a cDNA clone encoding rat insulin-like growth factor-II precursor. *Nature, Lond.* **312**, 277–280.

WILKINS, J. R. & D'ERCOLE, J. A. (1985). Affinity labeled plasma somatomedin-C/insulin-like growth factor I binding proteins: evidence of growth hormone dependence and subunit structure. *J. clin. Invest.* **75**, 1350–1358.

ZAPF, J., SCHOENLE, E., JAGARS, G., SAND, I., GRUNWALD, J. & FROESCH, E. R. (1979). Inhibition of the action of nonsuppressible insulin-like activity on isolated rat fat cells by binding to its carrier protein. *J. clin. Invest.* **63**, 1077–1084.

ZICK, Y., SASAKI, N., REES-JONES, R. W., GRUNBERGER, G., NISSLEY, S. P. & RECHLER, M. M. (1984). Insulin-like growth factor-I (IGF-I) stimulates tyrosine kinase activity in purified receptors from a rat liver cell line. *Biochem. biophys. Res. Commun.* **119**, 6–13.

J. Cell Sci. Suppl. 3, 53–64 (1985)
Printed in Great Britain © *The Company of Biologists Limited 1985*

THE CONFORMATION OF INSULIN-LIKE GROWTH FACTORS: RELATIONSHIPS WITH INSULINS

EVA DAFGÅRD, MONA BAJAJ, ANNE MARIE HONEGGER, JIM PITTS, STEPHEN WOOD and TOM BLUNDELL

Laboratory of Molecular Biology, Department of Crystallography, Birkbeck College, London University, Malet Street, London WC1E 7HX, U.K.

SUMMARY

The insulin-like growth factors and hystricomorph insulins have been modelled by interactive computer graphics on the assumption that their sequence homology to insulin implies that they will have a similar tertiary structure. These studies suggest that, although the insulin-related molecules can adopt the insulin fold, they are unlikely to form hexamers and if they form dimers they will be of reduced stability. The non-suppressibility of insulin-like growth factors by anti-insulin antibodies is explained in terms of differences of surface residues in the region A8–A10 and B1–B5. Receptor affinity of insulins and insulin-like growth factors for insulin receptors is explicable in terms of a receptor-binding site in the vicinity of B25 Phe on the insulin surface. An equivalent region around B25 Tyr of insulin-like growth factors may be responsible for their binding to type 1 receptors, although binding type 2 receptors must involve a different surface region not shared by insulin.

INTRODUCTION

The evolution of hormones and growth factors has led to families of polypeptides that often have overlapping activities (Blundell & Humbel, 1980). The insulins and insulin-like growth factors (IGFs) comprise such a divergently evolved family (Rinderknecht & Humbel, 1976, 1978; Humbel *et al.* 1979; Marquardt, Todaro, Henderson & Oroszalan, 1981; Rubin *et al.* 1982). Comparison of their sequences shows that the ability to attain an insulin-like tertiary structure (the insulin fold) has been retained (Blundell, Bedarkar, Rinderknecht & Humbel, 1978; Blundell, Bedarkar & Humbel, 1983). They have also retained a few surface residues in common, which mediate their interactions with insulin and type 1 receptors, although their ability to form dimers, hexamers, bind antibodies and interact with type II receptors has not been universally retained in evolution (for a review, see Rechler & Nissley, 1985).

In this article we review the computer-aided modelling of the insulin-like growth factors and some unusual insulins, based on the structures of porcine, human and hagfish insulins that have been defined by X-ray analysis. We then discuss differences in the ability to form oligomers that are suggested by these models and compare them with experimental data where available. Finally, we consider possible models for receptor interactions. Of particular interest is the evolution of the insulins of some hystricomorph rodents, which include the porcupine and the guinea pig. These insulins have accepted mutations that lead to molecules that are monomeric, have reduced affinity for insulin receptors and have some similarities to the insulin-like growth factors.

COMPUTER-AIDED MODELLING OF INSULIN-LIKE GROWTH FACTORS

Table 1 shows the sequences of some representative insulins, including those from mammalian, reptilian, avian, teleost, elasmobranch, cyclostome and hystricomorph sources. The residues that are conserved in this family include the three cystine bridges, glycines at residues B8 and B23 that allow turns in the main chain, and the residues contributing towards the hydrophobic core: A2 Ile, A16 Leu, B12 Val, B15 Leu, B24 Phe (Blundell, Dodson, Hodgkin & Mercola, 1972; Blundell & Humbel, 1980). The alignment of IGF I and IGF II with these sequences (Table 1) shows that these residues are all conserved in the growth factors (Blundell *et al.* 1978, 1983; Blundell & Humbel, 1980). This implies that the homologous regions of the IGFs may assume conformations identical to those defined by the X-ray analysis of insulin. The short connecting peptides (Table 2) of the IGFs are eight and twelve residues in length but they can easily span the short distance between residues B30 and A1 in the three-dimensional structure of insulin. We have modelled their main-chain conformations using predicted secondary structures that were consistent with a close packing with the body of the globular insulin-like molecule (see Blundell *et al.* 1978, for a discussion). The conformations of the D-peptides were modelled in a similar way. The IGF I molecule was originally modelled using plastic model parts (Blundell *et al.* 1978), but both insulin-like growth factors were later modelled using interactive computer graphics (Blundell *et al.* 1983). The orientations and conformations of surface side-chains were placed using the insulin side-chain positions as guides but optimizing side-chain interactions including hydrogen bonds, ion pairs and van der Waals' contacts. For example, the sequence of rat IGF II (or MSA) has a serine at B20 (Marquardt *et al.* 1981). In most insulins this is glycine, which allows torsion angles (positive ϕ values) in the main chain that are less favourable for L-amino acid side-chains. We have found that the main chain in this region can be remodelled with small local conformational changes to accommodate this substitution. However, it is possible that the conformation is not different from that of porcine insulin, although it would be of higher energy. The orientations and conformations of surface side-chains were placed using the insulin side-chain positions as guides but optimizing side-chain interactions including hydrogen bonds, ion pairs and van der Waals' contacts. Finally, both structures were refined to minimize their energies. The models are shown schematically in Figs 1 and 2. The recently identified variations in the length of the C-peptide of IGF II molecules are also compatible with these models (Jansen *et al.* 1985; Zumstein, Luthi & Humbel, 1985). At the present time these models must be considered as approximate although their excellent internal consistencies (close-packed hydrophobic core, low-energy conformations etc.) are strong indications of their correctness.

COMPUTER-AIDED MODELLING OF INSULINS

As the crystal structures of only porcine, bovine, human and hagfish insulins have been defined at high resolution by X-ray analysis, we have carried out similar model building studies of some other representative insulins including those from an elasmobranch, the dogfish (Bajaj *et al.* 1983) and some hystricomorphs including guinea pig (Horuk *et al.* 1980), casiragua (Blundell & Horuk, 1981), coypu (Bajaj, 1984; Bajaj *et al.* 1985) and cuis (Bajaj, 1984; Bajaj, Blundell, Waterfield & Wollmer, unpublished data). Although the cystine residues, glycines at B8 and B23, and the hydrophobic core residues are all conserved, there are several substitutions in the hystricomorph insulins that present difficulties and may indicate small confor-mational differences. As in rat IGF II (MSA), there is a variety of residues other than glycine at B20, including glutamine (guinea pig), lysine (casiragua and cuis) and arginine (coypu). In a similar way to rat IGF II these may assume the same conformation as the B20 Gly, in which case the energy will be increased, or there may be a small local rearrangement in the conformation, which we believe to be most probable. The substitution of B26 Tyr, which is found in most insulins, by an arginine in casiragua and coypu and by a serine in cuis, may cause small local rearrangements in the adjacent core, but can be accommodated because B26 Tyr is not a completely inaccessible residue. This is consistent with the circular dichroism of casiragua, coypu and cuis insulins, which indicate only small differences in the main-chain conformations compared to porcine insulin (Horuk *et al.* 1980*a,b*; Bajaj, Blundell & Wood, 1984). However, substitution of the surface B22 Arg by aspartate in porcupine and guinea pig insulins leads to a loss of the ion-pair interaction with the neighbouring COOH terminus of the A-chain, and introduces a destabilizing negative charge when both residues are ionized. Thus guinea pig (Wood *et al.* 1975) and porcupine (Horuk *et al.* 1979) insulin circular dichroism spectra are greatly altered at neutral pH where the B22 Asp would be deprotonated, but the spectra become more insulin-like at lower pH. Our computer graphics models (e.g. see Fig. 3) are consistent with these experimental data.

OLIGOMER FORMATION?

Porcine, bovine and human insulins associate to dimers and in the presence of zinc ions to hexamers. Spectroscopic and sedimentation data indicate that avian, teleost, elasmobranchial and most other insulins can also form dimers and hexamers although the dogfish (elasmobranch) insulin appears to form hexamers more weakly (Bajaj *et al.* 1983). On the other hand, hagfish (cyclostome) insulin forms only dimers (Falkmer & Emdin, 1981). These data can be rationalized in terms of maintenance of complementary sets of side-chain residues on surfaces that become inaccessible in the zinc hexamers (Blundell & Wood, 1975). In fact the residues on the periphery of the surfaces involved in hexamer formation at B1–B3 are quite variable in the lower vertebrates. In the elasmobranch the presence of a phenylalanine at B17 probably accounts for the instability of the zinc hexamers (Bajaj *et al.* 1984).

Table 1. *Comparison of the amino acid sequences of insulin and insulin-like growth factors*

A/D-chains	1	2	3	4	5	6	7	8	9	10	11	12	13	14	15	16	17	18	19	20	21	22	23	24	25	26	27	28	29
	Gly	Ile	Val	Glu	Gln	Cys	Cys	Thr	Ser	Ile	Cys	Ser	Leu	Tyr	Gln	Leu	Glu	Asn	Tyr	Cys	Asn								
Mammalian																													
Human																						—	—	—	—	—	—	—	—
Porcine																						—	—	—	—	—	—	—	—
Avian																													
Turkey								His	Asn	Thr												—	—	—	—	—	—	—	—
Reptilian																													
Rattlesnake								Glu	Asn	Thr												—	—	—	—	—	—	—	—
Teleost																													
Cod				Asp				His	Arg	Pro		Asp	Ile	Phe	Asp		Gln					—	—	—	—	—	—	—	—
Elasmobranch																													
Dogfish					His			His	Asn	Thr					Asp			Gly				Gln	—	—	—	—	—	—	—
Clyclostome																													
Hagfish								His	Lys	Arg			Ile		Asn		Gln					—	—	—	—	—	—	—	—
Hystricomorph																													
Guinea pig				Asp					Gly	Thr		Thr	Arg	His		Arg	Gln	Ser				—	—	—	—	—	—	—	—
Chinchilla				Asp								Thr										—	—	—	—	—	—	—	—
Casiragua				Asp					Asn				Arg	Asn			Leu	Thr				—	—	—	—	—	—	—	—
Coypu				Asp					Asn				Arg	Asn			Met	Ser				Asp	—	—	—	—	—	—	—
Porcupine				Asp					Gly	Val							Gln					—	—	—	—	—	—	—	—
Cuis				Asp					Arg			Thr	Ser			Arg	Arg					—	—	—	—	—	—	—	—
IGFs																													
hIGF I				Asp	Glu			Phe	Arg	Ser		Asp		Arg	Arg			Met			Ala	Pro	Leu	Lys	Pro	Ala	Lys	Ser	Ala
hIGF II					Glu			Phe	Arg	Ser		Asp		Ala	Leu			Thr			Ala	Thr	—	—	Pro	Ala	Lys	Ser	Glu
MSA					Glu			Phe	Arg	Ser		Asp		Ala	Leu			Thr			Ala	Thr	—	—	Pro	Ala	Lys	Ser	Glu

Table 1. *Continued*

B-chain	-2	-1	1	2	3	4	5	6	7	8	9	10	11	12	13	14	15	16	17	18	19	20	21	22	23	24	25	26	27	28	29	30	31	32
Mammalian																																		
Human	—	—	Phe	Val	Asn	Gln	His	Leu	Cys	Gly	Ser	His	Leu	Val	Glu	Ala	Leu	Tyr	Leu	Val	Cys	Gly	Glu	Arg	Gly	Phe	Phe	Tyr	Thr	Pro	Lys	Thr	—	—
Porcine	—	—																														Ala	—	—
Avian																																		
Turkey	—	—	Ala	Ala																									Ser			Ala	—	—
Reptilian																																		
Rattlesnake	—	—	Ala	Pro			Arg											Phe		Ile						Tyr			Ser		Arg	Ser	—	—
Teleost																																		
Cod	—	—	Met	Ala	Pro	Pro									Asp								Asp						Asn				—	—
Elasmobranch																																		
Dogfish	—	—	Leu	Pro	Ser														Phe				Pro	Lys		Tyr			Leu			(Asx	Glx	Val)
Cyclostome																																		
Hagfish	—	—	Arg	Thr	Thr	Gly					Lys	Asp			Asn				Ile	Ala			Val			Val			Asp	Tyr	Lys	Met	—	—
Hystricomorph																																		
Guinea pig	—	—			Ser	Arg					Asn					Thr			Ser			Gln	Asp	Asp					Ile	Asp			—	—
Chinchilla	—	—				Lys									Asp								Asp							Met	Ala		—	—
Casiragua	—	—			Tyr	Gly	Arg						Gln		Asp	Thr			Ser			Lys	His	Tyr	Arg	Pro	Ser	Glu					—	—
Coypu	—	—			Tyr	Ser	Arg						Gln		Asp	Thr			Ser			Arg	His	Tyr	Arg	Pro	Asn	Asp					—	—
Porcupine	—	—																				Asn	Asp			Arg					Ala		—	—
Cuis	—	—			Phe	Asn	Arg				Asn				Asp				Val			Lys	Asp	Lys	Ser	Arg							—	—
IGFs																																		
hIGF I	—	—	Gly	Pro	Glu	Thr					Ala	Glu			Asp			Gln	Phe			Asp		Tyr	Phe	Asn	Lys	Pro	Thr				—	—
hIGF II	Ala	Tyr	Arg	Pro	Ser	Glu	Thr				Gly	Glu			Asp			Gln	Phe			Asp		Tyr	Phe	Ser	Arg	Pro	Ala				—	—
MSA	Ala	Tyr	Arg	Pro	Ser	Glu	Thr				Gly	Glu			Asp	Thr		Gln	Phe			Ser	Asp	Tyr	Phe	Ser	Arg	Pro	Ser				—	—

Numbers of residues involved in formation of insulin dimers are underlined; those involved in receptor binding are boxed; other possible receptor residues are encircled. Residues in the human insulin sequence that are conserved in all insulins and IGFs are encircled. Gaps are introduced to maximize homology.

Table 2. *Comparison of the C-peptide sequences of the insulin-like growth factors (IGF I and IGF II) with that of porcine proinsulin*

Amino acid no.	1	2	3	4	5	6	7	8	9	10	11	12	13	14	15	16	17	18	19	20	21	22	23	24	25	26	27	28	29	30	31	32
Porcine	Glu	Ala	Glu	Asn	Pro	Gln	Ala	Gly	Ala	Val	Glu	Leu	Gly	Gly	Gly	Leu	Gly	Gly	Gly	—	Leu	Gln	Ala	Leu	Ala	Leu	Glu	Gly	Pro	Pro	Gln	—
IGF I	—	—	—	—	—	—	—	—	—	—	—	—	—	—	Gly	Tyr	Gly	Ser	Ser	Ser	Arg	Arg	—	—	—	—	—	—	Ala	Pro	Gln	Thr
IGF II	—	—	—	—	—	—	—	—	—	—	—	—	—	—	—	Ser	Arg	Val	Ser	Arg	Arg	Ser	Arg	—	—	—	—	—	—	—	—	—

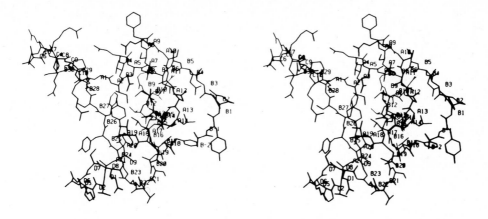

Fig. 1. Stereo view of rat IGF II (MSA).

The central residues responsible for hexamer formation include B10 His, which binds zinc ions, and B14, B17, B20 and A13, which are involved in close-packed hydrophobic interactions. In hagfish insulin, the absence of hexamers is accounted for by the substitution of B10 as aspartate, although the surface is retained as hydrophobic but conservatively varied. In the insulins from the hystricomorphs, guinea pig, cuis, coypu and casiragua the B10 His is also substituted (by asparagine or glutamine), accounting for their inability to form hexamers, and the monomer is further stabilized by larger or more hydrophilic residues at B14 (Thr), B17 (Ser or Val), B20 (Gln, Lys or Arg) and A13 (Arg or Ser) (Bajaj *et al.* 1984). The insulin-like growth factors have substitutions at both B10 (Glu) and B14 (Thr, only in IGF II), and B17 (Phe), indicating that they also do not bind zinc. Zinc insulin hexamers appear to have an intracellular role in transport and storage within the B-granules of the pancreas. It appears therefore that this is a recently evolved aspect of insulin's molecular action (Blundell *et al.* 1972) and is unnecessary for receptor affinity. Its loss in the hystricomorph insulins is therefore not catastrophic. The inability of insulin-like growth factors to form hexamers is not unexpected as these are not stored in granules before release into the circulation (for a review, see Froesch *et al.* 1979).

The ability to form dimers is mediated by hydrophobic interactions involving B12 Val, B16 Tyr, B24 Phe, B25 Phe and B26 Tyr in addition to hydrogen bonding between the antiparallel β-strands B24–B26 of each molecule. These are retained or very conservatively varied (e.g. B16 Tyr→ Phe in reptiles and B25 Phe→ Tyr in reptiles and elasmobranchs) in all insulins except the hystricomorphs where the topologically equivalent residue to B26 in our models is arginine or serine in casiragua, coypu and cuis. This explains the inability of these insulins to form dimers (Bajaj *et al.* 1984). The porcupine and guinea pig insulins are also unable to dimerize at neutral pH but this appears to be due to the conformational changes noted above; the ability to dimerize is almost certainly restored at low pH when the conformation becomes more porcine-insulin-like (Wood, 1976; Horuk *et al.* 1979). For the insulin-like growth factors, the most radical change in the dimer-forming residues is the substitution of glutamine for tyrosine at B16. Otherwise B25 (Phe→ Tyr) and B26 (Tyr→ Phe) are relatively conservative substitutions. We conclude that insulin-like growth factors may have a reduced ability to form dimers.

Of the 51 residues in the human insulin molecule, substitutions have been accepted at between 16 and 20 positions in the guinea pig, cuis, coypu and casiragua compared to seven or less in the closely related hystricomorph, the chinchilla, and other mammal insulins. Much of this variation is in the residues involved in oligomer formation, which accounts for the differences being greater in extent between hystricomorph and human insulins, than between the fish and human insulins (16 substitutions). In a similar way, differences in sequence between both hagfish insulin (19 substitutions) and the human insulin-like growth factors (26 and 27 substitutions) when compared with human insulin are partly accounted for by probable differences in oligomer formation.

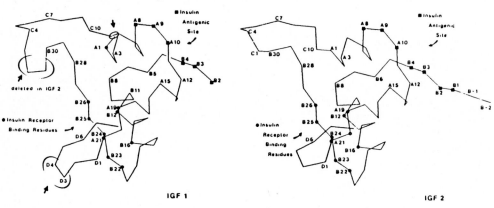

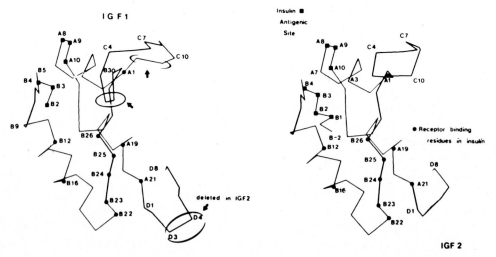

Fig. 2. Schematic diagrams of human IGF I and II (only C_α positions shown) showing positions equivalent to the receptor binding (●) and antigenic (■) sites of insulin.

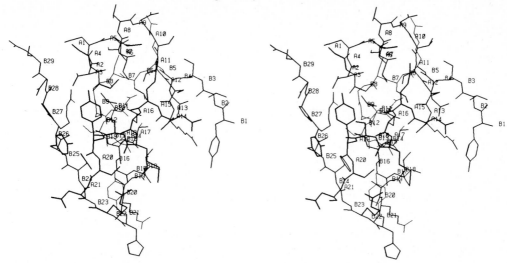

Fig. 3. A stereo view of the proposed three-dimensional structure of the insulin from the hystricomorph rodent, the coypu.

ANTIGENICITY

When antibodies to human or porcine insulin are raised in rabbits they appear to be mainly directed at a surface region involving A8–A10 and the adjacent B1–B4 (see Blundell *et al.* 1972, for a review), although in guinea pigs there appear to be two types, one of which binds a similar region and the other a region involving A1, A19, B22 and surrounding residues (Arquilla, Bromer & Mercola, 1969). This reflects differences in self-association of guinea pig insulin, the further differences in surface residues and possibly the disturbed conformation of the guinea pig insulin itself. The significant differences between both human and bovine insulins and insulin-like growth factors in this region are consistent with the inability of insulin-like growth factors to bind anti-insulin antibodies (see Fig. 2).

RECEPTOR BINDING

Comparative studies of the receptor binding of different insulins to insulin receptors on a variety of cells have suggested that a conservatively varied region is involved in receptor recognition and binding (Blundell *et al.* 1971, 1972; Pullen *et al.* 1976; Dodson, Dodson, Hodgkin & Reynolds, 1979). This appears to include surface residues in the vicinity of B25 Phe. The low affinity of coypu, casiragua and cuis insulins for the insulin receptor is probably due to the substitutions of B26 Thr by arginine or serine. The reduced affinity of guinea pig and porcupine insulins may be a consequence of the substitution of B22 Arg by an aspartate directly, or indirectly through the conformational change induced. The low affinity of proinsulin for insulin receptors must be due to the long connecting peptide that covers part of the receptor binding region.

Fig. 2 shows that some of the receptor binding region of insulin is conserved in the insulin-like growth factor models, although the substitution of B25 Phe → Tyr may lead to a decrease in affinity. More significantly, the C- and D-peptides are arranged on the surface close to this region and these may further interfere with receptor affinity in the same way as the connecting peptide of proinsulin.

Consideration of the affinity of the insulin-like family of growth factors and hormones to the type 1 receptors is more difficult in the absence of extensive binding data of the kind available for insulin receptors. However, the fact that insulin binds, albeit weakly, to such receptors, implies that part of the topologically equivalent region in insulins and growth factors must be involved. It is an attractive hypothesis that a similar region of the insulin-like growth factors is involved, which includes B25 Tyr and the adjacent surface residues including part of the C- and D-peptides (King et al. 1982). In this case it is possible that coypu, casiragua and dogfish insulins might bind more strongly to type 1 receptors. This is consistent with the ability of the hystricomorph insulins to stimulate thymidine incorporation to a greater maximum than other mammalian insulins (King & Kahn, 1981; Bajaj, 1984; Bajaj et al. 1984), although this was not confirmed by the work of King, Kahn & Heldin (1983). Other residues in the B-chain that reduce oligomer formation in both insulin-like growth factors and some hystricomorph insulins may also be involved in binding type 1 receptors.

The observation that insulins do not bind to IGF type II receptors (Czech et al. 1984) implies that these receptor interactions are mediated by a very different region possibly involving the C- and D-peptides and other residues that are unique to the insulin-like growth factors.

NEW APPROACHES TO THE UNDERSTANDING OF RECEPTOR INTERACTIONS

Of course the ultimate description of hormone and growth factor–receptor interactions will come from a study of the direct binding to the purified receptors, which now seems possible. We are pursuing this attractive possibility by isolating and characterizing complexes between the hormones and growth factors and the receptor binding domains, which appear to be largely extrinsic to the membrane. Such complexes may be studied by both nuclear magnetic resonance and X-ray techniques.

In the meantime other approaches may be helpful in further defining receptor interactions. Site-specific mutagenesis combined with recently developed computer-aided design appears to offer particular advantages. At Birkbeck we have clones of proinsulin, IGF I and IGF II, which we can engineer using mismatch priming and express in Escherichia coli to give specifically substituted growth factors and hormones. The location and nature of the engineered changes is aided by computer graphics techniques, which enable volumes of the molecular structures to be mapped onto a three-dimensional bit grid in the computer and compared using logical operations such as 'and' to get inclusive volumes and surfaces, 'and not' to get differences etc. (Honegger & Blundell, 1983). These methods can be used to compare molecular topographies of natural and engineered molecules and correlated with biological data on the recombinant DNA molecules.

We thank Professor Axel Wollmer, Dr Norman Lazarus, Dr Richard Horuk, Dr Linda Gowan, Dr Michael Waterfield, Dr Ian Tickle, Dr Sudhir Bedarkar, Dr Guy Dodson, Professor Dorothy Hodgkin, Dr Rene Humbel, Professor Sture Falkmer, Dr Stefan Emdin, Dr Wilhelm Engstrom and others who have contributed to the ideas reviewed here, which have evolved since the successful elucidation of the 3-D structure of insulin in 1969. This work was supported by grants from the Swedish Medical Research Council (project no. 12X-718) and the U.K. Science and Engineering Research Council.

REFERENCES

ARQUILLA, E. R., BROMER, W. W. & MERCOLA, D. A. (1969). *Diabetes* **18**, 193–198.

BAJAJ, M. (1984). Ph.D. thesis, University of London, U.K.

BAJAJ, M., BLUNDELL, T. L., PITTS, J. E., WOOD, S. P., TATNELL, M. A., FALKMER, S., EMDIN, S. O., GOWAN, L. K., CROW, H., SCHWABE, C., WOLLMER, A. & STRASSBURGER, W. (1983). *Eur. J. Biochem.* **135**, 532–542.

BAJAJ, M., BLUNDELL, T. L., HORUK, R., PITTS, J. E., WOOD, S. P., GOWAN, L. K., SCHWABE, C., WOLLMER, A., GLIEMAN, J. & GAMMELTOFT, S. (1985). *Biochem. J.* (in press).

BAJAJ, M., BLUNDELL, T. L. & WOOD, S. P. (1984). *Biochem. Soc. Symp.* **49**, 45–54.

BLUNDELL, T. L., BEDARKAR, S. & HUMBEL, R. E. (1983). *Fedn Proc. Fedn Am. Socs exp. Biol.* **42**, 2592–2597.

BLUNDELL, T. L., BEDARKAR, S., RINDERKNECHT, E. & HUMBEL, R. E. (1978). *Proc. natn. Acad. Sci. U.S.A.* **75**, 180–184.

BLUNDELL, T. L., DODSON, G. G., DODSON, E. J., HODGKIN, D. C. & VIJAYAN, M. (1971). *Recent Prog. Horm. Res.* **27**, 1–40.

BLUNDELL, T. L., DODSON, G. G., HODGKIN, D. C. & MERCOLA, D. A. (1972). *Adv. Protein Chem.* **26**, 279–402.

BLUNDELL, T. L. & HORUK, R. E. (1981). *Hoppe-Seyler's Z. physiol. Chem.* **362**, 727–737.

BLUNDELL, T. L. & HUMBEL, R. E. (1980). *Nature, Lond.* **287**, 781–787.

BLUNDELL, T. L. & WOOD, S. P. (1975). *Nature, Lond.* **257**, 197–203.

CZECH, M. D., MASSAGUE, J., YU, K., OPPENHEIMER, C. L. & MOTTALA, C. (1984). In *The Importance of Islets of Langerhans for Modern Endocrinology*, pp. 41–53. New York: Raven Press.

DODSON, E. J., DODSON, G. G., HODGKIN, D. C. & REYNOLDS, C. D. (1979). *Can. J. Biochem.* **57**, 469–479.

FALKMER, S. & EMDIN, S. O. (1981). In *Structural Studies on Molecules of Biological Interest* (ed. G. G. Dodson, J. P. Glusker & D. Sayre), pp. 420–440. Oxford: Clarendon Press.

FROESCH, E. R., ANDRES, R., ERNEST, C., HASELBACHES, G. K., RINDERKNECHT, E. & WILSON, K. (1979). *Nature, Lond.* **279**, 439–440.

HONEGGER, A. & BLUNDELL, T. L. (1983). In *Insulin-like Growth Factors/Somatomedins: Basic Chemistry, Biology and Clinical Importance* (ed. E. M. Spencer), pp. 93–113. New York: Walter de Gruyter & Co.

HORUK, R., BLUNDELL, T. L., LAZARUS, N. R., NEVILLE, R. W. J., STONE, D. & WOLLMER, A. (1980a). *Nature, Lond.* **286**, 822–824.

HORUK, R., GOODWIN, P., O'CONNOR, K., NEVILLE, R. W. J., LAZARUS, N. R. & STONE, D. (1979). *Nature, Lond.* **279**, 439–440.

HORUK, R., WOOD, S. P., BLUNDELL, T. L., LAZARUS, N. R., NEVILLE, R. W. J., RAPER, J. H. & WOLLMER, A. (1980b). *Horm. Cell. Reguln* **4**, 123–139.

HUMBEL, R. E., ANDRES, R., ERNEST, C., HASELBACHES, G. K., RINDERKNECHT, E. & WILSON, K. (1979). *Diabetes Int. Congr. Series* **506**, 254–258.

JANSEN, M., VAN SCHAIK, F. M. A., VAN TOL, H., VAN DEN BRANDE, J. L. & SUSSENBACH, J. S. (1985). *FEBS Lett.* **179**, 243–246.

KING, G. L. & KAHN, C. R. (1981). *Nature, Lond.* **292**, 644–646.

KING, G. L., KAHN, D. R. & HELDIN, C-H. (1983). *Proc. natn. Acad. Sci. U.S.A.* **80**, 1308–1312.

KING, G. L., KAHN, D. R., SAMUELS, B., DANHO, W., BULLESBACH, E. E. & GATTNER, H. G. (1982). *J. Cell Chem.* **257**, 10 869–10 873.

MARQUARDT, H., TODARO, G. J., HENDERSON, L. E. & OROSZLAN, S. (1981). *J. biol. Chem.* **256**, 6859–6863.

PULLEN, R. A., LINDSAY, D. G., WOOD, S. P., TICKLE, I. J., BLUNDELL, T. L., WOLLMER, A., KRAIL, G., BRANDENBURG, D., ZAHN, H., GLIEMANN, J. & GAMMELTOFT, S. (1976). *Nature, Lond.* **259**, 369–373.

RECHLER, M. M. & NISSLEY, S. D. (1985). *Annu. Rev. Physiol.* **47**, 425–442.

RINDERKNECHT, E. & HUMBEL, R. E. (1976). *Proc. natn. Acad. Sci. U.S.A.* **73**, 2365–2369.

RINDERKNECHT, E. & HUMBEL, R. E. (1978). *J. biol. Chem.* **253**, 2769–2776.

RUBIN, R. S., MARIZ, I., JACOBS, J. W., DAUGHADAY, W. H. & BRADSHAW, R. A. (1982). *Endocrinology* **110**, 734–740.

WOOD, S. P. (1976). Ph.D. thesis, University of Sussex, U.K.

WOOD, S. P., BLUNDELL, T. L., WOLLMER, A., LAZARUS, N. R. & NEVILLE, R. W. J. (1975). *Eur. J. Biochem.* **55**, 532–542.

ZUMSTEIN, P. P., LUTHI, C. & HUMBEL, R. E. (1985). *Proc. natn. Acad. Sci. U.S.A.* (in press).

J. Cell Sci. Suppl. 3, 65–76 (1985)
Printed in Great Britain © The Company of Biologists Limited 1985

PLATELET-DERIVED GROWTH FACTOR: MECHANISM OF ACTION AND RELATION TO ONCOGENES

C.-H. HELDIN[1,*], C. BETSHOLTZ[2], A. JOHNSSON[1], M. NISTÉR[2], B. EK[1], L. RÖNNSTRAND[1], Å. WASTESON[3] AND B. WESTERMARK[2]

[1]*Department of Medical and Physiological Chemistry, Box 575, Biomedical Center, S-751 23 Uppsala, Sweden*
[2]*Department of Pathology, University Hospital, S-751 85 Uppsala, Sweden*
[3]*Clinical Research Center, University Hospital, S-581 85 Linköping, Sweden*

SUMMARY

Recent studies of platelet-derived growth factor (PDGF) have revealed several structural and functional similarities between this growth factor or components linked to its mechanism of action and certain oncogene products: PDGF itself has a structural homology with the transforming protein of simian sarcoma virus, the PDGF receptor has a functional homology (tyrosine kinase activity) with a family of oncogene products, and PDGF induces the expression of the cellular counterparts of *myc* and *fos*. In addition, several tumour cell lines have been found to produce PDGF-like growth factors, which may cause autocrine stimulation of growth. We interpret these findings as indicating that regulatory components along the PDGF-dependent mitogenic pathway may have oncogenic properties if they are inappropriately expressed or activated.

INTRODUCTION

Platelet-derived growth factor (PDGF) is the major mitogen in serum for connective tissue-derived cells (for a recent review on PDGF, see Heldin, Wasteson & Westermark, 1985). The *in vivo* function of PDGF is not known, but it has been speculated that it has a role in normal as well as pathological cell proliferation, e.g. in conjunction with wound healing, atherosclerosis, myelofibrosis and neoplasia. Our major interest in PDGF research comes from studies on the control of growth of cells in culture. Several recent findings link growth factors and components involved in their mechanism of action to oncogene products. As will be reviewed in this article, studies on PDGF have been particularly illustrative in this context.

THE STRUCTURE OF PDGF AND ITS RELATION TO p28^{sis}

The native PDGF-molecule has an M_r of about 30×10^3 and consists of two different disulphide-bonded polypeptide chains of similar size, designated A and B (Johnsson, Heldin, Westermark & Wasteson, 1982). The molecule is probably a heterodimer of one A chain and one B chain, but the existence of homodimers A–A and B–B has not been ruled out. A dimer structure for PDGF appears to be important for the mitogenic activity, since reduction irreversibly inactivates PDGF.

---

*Author for correspondence.

Determination of a partial amino acid sequence for PDGF has shown that the two polypeptide chains are homologous with each other and that one of them is almost identical to part of p28[sis], the transforming protein of simian sarcoma virus (SSV) (Waterfield *et al.* 1983; Doolittle *et al.* 1983; Devare *et al.* 1983; Johnsson *et al.* 1984). Sequence analysis of the human c-*sis* gene has established that it is identical to the gene for the B chain of PDGF (Josephs, Guo, Ratner & Wong-Staal, 1984; Chiu *et al.* 1984; Johnsson *et al.* 1984).

The close structural relationship between the B chain of PDGF and p28[sis] infers a corresponding functional homology; i.e. a PDGF-like growth factor may operate in SSV-induced transformation via interaction with the PDGF receptor and autocrine stimulation of growth. In support of this hypothesis, cell lysates and conditioned media of SSV-transformed cells have been found to contain growth factor activity that can be inhibited by PDGF antibodies (Deuel *et al.* 1983; Bowen-Pope, Vogel & Ross, 1984; Owen, Pantazis & Antoniades, 1984; Garrett *et al.* 1984; Johnsson *et al.* 1985*b*). Studies on the biosynthesis and maturation of p28[sis] have revealed that the product is rapidly dimerized and then proteolytically cleaved at both the N terminus and the C terminus (Robbins *et al.* 1983). The structure of the active protein is thus probably very similar to a PDGF B–B homodimer.

If a secreted PDGF-like growth factor causes autocrine stimulation of growth via binding to cell surface PDGF receptors, one would expect that exogenously added PDGF antibodies would inhibit the growth of the producer cells. In order to test this prediction we have used human foreskin fibroblasts infected with SSV. Indeed, PDGF antibodies added to these cells inhibit their growth as well as normalize their transformed phenotype (Johnsson *et al.* 1985*a*). Similarly PDGF antibodies have been found to inhibit the growth of other SSV-transformed cells (Huang, Huang & Deuel, 1984). These data thus support the hypothesis that a PDGF-like growth factor is involved in SSV-induced cell transformation.

PRODUCTION OF PDGF-LIKE GROWTH FACTORS BY NORMAL AND MALIGNANT CELLS

Several recent observations indicate that PDGF-like growth factors may be implicated in autocrine stimulation of growth also in cell types other than SSV-transformed cells. Thus PDGF-like growth factors have been identified in the conditioned media of a variety of different cell types, normal as well as malignant (Table 1). We have partially purified and characterized the factors produced by human osteosarcoma and glioma cell lines. Their structural and functional characteristics are similar and possibly identical to PDGF (Heldin, Westermark & Wasteson, 1980; Nistér, Heldin, Wasteson & Westermark, 1984; Betsholtz *et al.* 1983). Thus it is possible that the normal gene(s) for PDGF are aberrantly expressed in these cell lines. An involvement of PDGF-like growth factors in certain forms of neoplasia may not be uncommon since *sis*-related $4 \cdot 2 \times 10^3$ base-pair transcripts have been found in a high proportion of sarcoma and glioma cell lines, i.e. cell types that carry PDGF receptors (Eva *et al.* 1982).

In order to investigate whether the endogenous production of a PDGF-like growth factor causes autocrine stimulation of growth, we studied the human osteosarcoma cell line U-2 OS. These cells do not show any specific binding of PDGF (Heldin, Westermark & Wasteson, 1981). Though this is probably due to receptor blocking and down regulation, and may as such be a sign of functional activity of the endogenously produced growth factor, it poses a practical problem when one wants to prove that the same cells that produce the growth factor also respond to it. If there is an inverse relationship between growth factor production and receptor number, one would expect to find receptors on cells that produce less growth factor. Indeed a low-producer clone of the osteosarcoma cells had a certain number of specific binding sites for [^{125}I]PDGF (Betsholtz, Westermark, Ek & Heldin, 1984). These receptors were functional; PDGF stimulated tyrosine phosphorylation of a $185 \times 10^3 M_r$ component, which is probably the PDGF receptor itself (see below), in membranes as well as in intact cells (Betsholtz *et al.* 1984). Immunoprecipitation of metabolically labelled osteosarcoma cells using an antiserum against phosphotyrosine revealed that

Table 1. *Production by various cell types of PDGF-like growth factors*

Cell type	References
Non-transformed cells	
Smooth muscle cells	Seifert *et al.* (1984); Nilsson *et al.* (1985)
Endothelial cells	DiCorleto & Bowen-Pope (1983)
Cytotrophoblasts	Goustin *et al.* (1985)
Cell lines derived from 'spontaneous' tumours	
U-2 OS, SAOS-2 (osteosarcoma)	Heldin *et al.* (1980); Betsholtz *et al.* (unpublished)
U-4 SS (synovial sarcoma)	Betsholtz *et al.* (unpublished)
B-5 GT (giant cell sarcoma)	Betsholtz *et al.* (unpublished)
U-343 MGa, U-178 MG (glioma)	Nistér *et al.* (1984); Nistér *et al.* (unpublished)
RD (rhabdomyosarcoma)	Betsholtz *et al.* (1983)
L5 (myogenic cell line)	Sejersen *et al.* (unpublished)
PSA-1-G (teratocarcinoma)	Gudas *et al.* (1983)
Hep G2 (hepatoma)	Bowen-Pope *et al.* (1984)
U-1810 (lung carcinoma)	Betsholtz *et al.* (unpublished)
T24 (bladder carcinoma)	Bowen-Pope *et al.* (1984)
Neuro 2A (neuroblastoma)	Van Zoelen *et al.* (1985)
Virus transformed cells	
SSV-transformed cells	Deuel *et al.* (1983)
Kirsten murine sarcoma virus transformed cells	Bowen-Pope *et al.* (1984)
Moloney murine sarcoma virus transformed cells	Bowen-Pope *et al.* (1984)
Adenovirus-transformed cells	Bowen-Pope *et al.* (1984)
SV40-transformed cells	Dicker *et al.* (1981)

The table lists cells that have been shown to produce components that compete with [^{125}I]PDGF for binding to its receptor. In addition, HTLV-transformed cells (Josephs *et al.* 1984), several additional osteosarcoma and glioma cell lines (Eva *et al.* 1982) and a smooth muscle tumour cell line (Norris *et al.* 1984), have been shown to express c-*sis* and are therefore likely to produce PDGF-like growth factors.

a $115 \times 10^3 \, M_r$ component was constitutively phosphorylated in these cells. Since a component of similar M_r is also phosphorylated in human fibroblasts, but only after stimulation with PDGF (Ek & Heldin, 1984), this may reflect the fact that the postreceptor pathway is permanently activated in these cells.

Evidence for autocrine receptor activation in this clone of osteosarcoma cells was thus obtained. However, contrary to our findings with SSV-transformed cells, antibodies against PDGF had no effect on the growth rate of these cells (Betsholtz *et al.* 1984, and unpublished). Similarly PDGF antibodies have no effect on the growth of human glioma cell lines producing PDGF-like growth factors (Nistér *et al.*, unpublished). Therefore, it is possible that the endogenous production of PDGF-like growth factors has no significance for the growth of the cells. Alternatively, the endogenously produced growth factor may activate the PDGF receptor at a site where it is inaccessible to exogenously added antibodies, e.g. the interaction may take place inside the cell and involve newly synthesized receptors before they are inserted in the membrane.

One of the PDGF-producing glioma cell lines was cloned and individual cell clones analysed with regard to PDGF production and PDGF binding. Examination of about 80 different clones revealed a remarkable variability between different clones in both these parameters (Nistér *et al.* 1985). Clones producing much of the PDGF-like growth factor were, as expected, found to have a low number of PDGF receptors. However, several low producers also showed a low binding of [^{125}I]PDGF, suggesting that a clonal variation in the expression of the genes for both the growth factor and the PDGF receptor. A correlation was found between the amount of PDGF produced and the growth rate of the cells under serum-free conditions, supporting the assumption that the endogenous growth factor production is of significance for autocrine growth stimulation. Furthermore, a correlation was noticed between PDGF production and passage level, indicating that high-producer cells may have a growth advantage over low-producer cells.

Taken together, the available data support the assumption that PDGF-like growth factors may participate in autocrine stimulation of growth. This may then occur via two different mechanisms. One is represented by SSV-transformed human fibroblasts, where the growth factor is secreted from the cell and where exogenously added PDGF antibodies inhibit the stimulation (Fig. 1A). The other one is represented by certain human osteosarcoma and glioma cell lines, where a significant portion of the receptor activation occurs in a compartment inaccessible to PDGF antibodies (Fig. 1B).

THE PDGF RECEPTOR

PDGF exerts its mitogenic action via binding to specific cell surface receptors on responsive cells (Heldin *et al.* 1981). The receptor is a transmembrane glycoprotein of M_r 185×10^3 (Glenn, Bowen-Pope & Ross, 1982; Heldin, Ek & Rönnstrand, 1983). It is composed of two functional parts, an extracellular ligand binding domain, and an intracellular effector domain with an associated PDGF-stimulatable

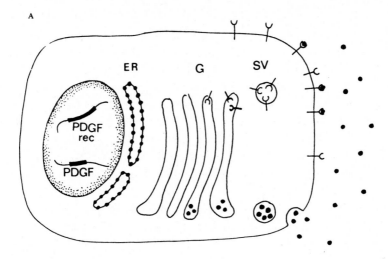

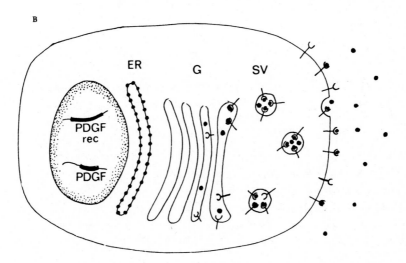

Fig. 1. Possible mechanisms for autocrine growth stimulation. A. The endogenously produced growth factor is exported from the cell and interacts with growth factor receptors at the cell surface. B. The endogenous growth factor interacts with and activates newly synthesized growth factor receptors inside the cell, before they have reached the cell surface. Reproduced with permission from Betsholtz *et al.* (1984). ER, endoplasmic reticulum; G, Golgi apparatus; SV, secretory vesicle.

tyrosine kinase activity (Ek, Westermark, Wasteson & Heldin, 1982; Nishimura, Huang & Deuel, 1982; Pike, Bowen-Pope, Ross & Krebs, 1983). The kinase activity is likely to be an integral part of the receptor molecule, since it has affinity for PDGF-Sepharose (Heldin *et al.* 1983) and since the kinase activity remains associated with highly purified receptor preparations (Rönnstrand *et al.*, unpublished). The functional organization of the PDGF receptor is thus very similar to that of other tyrosine kinase associated growth factor receptors, e.g. the receptors for epidermal growth factor (EGF) (Cohen, Ushiro, Stoscheck & Chinkers, 1982), insulin (Kasuga *et al.* 1983) and insulin-like growth factor I (Jacobs *et al.* 1983). That tyrosine phosphorylation is involved in control of cell proliferation is further supported by the findings that several oncogene products are tyrosine kinases (Bishop, 1983).

Incubation of membranes from human fibroblasts with PDGF and radioactively labelled ATP led to the phosphorylation of components of 185×10^3 and $130 \times 10^3 M_r$ (Ek *et al.* 1982; Ek & Heldin, 1982). The $185 \times 10^3 M_r$ component represents the PDGF receptor proper, which undergoes autophosphorylation (Heldin *et al.* 1983). The $130 \times 10^3 M_r$ component is a fragment of the receptor, formed after cleavage by an endogenous Ca^{2+}-dependent SH-protease (Ek & Heldin, unpublished). The degraded form of the receptor retains kinase activity. It is not known whether this proteolysis has any significance in the mechanism of action of PDGF.

Autophosphorylation of the PDGF receptor on tyrosine residues also occurs in intact cells (Ek & Heldin, 1984). Furthermore, the receptor of intact fibroblasts was also found to contain phosphate bound to serine residues. This suggests that the various functional properties of the receptor, i.e. ligand binding, kinase activity and receptor turnover, may be regulated by phosphorylations involving two different types of kinases: autophosphorylation on tyrosine residues and phosphorylation on serine residues by as yet unidentified kinases.

Mechanism of action of PDGF

The mechanism whereby the mitogenic signal is transmitted from the activated PDGF receptor further into the cell is largely unknown. In view of the functional homology between several growth factor receptors and certain oncogene products, it is likely that the receptor-associated tyrosine kinase is involved. Several methods have been used to identify substrates for the PDGF receptor kinase. Cooper *et al.* (1982) analysed lysates from metabolically labelled, PDGF-stimulated cells by two-dimensional electrophoresis; gels were then treated with alkali in order to hydrolyse phosphoserine. This method revealed certain components in the M_r region 45×10^3 to 43×10^3 in both 3T3 cells and human fibroblasts. Nakamura, Martinez & Weber (1983) found the major increase in tyrosine phosphorylation in PDGF-stimulated chick cells in the same M_r region. Another approach was taken by Ek & Heldin (1984) and Frackelton, Tremble & Williams (1984), who used antisera that specifically recognize phosphotyrosine. This method identified the PDGF receptor as the major tyrosine-phosphorylated component in PDGF-stimulated cells. In addition, several other components were found, including a $115 \times 10^3 M_r$ component. The function of these components, or their involvement in PDGF-stimulated mitogenesis, is not known.

Other rapid effects of PDGF on cells include activation of protein kinase C (Rozengurt, Rodriguez-Pena & Smith, 1983), a serine/threonine kinase, which is the target for certain tumour promoters (Castagna *et al.* 1982), as well as mobilization of Ca^{2+} from intracellular pools (Moolenar, Tertoolen & de Laat, 1984). Both these effects, which are likely to be important in the mitogenic pathway, can be explained by the stimulatory effect of PDGF on phosphatidylinositol metabolism (Habenicht *et al.* 1981; Berridge, Heslop, Irvine & Brown, 1984). This results in breakdown of phosphatidylinositol bisphosphate to diacylglycerol and inositol trisphosphate, which activates protein kinase C (Nishizuka, 1984) and mobilizes Ca^{2+} (Berridge & Irvine, 1984), respectively. PDGF also rapidly stimulates the amiloride-sensitive NA^+/H^+ exchanger (Burns & Rozengurt, 1983; Cassel *et al.* 1983), leading to an alkalinization of the cytoplasm.

It is known that gene expression is a necessary event in PDGF-stimulated mitogenesis since inhibitors of mRNA synthesis block cell proliferation (Smith & Stiles, 1981). Recent studies have indicated that PDGF induces the genes of several proteins (Pledger, Hart, Locatell & Scher, 1981; Cochran, Reffel & Stiles, 1983; Linzer & Nathans, 1983), including c-*myc* (Kelly, Cochran, Stiles & Leder, 1983) and c-*fos* (Greenberg & Ziff, 1984). It is possible that the products of c-*myc* and c-*fos*, which are localized in the nucleus, function as regulators of the expression of the genetic program that controls cell proliferation.

RELATIONSHIP BETWEEN THE MECHANISM OF ACTION OF GROWTH FACTORS AND ONCOGENE PRODUCTS

In conclusion, studies on PDGF and cellular components linked to its action have revealed several connections with retroviral oncogenes. Together with additional information from studies on other growth factors, this suggests that proto-oncogenes encode proteins that operate in the regulation of normal mitogenesis or differentiation; these genes may obtain transforming potential by aberrant expression, mutation or recombination, leading to the synthesis of proteins that perturb the mitogenic pathway at a regulatory point (see Heldin & Westermark, 1984).

Fig. 2 illustrates schematically the mitogenic pathway of growth factors and how one can envisage that various retroviral oncogenes interfere with this pathway at different levels. The basis for the assignment of the oncogenes to various levels of growth factor action is the current knowledge of their amino acid sequence, enzymic activity and subcellular localization (for references, see reviews by Bishop, 1983; Land, Parada & Weinberg, 1983; Heldin & Westermark, 1984; Hunter, 1984).

(1) Oncogenes may code for a growth factor that acts by autocrine stimulation of growth. The *sis* product, which is a PDGF agonist, is an example in this category.

(2) Oncogenes may code for proteins that mimic the action of activated growth factor receptors. The *erbB* product, which corresponds to a truncated EGF receptor

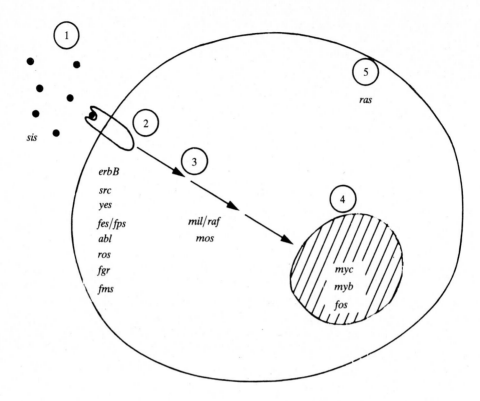

Fig. 2. Assignment of various retroviral oncogenes to functional groups along the growth factor dependent mitogenic pathway. For discussion see the text.

(Downward et al. 1984), is an example in this group. Other oncogene products with tyrosine kinase activity may also belong to this category. The fms product has not yet been shown to be a tyrosine kinase, but since it has an extensive amino acid homology with the tyrosine kinases and is probably a membrane protein (Hampe, Gobet, Sherr & Galibert, 1984), it has been placed in this group.

(3) The oncogene products of mos (Kloetzer, Maxwell & Arlinghaus, 1983) and raf/mil (Moelling et al. 1984) have been shown to have serine/threonine kinase activity. These proteins may thus be involved in growth stimulation in a manner similar to protein kinase C, which is a serine/threonine kinase that is activated by PDGF and other growth factors.

(4) Of the group of nuclear oncogene products, at least two, the products of myc and fos, have normal counterparts that are induced by growth factors.

(5) The ras family of oncogene products constitute a separate group. Their products are localized at the cell surface, have GTPase activity and have a structural homology with signal transducing G proteins linked to the adenylate cyclase or other effector systems (Hurley et al. 1984). Their activity is required late in G_1, immediately before the S phase (Mulcahy, Smith & Stacey, 1985).

The categorization of oncogenes above is not meant to be definitive but merely as an attempt to summarize the present knowledge. Future work is likely to lead to extensions and alterations of this model.

Our work cited in the text was supported by the Swedish Cancer Society, the Swedish Medical Research Council and The University of Uppsala.

REFERENCES

BERRIDGE, M. J., HESLOP, J. P., IRVINE, R. F. & BROWN, K. D. (1984). Inositol trisphosphate formation and calcium mobilization in Swiss 3T3 cells in response to platelet-derived growth factor. *Biochem. J.* **222**, 195–201.

BERRIDGE, M. J. & IRVINE, R. F. (1984). Inositol trisphosphate, a novel second messenger in cellular signal transduction. *Nature, Lond.* **312**, 315–321.

BETSHOLTZ, C., HELDIN, C.-H., NISTÉR, M., EK, B., WASTESON, Å & WESTERMARK, B. (1983). Synthesis of a PDGF-like growth factor in human glioma and sarcoma cells suggests the expression of the cellular homologue to the transforming protein of simian sarcoma virus. *Biochem. biophys. Res. Commun.* **117**, 176–182.

BETSHOLTZ, C., WESTERMARK, B., EK, B. & HELDIN, C.-H. (1984). Coexpression of a PDGF-like growth factor and PDGF receptors in a human osteosarcoma cell line: implications for autocrine receptor activation. *Cell* **39**, 447–457.

BISHOP, J. M. (1983). Cellular oncogenes and retroviruses. *A. Rev. Biochem.* **52**, 301–354.

BOWEN-POPE, D. F., VOGEL, A. & ROSS, R. (1984). Production of platelet-derived growth factor-like molecules and reduced expression of platelet-derived growth factor receptors accompany transformation by a wide spectrum of agents. *Proc. natn. Acad. Sci. U.S.A.* **81**, 2396–2400.

BURNS, C. P. & ROZENGURT, E. (1983). Serum, platelet-derived growth factor, vasopressin and phorbol esters increase intracellular pH in Swiss 3T3 cells. *Biochem. biophys. Res. Commun.* **116**, 931–938.

CASSEL, D., ROTHENBERG, P., ZHUANG, Y., DEUEL, T. F. & GLASER, L. (1983). Platelet-derived growth factor stimulates Na^+/H^+ exchange and induces cytoplasmic alkalinization in NR6 cells. *Proc. natn. Acad. Sci. U.S.A.* **80**, 6224–6228.

CASTAGNA, M., TAKAI, Y., KAIBUCHI, K., SANO, K., KIKKAWA, U. & NISHIZUKA, Y. (1982). Direct activation of calcium-activated, phospholipid-dependent protein kinase by tumor-promoting phorbol esters. *J. biol. Chem.* **257**, 7847–7851.

CHIU, I.-M., REDDY, E. P., GIVOL, D., ROBBINS, K. C., TRONICK, S. R. & AARONSON, S. A. (1984). Nucleotide sequence analysis identifies the human *c-sis* proto-oncogene as a structural gene for platelet-derived growth factor. *Cell* **37**, 123–129.

COCHRAN, B. H., REFFEL, A. C. & STILES, C. D. (1983). Cell specific regulation of the c-*myc* gene by lymphocyte mitogenes and platelet-derived growth factor. *Cell* **35**, 607–615.

COOPER, J. A., BOWEN-POPE, D. F., RAINES, E., ROSS, R. & HUNTER, T. (1982). Similar effects of platelet-derived growth factor and epidermal growth factor on the phosphorylation of tyrosine in cellular proteins. *Cell* **31**, 263–273.

COHEN, S., USHIRO, H., STOSCHECK, C. & CHINKERS, M. (1982). A native 170,000 epidermal growth factor receptor-kinase complex from shed plasma membrane vesicles. *J. biol. Chem.* **257**, 1523–1531.

DEUEL, T. F., HUANG, J. S., HUANG, S. S., STROOBANT, P. & WATERFIELD, M. D. (1983). Expression of a platelet-derived growth factor-like protein in simian sarcoma virus transformed cells. *Science* **221**, 1348–1350.

DEVARE, S. G., REDDY, E. P., LAW, J. D., ROBBINS, K. C. & AARONSON, S. A. (1983). Nucleotide sequence of the simian sarcoma virus genome: Demonstration that its acquired cellular sequences encode the transforming gene product p28[sis]. *Proc. natn. Acad. Sci. U.S.A.* **80**, 731–735.

DICKER, P., POHJANPELTO, P., PETTICAN, P. & ROZENGURT, E. (1981). Similarities between fibroblast-derived growth factor and platelet-derived growth factor. *Expl Cell Res.* **135**, 221–227.

DiCorleto, P. E. & Bowen-Pope, D. F. (1983). Cultured endothelial cells produce a platelet-derived growth factor-like protein. *Proc. natn. Acad. Sci. U.S.A.* **80**, 1919–1923.

Doolittle, R. F., Hunkapiller, M. W., Hood, L. E., Devare, S. G., Robbins, K. C., Aaronson, S. A. & Antoniades, H. N. (1983). Simian sarcoma virus oncogene, v-*sis*, is derived from the gene (or genes) encoding a platelet-derived growth factor. *Science* **221**, 275–277.

Downward, J., Yarden, Y., Mayes, E., Scrace, G., Totty, N., Stockwell, P., Ullrich, A., Schlessinger, J. & Waterfield, M. D. (1984). Close similarity of epidermal growth factor receptor and v-*erb*-B oncogene protein sequences. *Nature, Lond.* **307**, 521–527.

Ek, B. & Heldin, C.-H. (1982). Characterization of a tyrosine-specific kinase activity in human fibroblast membranes stimulated by platelet-derived growth factor. *J. biol. Chem.* **257**, 10486–10492.

Ek, B. & Heldin, C.-H. (1984). Use of an antiserum against phosphotyrosine for the identification of phosphorylated components in human fibroblasts stimulated by platelet-derived growth factor. *J. biol. Chem.* **259**, 11145–11152.

Ek, B., Westermark, B., Wasteson, Å & Heldin, C.-H. (1982). Stimulation of tyrosine-specific phosphorylation by platelet-derived growth factor. *Nature, Lond.* **295**, 419–420.

Eva, A., Robbins, K. C., Andersen, P. R., Srinavasan, A., Tronich, S. R., Reddy, E. P., Ellmore, N. W., Galen, A. T., Lautenberger, J. A., Papas, T. S., Westin, E.-H., Wong-Staal, F., Gallo, R. C. & Aaronson, S. A. (1982). Cellular genes analogous to retroviral oncogenes. *Nature, Lond.* **295**, 116–119.

Frackelton, A. R. Jr, Tremble, P. M. & Williams, L. T. (1984). Evidence for the platelet-derived growth factor-stimulated tyrosine phosphorylation of the platelet-derived growth factor receptor *in vivo*. *J. biol. Chem.* **259**, 7909–7915.

Garrett, J. S., Coughlin, S. R., Niman, H. L., Tremble, P. M., Giels, G. M. & Williams, L. T. (1984). Blockade of autocrine stimulation in simian sarcoma virus transformed cells reverses down-regulation of platelet-derived growth factor receptors. *Proc. natn. Acad. Sci. U.S.A.* **80**, 7466–7470.

Glenn, K., Bowen-Pope, D. F. & Ross, R. (1982). Platelet-derived growth factor. II. Identification of a platelet-derived growth factor receptor by affinity labeling. *J. biol. Chem.* **257**, 5172–5176.

Goustin, A. S., Betsholtz, C., Pfeifer-Ohlsson, S., Persson, H., Rydnert, J., Bywater, M., Holmgren, G., Heldin, C.-H., Westermark, B. & Ohlsson, R. (1985). Co-expression of the *sis* and *myc* proto-oncogenes in developing human placenta suggests autocrine control of trophoblast growth. *Cell* **41**, 301–312.

Greenberg, M. E. & Ziff, E. B. (1983). Stimulation of 3T3 cells induces transcription of the c-*fos* proto-oncogene. *Nature, Lond.* **311**, 433–438.

Gudas, L. J., Singh, J. P. & Stiles, C. D. (1983). Secretion of growth regulatory molecules by teratocarcinoma stem cells. In *Teratocarcinoma Stem Cells* (ed. Silver, Martin, & Strickland) *Cold Spring Harbor Conf Cell Proliferation*, vol. 10, pp. 229–236. New York: Cold Spring Harbor Press.

Habenicht, A. J. R., Glomset, J. A., King, W. C, Nist, C., Mitchell, C. D. & Ross, R. (1981). Early changes in phosphatidylinositol and arachidonic acid metabolism in quiescent Swiss 3T3 cells stimulated to divide by platelet-derived growth factor. *J. biol. Chem.* **256**, 12329–12335.

Hampe, A., Gobet, M., Sherr, C. J. & Galibert, F. (1984). Nucleotide sequence of the feline retroviral oncogene v-*fms* shows unexpected homology with oncogenes encoding tyrosine-specific protein kinases. *Proc. natn. Acad. Sci. U.S.A.* **81**, 81–85.

Heldin, C.-H., Ek, B. & Rönnstrand, L. (1983). Characterization of the receptor for platelet-derived growth factor on human fibroblasts. *J. biol. Chem.* **258**, 10054–10061.

Heldin, C.-H., Wasteson, Å. & Westermark, B. (1985). Platelet-derived growth factor. *Molec. cell. Endocrinol.* **39**, 169–187.

Heldin, C.-H. & Westermark, B. (1984). Growth factors: Mechanism of action and relation to oncogenes. *Cell* **37**, 9–20.

Heldin, C.-H., Westermark, B. & Wasteson, Å. (1980). Chemical and biological properties of a growth factor from human-cultured osteosarcoma cells: Resemblance with platelet-derived growth factor. *J. cell. Physiol.* **105**, 235–246.

HELDIN, C.-H., WESTERMARK, B. & WASTESON, Å. (1981). Specific receptors for platelet-derived growth factor on cells derived from connective tissue and glia. *Proc. natn. Acad. Sci. U.S.A.* **78**, 3664–3668.

HUANG, J. S., HUANG, S. S. & DEUEL, T. F. (1984). Transforming protein of simian sarcoma virus stimulates autocrine growth of SSV-transformed cells through PDGF cell-surface receptors. *Cell* **39**, 79–87.

HUNTER, T. (1984). The proteins of oncogenes. *Scient. Am.* **251**, 60–69.

HURLEY, J. B., SIMON, M. I., TEPLOW, D. B., ROBISHAW, J. D. & GILMAN, A. G. (1984). Homologies between signal transducing G proteins and ras gene products. *Science* **226**, 860–862.

JACOBS, S., KULL, F. C. JR, EARP, H. S., SVOBODA, M. E., VAN WYK, J. J. & CUATRECASAS, P. (1983). Somatomedin-C stimulates the phosphorylation of the β-subunit of its own receptor. *J. biol. Chem.* **258**, 9581–9584.

JOHNSSON, A., BETSHOLTZ, C., HELDIN, C.-H. & WESTERMARK, B. (1985). Antibodies to platelet-derived growth factor inhibit acute transformation by simian sarcoma virus. *Nature, Lond.* (in press).

JOHNSSON, A., BETSHOLTZ, C., VON DER HELM, K., HELDIN, C.-H. & WESTERMARK, B. (1985). Platelet-derived growth factor agonist activity of a secreted form of the *v-sis* oncogene product. *Proc. natn. Acad. Sci. U.S.A.* **82**, 1721–1725.

JOHNSSON, A., HELDIN, C.-H., WESTERMARK, B. & WASTESON, Å. (1982). Platelet-derived growth factor: Identification of constituent polypeptide chains. *Biochem. biophys. Res. Commun.* **104**, 66–74.

JOHNSSON, A., HELDIN, C.-H., WASTESON, Å., WESTERMARK, B., DEUEL, T. F., HUANG, J. S., SEEBURG, P. H., GRAY, A., ULLRICH, A., SCRACE, G., STROOBANT, P. & WATERFIELD, M.D. (1984). The *c-sis* gene encodes a precursor of the B chain of platelet-derived growth factor. *EMBO J.* **3**, 921–928.

JOSEPHS, S. F., GUO, C., RATNER, L. & WONG-STAAL, F. (1984). Human proto-oncogene nucleotide sequences corresponding to the transforming region of simian sarcoma virus. *Science* **223**, 487–490.

KASUGA, M., ZICK, Y., BLITHE, D. L., KARLSSON, F. A., HÄRING, H. U. & KAHN, C. R. (1982). Insulin stimulation of phosphorylation of the β-subunit of the insulin receptor. *J. biol. Chem.* **257**, 9891–9894.

KELLY, K., COCHRAN, B. H., STILES, C. D. & LEDER, P. (1983). Cell-specific regulation of the c-*myc* gene by lymphocyte mitogens and platelet-derived growth factor. *Cell* **35**, 603–610.

KLOETZER, W., MAXWELL, S. & ARLINGHAUS, R. (1983). P85^gag-mos encoded by ts110 Moloney murine sarcoma virus has an associated protein kinase activity. *Proc. natn. Acad. Sci. U.S.A.* **80**, 412–416.

LAND, H., PARADA, L. F. & WEINBERG, R. A. (1983). Cellular oncogenes and multistep carcinogenesis. *Science* **222**, 771–778.

LINZER, D. I. H. & NATHANS, D. (1983). Growth-related changes in specific mRNAs of cultured mouse cells. *Proc. natn. Acad. Sci. U.S.A.* **80**, 4271–4275.

MOELLING, K., HEIMANN, B., BEIMLING, P., RAPP, U. R. & SANDER, T. (1984). Serine- and threonine-specific protein kinase activities of purified *gag-mil* and *gag-raf* proteins. *Nature, Lond.* **312**, 558–561.

MOOLENAAR, W. H., TERTOOLEN, L. G. J. & DE LAAT, S. W. (1984). Growth factors immediately raise cytoplasmic free Ca^{2+} in human fibroblasts. *J. biol. Chem.* **259**, 8066–8068.

MULCAHY, L. S., SMITH, M. R. & STACEY, D. W. (1985). Requirement of *ras* proto-oncogene function during serum-stimulated growth of NIH 3T3 cells. *Nature, Lond.* **313**, 241–243.

NAKAMURA, K. D., MARTINEZ, R. & WEBER, M. J. (1983). Tyrosine phosphorylation of specific proteins after mitogen stimulation of chicken embryo fibroblasts. *Molec. cell. Biol.* **3**, 380–390.

NILSSON, J., SJÖLUND, M., PALMBERG, L., THYBERG, J. & HELDIN, C.-H. (1985). Arterial smooth muscle cells in primary culture produce a platelet-derived growth factor-like protein. *Proc. natn. Acad. Sci. U.S.A.* (in press).

NISHIMURA, J., HUANG, J. S. & DEUEL, T. F. (1982). Platelet-derived growth factor stimulates tyrosine-specific protein kinase activity in Swiss mouse 3T3 cell membranes. *Proc. natn. Acad. Sci. U.S.A.* **79**, 4303–4307.

NISHIZUKA, Y. (1984). The role of protein kinase C in cell surface signal transduction and tumour promotion. *Nature, Lond.* **308**, 693–698.

NISTÉR, M., HELDIN, C.-H., WASTESON, Å & WESTERMARK, B. (1984). A glioma-derived analog to platelet-derived growth factor: Demonstration of receptor competing activity and immunological crossreactivity. *Proc. natn. Acad. Sci. U.S.A.* **81**, 926–930.

NISTÉR, M., HELDIN, C.-H. & WESTERMARK, B. (1985). Clonal variation in the production of a PDGF-like growth factor and expression of PDGF receptors in a human malignant glioma. *Cancer Res.* (in press).

NORRIS, J. S., CORNETT, L. E., HARDIN, J. W., KOHLER, P. O., MACLEOD, S. L., SRIVASTAVA, A., SYMS, A. J. & SMITH, R. G. (1984). Autocrine regulation of growth: II. Glucocorticoids inhibit transcription of c-*sis* oncogene-specific RNA transcripts. *Biochem. biophys. Res. Commun.* **122**, 124–128.

OWEN, A. J., PANTAZIS, P. & ANTONIADES, H. N. (1984). Simian sarcoma virus-transformed cells secrete a mitogen identical to platelet-derived growth factor. *Science* **225**, 54–56.

PIKE, L. J., BOWEN-POPE, D. F., ROSS, R. & KREBS, E. G. (1983). Characterization of platelet-derived growth factor-stimulated phosphorylation in cell membranes. *J. biol. Chem.* **258**, 9383–9390.

PLEDGER, W. J., HART, C. A., LOCATELL, K. L. & SCHER, C. D. (1981). Platelet-derived growth factor-modulated proteins. Constitutive synthesis by a transformed cell line. *Proc. natn. Acad. Sci. U.S.A.* **78**, 4358–4362.

ROBBINS, K. C., ANTONIADES, H. N., DEVARE, S. G., HUNKAPILLER, M. W. & AARONSON, S. A. (1983). Structural and immunological similarities between simian sarcoma virus gene product(s) and human platelet-derived growth factor. *Nature, Lond.* **305**, 605–608.

ROZENGURT, E., RODRIGUEZ-PENA, M. & SMITH, K. A. (1983). Phorbol esters, phospholipase C, and growth factors rapidly stimulate the phosphorylation of a M_r 80,000 protein in intact quiescent 3T3 cells. *Proc. natn. Acad. Sci. U.S.A.* **80**, 7244–7248.

SEIFERT, R. A., SCHWARTZ, S. M. & BOWEN-POPE, D. F. (1984). Developmentally regulated production of platelet-derived growth factor-like molecules. *Nature, Lond.* **311**, 669–671.

SMITH, J. C. & STILES, C. D. (1981). Cytoplasmic transfer of the mitogenic response to platelet-derived growth factor. *Proc. natn. Acad. Sci. U.S.A.* **78**, 4363–4367.

VAN ZOELEN, E. J. J., VAN DE VEN, W. J. M., FRANSSEN, H. J., VAN OOSTWAARD, T. M. J., VAN DER SAAG, P. T., HELDIN, C.-H. & DE LAAT, S. W. (1985). Neuroblastoma cells express c-*sis* and produce a transforming growth factor antigenically related to platelet-derived growth factor. *Molec. Cell Biol.* (in press).

WATERFIELD, M. D., SCRACE, G. T., WHITTLE, N., STROOBANT, P., JOHNSSON, A., WASTESON, Å., WESTERMARK, B., HELDIN, C.-H., HUANG, J. S. & DEUEL, T. F. (1983). Platelet-derived growth factor is structurally related to the putative transforming protein p28[sis] of simian sarcoma virus. *Nature, Lond.* **304**, 35–39.

J. Cell Sci. Suppl. 3, 77–82 (1985)
Printed in Great Britain © The Company of Biologists Limited 1985

ACTIVATION AND CELL CYCLE CONTROL OF MURINE B LYMPHOCYTES

FRITZ MELCHERS*, CATHERINE CORBEL†, MARIA LEPTIN‡ AND
WALDEMAR LERNHARDT§

Basel Institute for Immunology, Grenzacherstrasse 487, CH-4005 Basel, Switzerland

SUMMARY

The cell cycle of activated murine B lymphocytes (B cells) is controlled by the occupancy of surface membrane-bound immunoglobulin (Ig) and by two types of growth factors, called α and β factors. These growth factors are produced in an endocrine fashion by the interaction of helper T lymphocytes (T cells) with antigen-presenting macrophages (A cells). Antigen is taken up, processed and presented on the surface of A cells in the context of class II major histocompatibility complex (MHC) glycoproteins. Helper T cells recognize this association of antigen and class II MHC molecules. A cells produce α factors and T cells produce β factors. The molecular nature of these factors and of the corresponding receptors on B cells has yet to be elucidated, although it can be shown that the complement component C3d replaces α factor action.

Resting, G_0 phase B cells are refractory to the action of α and β factors. They have to be excited, i.e. rendered susceptible to the action of these factors. This can be achieved by the interaction with helper T cells that recognize antigen, bound by surface membrane Ig, in the context of class II MHC glycoproteins on the surface of resting G_0 B cells. Excitation can also occur in a polyclonal fashion by cross-linking of suface Ig with immobilized, Ig-specific antibodies, or by the interaction with polyclonal activators of B cells, such as lipopolysaccharides. Entry into the cell cycle is asynchronous. Activated, cycling B cells can be synchronized by size separation, using velocity sedimentation. Synchronized B cells will retain their synchrony for several divisions, when they are stimulated by immobilized Ig-specific antibodies, α and β factors. They divide every 20 h at 37 °C. Omission of either of the three stimuli arrests B cells, though at different points in the cell cycle. Three restriction points are found: the first occurs immediately after mitosis and is controlled by the binding of immobilized Ig-specific antibodies to surface membrane-bound Ig. The second is observed in the G_1 phase, around 6–8 h after mitosis and 2–4 h before entry into S phase. It is controlled by α factors. The third is found 2–4 h before mitosis, in G_2 phase, and is controlled by β factors.

INTRODUCTION

Three steps can be distinguished in the activation of resting B lymphocytes to proliferation and maturation to immunoglobulin (Ig) secretion (Howard & Paul, 1983; Melchers & Andersson, 1984). The first is the endocrine production of growth and maturation factors for B cells by helper T lymphocytes and accessory (A) cells.

* Author for correspondence.
† Present address: CNRS, Institute d'Embryologie, 49, av. de la Belle Gabrielle, F-94130 Nogent-sur-Marne, France.
‡ Present address: MRC Laboratory of Molecular Biology, Hills Rd, Cambridge CB2 2QH, U.K.
§ Present address: La Jolla Cancer Foundation, 10901 Torrey Pines Road, La Jolla, CA 92037, U.S.A.

The second is the excitation of the resting B cells from their resting state to susceptibility to growth factor action. The third is the control of the B cell cycle by antigen, and by growth factors produced by A and T cells.

ENDOCRINE B CELL GROWTH FACTOR PRODUCTION

An endocrine system of helper T cells and accessory (A) cells produces growth and maturation factors for B cells. Initially, antigen is taken up, processed and presented on the surface of A cells in the context of class II major histocompatibility complex (MHC) molecules (Rosenthal & Shevach, 1973; Allen & Unanue, 1984). Helper T cells recognize with their receptors the combination of processed antigen and class II MHC molecules. This recognition leads to the production and secretion of factors called lymphokines. We have called the factors produced by A cells αfactors and those produced by helper T cells, βfactors (Melchers & Andersson, 1984). Factor production can also be achieved in antigen-independent, polyclonal activations. T cells can be polyclonally activated by concanavalin A, phytohemagglutinin or by phorbol myristic acid. Polyanions such as lipopolysaccharide, lipoprotein, dextran sulphate and other polyclonally activate A cells (Corbel & Melchers, 1984a).

THE ROLE OF A CELLS IN B CELL RESPONSES

Murine B cell populations of spleen or lymph nodes can be depleted of A cells by a series of procedures that leads to unresponsiveness of these B cells to polyclonal stimuli (Corbel & Melchers, 1984b). Lipopolysaccharide or lipoprotein can no longer stimulate such A cell-depleted B cells to proliferation and maturation to Ig secretion. This, therefore, is the extreme, polyclonal, case of an apparently general rule that no B cell responses to any form of stimuli occur in the absence of A cells (Mosier & Subbara, 1982). When small numbers of A cells are added to the A cell-depleted B cell populations the responses are restored. A total of 10–50 A cells either from the macrophage line P388DI or from colonies of macrophages grown in the presence of colony-stimulating factor are sufficient for 10 000 B cells (Corbel & Melchers, 1984b). The requirement of A cells can be replaced by soluble factors produced by activated A cells, i.e. by αfactors. This has led to an assay for αfactors; αfactors can also be assayed by their requirement for growth of A cell-depleted B cell blasts and of a plasmacytoma cell line, J558.

We have recently found that αfactors can be replaced by the complement components C3b and C3d (Erdei & Melchers, 1985). Both have to be presented to the B cell in insoluble, aggregated forms, i.e. either bound to Sepharose beads or cross-linked by glutaraldehyde. This implies that the corresponding receptor on B cells is the C3d-specific complement receptor CR2 (Fearon, 1984; Ross, 1980), although that receptor has only been identified on human, but not murine cells.

Soluble C3d, by contrast, inhibits the αfactor-mediated activities on B cells (Melchers, Erdei, Schulz & Dierich, 1985). This may indicate that the same CR2 receptor signals positively for growth when cross-linked, and negatively when occupied by non-cross-linking forms of the same ligand, C3d.

It remains to be noted that a wide variety of cell lines of different differentiation lineages have been found to produce α factor-like activities, including those of the B lineage (Corbel & Melchers, 1984b). The latter points to a potential autocrine production of one B cell growth factor in some established lines and tumours. A considerable molecular heterogeneity of α factor activities has been observed. This makes us speculate that more complex reactions occur with the binding of the ligand to the CR2 receptors, not unlike the complex reactions that occur when the C3 components are activated.

THE ROLES OF HELPER T CELLS IN B CELL RESPONSES

It has long been known that most responses of B cells to proliferate and mature to Ig secreting cells are helper T cell-dependent (Miller & Mitchell, 1969). This cellular dependence is governed by class II MHC molecules: helper T cells have to possess the same MHC genotype as the B cell for a successful T cell-dependent B cell response (Katz, Hamaoka, Dorf & Benacerraf, 1973). Helper T cells, in fact, learn to interact with class II-MHC molecules of A cells and B cells during their differentiation from stem cells in the thymus. Thus, helper T cells with an incompatible MHC haplotype (a) can learn the interaction with a foreign MHC haplotype (b) when this foreign haplotpye (b) is presented to them during their differentiation in the MHC-foreign environment of a thymus in a chimeric mouse (Von Boehmer & Sprent, 1976). T cells of haplotype (a) then cooperate with B cells and A cells of haplotype (b), and not with B cells and A cells of their own haplotype. We think that the T cell receptor repertoire of (a) T cells adapts to the recognition of environment (b). This antigen-specific, MHC class II-restricted interaction of helper T cells plays a role in B cell activation at least twice: first, when T cells and A cells make B cell growth factors; and second, when B cells are activated from their resting state.

Lymphokines produced by T cells include a series of growth factors that are active on different cells of blood. T cells have been shown to produce T cell growth factor (interleukin-2), B cell growth factors (β factors), growth factors for early stages of blood cell differentiation (such as interleukin-3), colony-stimulating factors for monocytes, macrophages and granulocytes, and possibly other factors (Schreier, Andersson, Lernhardt & Melchers, 1980). We have cloned a series of helper T cells with different specificities for antigen as continuously growing lines and have made T cell hybridomas from them (Melchers *et al.* 1982). These T cell lines and hybridomas have been found to be convenient and clean sources for these factors, including β factors. The factors are produced upon stimulation either by antigen, presented on MHC-compatible A cells, or, polyclonally and antigen-unspecifically, MHC-unrestrictedly and A cell-independently by exposure to concanavalin A. In practically all situations such clones of T cells produce a spectrum of different factors. Any preparation of β factors, therefore, is likely to contain other factors. Clearly, cloning of the corresponding genes will obviate this problem. Nevertheless,

T cell-derived β factor preparations can be obtained that are devoid of α factor activities, and α factor preparations from P388DI macrophages are devoid of β factor activities.

EXCITATION OF RESTING B CELLS TO FACTOR SUSCEPTIBILITY

Resting, G_0 phase B cells are refractory to the action of α and β factors, and to combinations of them, as they will not enter S phase and divide (Melchers, Andersson, Lernhardt & Schreier, 1980). However, maturation will sometimes be induced without proliferation by mixtures of lymphokines that need further characterization and are often called B cell maturation factors. In order to become susceptible to the action of α and β factors and to enter S phase and mitosis resting B cells must be excited. Excitation is the second role that T cells play in the activation of B cells. Recognition of antigen and MHC class II molecules on resting B cells not only stimulates T cells, but also renders B cells susceptible to α and β factor action. B cells of an incompatible MHC haplotype are not excited; neither are B cells that do not have the antigen bound. Therefore, only MHC-compatible, antigen-specific B cells are stimulated by α and β factors. This secures the antigen selectivity of the B cell response.

There are two ways in which B cells can be excited from their resting state in a T independent, MHC-unrestricted, polyclonal fashion. One is through lipopolysaccharide (Andersson, Sjöberg & Möller, 1972) or lipoprotein (Melchers, Braun & Galanos, 1975), the other through Ig-specific antibodies (Parker, 1975). Monoclonal antibodies with specificities against the four constant region domains of μ heavy chains (Leptin et al. 1984), cross-linked on Sepharose beads, can all act to excite B cells from their resting state (Leptin, 1985).

The excitation from the resting state is likely to be connected with a series of molecular changes that have been observed in B cells early after activation (Cambier, Monroe, Coggeshall & Ransom, 1985). Amongst these changes are the inductions of expression of myc (Kelly, Cochran, Stiles & Leder, 1983), a process that is deregulated in many B cell tumours (Shen-Ong, Keath, Piccoli & Cole, 1982).

CELL CYCLE CONTROL

We have recently been able to synchronize activated B cell blasts (Melchers & Lernhardt, 1985). This was done by selection of a given size of activated B cell through velocity sedimentation. Surprisingly, these activated B cells remain synchronous for at least four to five divisions, with a 20-h cell cycle at 37 °C. For stimulation of continuous cell cycles three stimuli have to act in synergistic fashion: Ig-specific immobilized antibodies, α and β factors. The activated B cell will undergo one division and then stop, when only α and β factors are present. After this one division they can be re-excited by an exposure to Ig-specific antibodies that can be as short as 15 min and as long as 36 h. This exposure will permit α and β factors to induce one more division in the absence of Ig-specific antibodies, and continuous cycling in their presence. When α factors are present during a 36-h excitation phase with Ig-specific antibodies, cells will divide 2–4 h later, while they need 12–14 h until division when α factors are absent in the excitation phase. These experiments have defined three restriction points in the cell cycle of activated B cells that are controlled by three different interactions: the first occurs directly after mitosis and is controlled by the interaction of membrane-bound Ig with either Ig-specific antibodies or, naturally, with antigen and helper T cells specific for the antigen and restricted to class II MHC antigens. The second occurs 6–8 h after mitosis, before entry into S phase, and is controlled by α factors, or alternatively, by C3d. It is likely that the complement C3d-specific receptor CR2 regulates these interactions. The third restriction point occurs 2–4 h before mitosis and is regulated by β factors. While the second restriction point, therefore, appears to be regulated by cell interactions with A cells, the third is likely to be dependent on helper T cells.

This dissection of the cell cycle will now permit a more specified analysis of the biochemical steps that regulate B cell cycle. They will also permit the analysis of the nature of T cell-independent responses and, in the polyclonal case, of the mitogenic responses to lipopolysaccharide and lipoprotein. They may give insight into de-regulations in immunodeficiency and autoimmunities involving B cells. Finally, a B cell should become transformed by a series of different steps that should have to act synergistically to achieve the fully malignant state by becoming independent of the actions of α and β factors and of antigen.

The Basel Institute for Immunology was founded and is supported by F. Hoffmann–La Roche & Co. Ltd, Basel, Switzerland.

REFERENCES

ALLEN, P. M. & UNANUE, E. R. (1984). Differential requirements for antigen processing by macrophages for lysozyme-specific T cell hybridomas. *J. Immun.* **132**, 1077–1084.

ANDERSSON, J., SJÖBERG, O. & MÖLLER, G. (1972). Induction of immunoglobulin and antibody synthesis in vitro by lipopolysaccharide. *Eur. J. Immun.* **2**, 349–353.

CAMBIER, J. C., MONROE, J. G., COGGESHALL, K. M. & RANSOM, J. T. (1985). On the biochemical basis of transmembrane signalling by B lymphocyte surface immunoglobulin. *Immun. Today* (in press).

CORBEL, C. & MELCHERS, F. (1984a). The synergism of accessory cells and of soluble α-factors derived from them in the activation of B cells to proliferation. *Immun. Rev.* **78**, 51–74.

CORBEL, C. & MELCHERS, F. (1984b). Requirement for macrophages or for macrophage- or T cell-derived factors in the mitogenic stimulation of murine B-lymphocytes by lipopolysaccharides. *Eur. J. Immun.* **13**, 528–533.

ERDEI, A., MELCHERS, F., SCHULZ THOMAS, F. & MANFRED, D. (1985). The action of human C3 in soluble or cross-linked form with resting and activated murine B lymphocytes. *Eur. J. Immun.* **15**, 184–188.

FEARON, D. T. (1984). Cellular receptors for fragments of the third component of complement. *Immun. Today* **5**, 105–110.

HOWARD, E. G. & PAUL, W. E. (1983). Regulation of B cell growth and differentiation by soluble factors. *A. Rev. Immun.* **1**, 307–720.

KATZ, D. H., HAMAOKA, T., DORF, M. E., BENACERRAF, B. (1973). Cell interactions between histocompatible T and B lymphocytes. III. Determination that the H-2 complex determines successful physiological lymphocyte interactions. *Proc. natn. Acad. Sci. U.S.A.* **70**, 2624–2628.

KELLY, K., COCHRAN, B. H., STILES, C. D. & LEDER, P. (1983). Cell-specific regulation of the c-myc gene by lymphocyte mitogens and platelet-derived growth factor. *Cell* **35**, 603–610.

LEPTIN, M. (1985). Monoclonal antibodies specific for murine IgM. II. Activation of B lymphocytes by monoclonal antibodies specific for the four constant domains of IgM. *Eur. J. Immun.* **15**, 131–137.

LEPTIN, M., POTASH, M. J., GRÜTZMANN, R., HEUSSER, C., SCHULMAN, M., KÖHLER, G. & MELCHERS, F. (1984). Monoclonal antibodies specific for murine IgM I. Characterization of antigenic determinants on the four constant domains of the μ-heavy chain. *Eur. J. Immun.* **14**, 534–542.

MELCHERS, F. & ANDERSSON, J. (1984). B cell activation: Three steps and their variations. *Cell* **37**, 715–720.

MELCHERS, F., ANDERSSON, J., CORBEL, C., LEPTIN, M., LERNHARDT, W., GERHARD, W. & ZEUTHEN, J. (1982). Regulation of B lymphocyte replication and maturation. *J. cell. Biochem.* **19**, 315–332.

MELCHERS, F., ANDERSSON, J., LERNHARDT, W. & SCHREIER, M. H. (1980). H-2-unrestricted polyclonal maturation without replication of small B cells induced by antigen-activated T cell helper factors. *Eur J. Immun.* **10**, 679–685.

MELCHERS, F., BRAUN, D. & GALANOS, C. (1975). The lipoprotein of the outer membrane of *Escherichia coli*: a B lymphocyte mitogen. *J. exp. Med.* **142**, 473–482.

MELCHERS, F., ERDEI, A., SCHULZ, T. & DIERICH, M. (1985). Growth control of activated, synchronized murine B cells by the C3d fragment of human complement. *Nature, Lond.* (in press).

MELCHERS, F. & LERNHARDT, W. (1985). Three restriction points in the cell cycle of activated murine B lymphocytes. *Proc. natn. Acad. Sci. U.S.A.* (in press).

MILLER, J. F. A. P. & MITCHELL, G. F. (1969). Thymus and antigen-reactive cells. *Transpl. Rev.* **1**, 3–79.

MOSIER, D. H. & SUBBARA, B. (1982). Thymus-independent antigens: complexity of B-lymphocyte activation revealed. *Immun. Today* **3**, 217–222.

PARKER, D. C. (1975). Stimulation of mouse lymphocytes by insoluble anti-mouse immunoglobulins. *Nature, Lond.* **258**, 365.

ROSENTHAL, A. S. & SHEVACH, E. M. (1973). Function of macrophages in antigen recognition by guinea-pig T lymphocytes. I. Requirements for histocompatible macrophages and lymphocytes. *J. exp. Med.* **138**, 1194–1212.

ROSS, G. D. (1980). Analysis of the different types of leukocyte membrane complement receptors and their interaction with the complement system. *J. Immun. Meth.* **37**, 197–211.

SCHREIER, M. H., ANDERSSON, J., LERNHARDT, W. & MELCHERS, F. (1980). Antigen-specific T helper cells stimulate H-2-compatible and H-2-incompatible B-cell blasts polyclonally. *J. exp. Med.* **151**, 194–203.

SHEN-ONG, G. L. C., KEATH, E. J., PICCOLI, S. P. & COLE M. D. (1982). Novel myc oncogene RNA from abortive immunoglobulin-gene recombination in mouse plasmacytomas. *Cell* **31**, 443–452.

VON BOEHMER, H. & SPRENT, J. (1976). T cell function in bone marrow chimeras – absence of host-reactive T cells and cooperation of helper cells across allogeneic barriers. *Transpl. Rev.* **29**, 3–23.

J. Cell Sci. Suppl. 3, 83–95 (1985)
Printed in Great Britain © The Company of Biologists Limited 1985

THE ROLE OF STROMAL CELLS AND GROWTH FACTORS IN HAEMOPOIESIS AND MODULATION OF THEIR EFFECTS BY THE src ONCOGENE

T. M. DEXTER, A. D. WHETTON, E. SPOONCER, C. HEYWORTH AND P. SIMMONS

Paterson Laboratories, Christie Hospital and Holt Radium Institute, Withington, Manchester M20 9HX, U.K.

SUMMARY

In the haemopoietic system the mature blood cells have only a finite lifetime. For example, a circulating granulocyte in the peripheral blood has an approximate half-life of 7h (Cartwright, Athens & Wintrobe, 1964; Dancey, Dubelbeiss, Harker & Finch, 1976) whilst the lifetime of an erythrocyte is approximately 120 days (Wickramasinghe & Weatherall, 1982). This constant 'death' of mature functional haemopoietic cells means that new blood cells must replace those that are removed. The process of haemopoiesis provides the mature functional blood cells to replace those lost as a consequence of performing their biological functions (e.g. lymphocytes and macrophages in the immune response) or through apparent old age and breakdown (e.g. erythrocytes that are 110–120 days old). The major questions that we are required to answer about this process are 'where do all these new cells come from?', 'what regulates their production?' and 'how is this mechanism of control lost in haemopoietic disorders such as leukaemia, hyperproliferative diseases and anaemias?'. Recent work in the field of haemopoiesis has given some clues to the answers to the questions, which provide an intriguing insight into not only haemopoiesis itself but the possible lesions associated with the various blood disorders.

The process of blood cell production occurs mainly in the bone marrow. Within the marrow resides a population of pluripotent self-renewing stem cells; it is these cells that give rise to all the blood cells required by the adult animal. Upon cell division a stem cell can do one of two things; self-renew (produce two *exact* copies of itself) or become committed to differentiation and development (Fig. 1). The process of self-renewal ensures that the stem cell population is maintained throughout the lifespan of the animal, whilst the commitment to differentiate will yield the mature, functional cells required by the peripheral blood and tissues.

In general, the stem cell compartment is thought to be a population of cells the majority of which are withdrawn from the cell cycle (Lajtha, Pozzi, Schofield & Fox, 1969; Hodgson & Bradley, 1984). However, upon commitment to development these cells enter another compartment, the committed progenitor cell compartment (Fig. 1), which is a rapidly cycling population (Eaves & Eaves, 1984; Iscove, Till & McCulloch, 1970). When stem cells enter into the committed progenitor cell compartment there is little self-renewal, in this case the process of cell division is coupled to differentiation leading to development into mature cells.

How have these stages in haemopoiesis been identified? Classical histological and morphological studies have in the past revealed some features of precursor cells in the

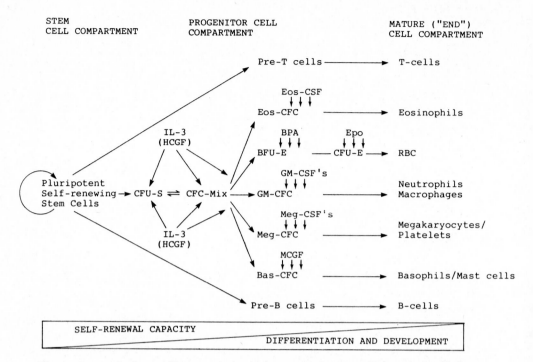

STEM   PROGENITOR CELL   MATURE ("END")
CELL COMPARTMENT   COMPARTMENT   CELL COMPARTMENT

Fig. 1. A general scheme of haemopoiesis: the haemopoietic stem cell gives rise to all the cells of the haemopoietic system shown in this scheme. As cells progress from the stem cell compartment through the committed progenitor cell compartment to maturity amplification of cell numbers is achieved by proliferation; mature cells generally have no capacity for proliferation.

Cells. CFU–S (colony forming unit–spleen). A functional assay in mice detects CFU–S, which belong to the stem cell compartment, but almost certainly do not represent the whole stem cell population; CFC–Mix (colony-forming cells–mixed). A functional assay detects CFC–Mix, a cell type that can produce multilineage colonies in semi-solid media, has some overlap with the CFU–S and represents part of the stem cell compartment: Eos–CFC (eosinophil–CFC); GM–CFC (granulocyte/macrophage–CFC); Meg–CFC (megakaryocyte–CFC); Bas–CFC (basophil–CFC); BFU–E (burst-forming unit–erythroid), primitive erythroid progenitor cell; CFU–E (colony-forming unit–erythroid), more mature erythroid precursor; RBC (red blood cell).

The self-renewal, differentiation, proliferation and development of haemopoietic cells occur in response to growth factors. IL3 (interleukin 3); HCGF (haemopoietic cell growth factor): this growth factor has a wide range of target cells and can elicit either self-renewal or differentiation. It is a 'lineage indifferent' growth factor. Eos–CSF (eosinophil-colony stimulating factor): GM–CSFs (granulocyte/macrophage–CSFs), a family of discrete molecules including the granulocyte-specific G–CSF, the macrophage specific M–CSF and the granulocyte/macrophage specific GM–CSF; Meg–CSF (mega karyocyte–CSF); BPA (burst-promoting activity); Epo (erythropoietin); MCGF (mast cell growth factor). The growth factors that act on committed progenitor cells only are 'lineage-restricted'.

bone marrow but two recent developments have revolutionized the field of experimental haematology allowing the scheme shown in Fig. 1 to be elucidated. The first major landmark was the development of the spleen colony forming assay by Till & McCulloch (1961). Essentially, this technique permits the identification and assay of pluripotent self-renewing (stem) cells in the mouse by their ability to form colonies in the spleen of an irradiated host mouse. These colonies can be shown to contain, or give rise to, all the haemopoietic cell types shown in Fig. 1, and also to contain further CFU–S (colony forming unit–spleen) cells, that is to say self-renewal of the CFU–S population can occur (Till & McCulloch, 1980).

The second important experimental advance was the development of *in vitro* assays for all of the committed progenitor cell types. (Metcalf, 1977; shown in Fig. 1). Assays *in vitro* are performed by culturing cells in semi-solid medium in the presence of a regulatory factor found in medium conditioned by the growth of various cell types in liquid culture. Under these conditions a single progenitor cell can give rise to a colony that may contain thousands of mature cells after several days. However, the self-renewal capacity of lineage-restricted progenitor cells is limited. In this respect they are a transit population that undergoes a developmental programme of proliferation and development, so that after a few days mature cells only are present. The survival of progenitor cells, their proliferation and the formation of a colony containing mature cells are absolutely dependent on the presence of specific regulatory factors (Burgess, Metcalf, Russell & Nicola, 1980; Metcalf & Merchav, 1982); in the absence of such regulators the progenitor cells die.

Many of these regulatory factors have now been characterized. These include granulocyte/macrophage colony-stimulating factor (GM–CSF), which can stimulate the development of mixed granulocyte/macrophage colonies as well as colonies containing only granulocytes or macrophages (Nicola, Burgess & Metcalf, 1979; Nicola, Metcalf, Johnson & Burgess, 1979). Two other distinct growth factors, granulocyte colony-stimulating factor (G–CSF) (Nicola, Metcalf, Matsumoto & Johnson, 1983) and macrophage colony-stimulating factor (M–CSF or CSF–1) (Stanley, Guilbert, Tushinski & Bartelmez, 1983), can stimulate the survival, proliferation and development of progenitor cells that each give rise to one form of colony only, i.e. granulocyte (G–CSF) and macrophage (CSF–1) colonies, respectively. Similarly, erythropoietin acts on committed erythroid precursor cells to promote the development of mature erythrocytes (Eaves & Eaves, 1984, Miyake, Kung & Goldwasser, 1977). All these growth factors show some lineage restriction. That is to say the target cells are a progenitor cell population of a distinct cellular lineage(s). However, a murine haemopoietic growth factor (interleukin 3 (Ihle *et al.* 1983) or Haemopoietic Cell Growth Factor (HCGF)) has been described that has a multi-lineage stimulatory capacity (Bazill, Haynes, Garland & Dexter, 1983). In the murine *in vitro* systems HCGF promotes the self-renewal of CFU–S, the survival, proliferation and development of megakaryocyte, granulocyte, basophilic, macrophage and erythroid progenitor cells, and the formation of mixed colonies from multipotent 'stem' cells (CFC–Mix) (see Fig. 1). The ability of HCGF to promote such a variety of lineage-restricted cells to survive, proliferate and develop whilst also allowing the self-renewal of CFU–S argues that this molecule may be of key importance in the regulation of haemopoiesis.

Recently, we have studied the means whereby HCGF/IL-3 can control survival and proliferation in haemopoietic progenitor cells using a granulocyte precursor

(FDC–P2) cell line (Bazill *et al.* 1983), which is absolutely dependent on HCGF for its survival; in its absence the cells die within 24–48 h. We have discovered that this growth factor mediates the survival of FDC–P2 cells by maintaining intracellular ATP levels (in the absence of HCGF, ATP levels undergo a steady decline that *precedes* any sign of loss of viability by several hours). This control of ATP levels is achieved by the ability of HCGF to control glucose transport and glycolysis (which are key elements in the ATP synthetic machinery of the cell) (Whetton & Dexter, 1983; Whetton, Bazill & Dexter, 1984). However, these biochemical studies tell us little of the factors controlling haemopoiesis *in vivo*. Another complementary approach to the elucidation of the elements controlling haemopoiesis has been the identification of the *environmental* requirements that can permit this process to occur. A culture system has been devised (the long-term marrow culture) that allows the self-renewal of stem cells and their development into mature cells in the absence of any exogenously added haemopoietic colony stimulating factors (Dexter, Allen & Lajtha, 1977). This is due to the formation of an adherent layer of (stromal) cells from the bone marrow that are absolutely required to maintain the stem cells *in vitro*. Thus it appears that an important determinative role is played by the stromal environment of the marrow in the survival, proliferation and development of haemopoietic precursor cells. This role of the stromal cells may (to some extent) be related to their ability to release haemopoietic growth factors into the extracellular medium.

Recently, stromal cell cultures have been shown to elaborate at least three colony-stimulating activities, a macrophage colony-stimulating factor, a granulocyte/macrophage colony-stimulating factor and also a megakaryocyte colony-stimulating factor (Gualtieri, Shadduck, Baker & Quesenberry, 1984) although no biochemical characterization of these factors has been undertaken. Nonetheless, these results imply that the stromal environment, as well as providing important cell–cell inter-actions (Dexter, 1982; Allen & Dexter, 1984), may also secrete growth factors into the medium. The role of these factors in self-renewal, commitment to differ-entiation, and the survival, proliferation and development of committed progenitor cells is still unclear.

How does this model of control of haemopoiesis explain the number of diverse diseases associated with blood cell production? In the case of malignant diseases the aberrant expression of oncogene protein products is associated with transformation of specific cells, which can then proliferate in an uncontrolled fashion. This is known to be the case in some leukaemias, but the *type* of cell that is transformed is of some significance. It has already been said that most mature haemopoietic cells cannot proliferate (indeed erythrocytes and platelets have lost their genetic material). The target cells for transformation must therefore be the stem cells or the committed progenitor cell compartment. In normal haemopoiesis the committed progenitor cells can proliferate *and* develop to mature cells. It is possible, therefore, that an imbalance between development and proliferation occurs that leads to proliferation with no development, i.e. a self-renewing population in the progenitor cell compartment (Dexter & Lajtha, 1981) or, indeed, uncontrolled self-renewal in the stem cell compartment. Many leukaemic cells have a phenotype that is very similar to committed progenitor cells (Greaves, 1982). Thus, an aberrant response to a growth factor (which normally signals 'proliferate and develop'), leading to proliferation alone, may well be a key step in the process of leukaemogenesis.

It is now well known that some oncogene protein products are related to growth factors or agents involved in eliciting an intracellular response to growth factors (Downward *et al.* 1984; Sugimoto, Whitman, Cantley & Erikson, 1984). As haemopoietic growth factors such as haemopoietic cell growth factor (interleukin 3) can control survival, proliferation, development and self-renewal, the aberrant expression of such a protein may have profound effects on the process of haemopoiesis. Similarly, autoproduction of a required growth factor would mean that some cells could survive and proliferate autonomously (Schrader & Crapper, 1983) (should this growth factor be able to promote self-renewal). To investigate the role of oncogenes in these processes, we have treated marrow cultures *in vitro* with a variety of retroviruses containing oncogenes of known specificity.

The effects have been diverse, ranging from inhibition of haemopoiesis (Teich, Rowe, Testa & Dexter, 1981), through increased longevity of haemopoiesis (Dexter, Scott & Teich, 1977) – to the development of leukaemic cells. Although some of the effects seen are almost certainly produced via changes in the regulatory stromal cell environment occurring as a consequence of retrovirus infection, the retroviruses used so far have carried oncogenes with a known tropism for haemopoietic cells. Because of this, we were interested in determining the effects of an oncogene with a known ability to transform 'connective tissue' cells – and in determining the subsequent effect upon haemopoietic cell proliferation and development. To this end, the *src* oncogene seemed to be a suitable candidate.

src was initially described as the oncogene present in Rous sarcoma virus, which conferred on this virus the ability to induce sarcomas and carcinomas in chickens (Beard, 1963). However, in common with other oncogenes, the normal cellular equivalent (c-*src*) has been found in many species, including man. The viral *src* (v-*src*) codes for a protein kinase (pp60^{src}) that is found in the cytoplasm of virus-infected cells. Although the function of the normal c-*src* gene product is unknown, the cell lineage and tissue-specific patterns of expression of the protein suggests that it has a role to play in normal cell growth and development. For various reasons, it is difficult to infect mammalian cells with chicken retroviruses (like the Rous sarcoma virus). Therefore, to investigate the effects of v-*src* on murine haemopoiesis, we used a recombinant retrovirus in which the avian v-*src* oncogene was inserted into an amphotropic murine leukaemia virus. This recombinant virus *src*(MoMuLV) was then used to infect long-term marrow cultures (Boettiger, Anderson & Dexter, 1984; Spooncer, Boettiger & Dexter, 1984).

For several weeks after infection, there was little change in the cultures. Commencing about 5 weeks after infection, however, we saw a marked alteration in the stromal cells of these cultures (Fig. 2), which progressively assumed a 'transformed' phenotype, i.e. marrow adipocytes disappeared and there was an overgrowth of large, highly basophilic adherent cells. At the same time, there was an increase in the numbers of macrophages. (Note: antigenic characteristics show that the macrophages and the transformed stromal cells do indeed represent different cell populations (P. Simmons, unpublished data).) Obviously, the changes in the stromal cells could have been anticipated, because of the known tropism of the *src* oncogene. What were surprising, however, were the changes seen in the haemopoietic activity in these cultures.

Concomitantly with the changes occurring in the stroma, there was a progressive reduction in the production of mature myeloid cells, which eventually reached levels less than 5 % of untreated controls. However, the stem cell (CFU–S) and committed progenitor cell (CFC–Mix and early GM–CFC) populations increased dramatically to reach levels 20× to 50× above control values. In other words, infection with *src*(MoMuLV) had induced a maturation block in the cultures. Superficially, therefore, the haemopoietic cells appeared to be 'leukaemic'. When examined further, however, we found the CFU–S to be quite capable of colonizing the haemopoietic system when injected into potentially lethally irradiated mice; the

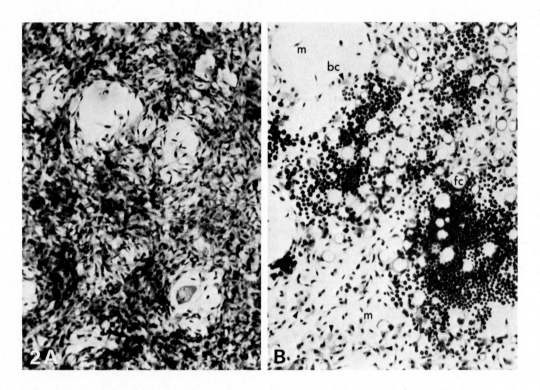

Fig. 2. Light micrographs of preparations stained with May-Grunwald-Giemsa. ×142. A. A region of the adherent layer of a *src*(MoMuLV)-infected culture. Note the disorganized pattern of growth, the predominance of spindle-shaped cells (bipolar macrophages) and the apparent absence of haemopoietic cells and fat cells. B. A region of the adherent layer of a control (age-matched) culture. Note the organized pattern of growth of the adherent layer, which includes fat cells (fc), macrophages (m), blanket cells (bc, nuclei arrowed) and large cobblestone regions of developing granulocytes (composed of small round cells).

reconstituted animals lived a normal lifespan and did not develop a leukaemia. This means that the maturation block seen in the *src*(MoMuLV)-infected cultures was overcome when the cells were injected *in vivo* – indicating that the block did not occur as a result of intrinsic changes in the haemopoietic cells, but was *imposed* upon the cells by the *src*(MoMuLV)-infected, transformed, stromal cell environment. Following further investigations, however, we found that the CFU–S from the *src*-infected cultures differed from their normal counterparts in one fundamental respect: namely, their ability to self-renew in situations unfavourable for self-renewal of normal stem cells.

If normal bone marrow, or long-term cultured CFU–S, are serially passaged *in vivo* (into irradiated mice) or *in vitro* (onto irradiated marrow stromal cells), they rapidly lose their ability to produce daughter stem cells and reconstitute hae-mopoiesis (Schofield & Dexter, 1985), i.e. their capacity for self-renewal declines. With cells from the *src*(MoMuLV)-infected cultures, however, no such decline occurs. The CFU–S could be passaged repeatedly *in vivo* with no apparent loss in their ability to reconstitute haemopoiesis; and could also be transferred repeatedly *in vitro* onto irradiated, but otherwise normal, marrow stromal cells. This was a puzzle, since it indicated that the CFU–S from the *src*-infected cultures *were* intrinsically different from normal CFU–S. However, it was possible that the increased self-renewal observed *in vivo* and *in vitro* was not a result of intrinsic changes in the stem cells, but was occurring as a result of modulation of self-renewal by contaminating transformed 'stromal' cells. To check this, we plated out the cells in soft agar, in the absence of stromal cells, using HCGF as the growth stimulus (Dexter, Boettiger & Spooncer, 1985; Spooncer *et al.* 1984). Individual colonies arising in this assay were isolated and expanded in liquid culture in the presence of HCGF. The majority of such clones produced permanently growing, HCGF–dependent cell lines.

These cells have a primitive morphology, a diploid karyotype, are non-leukaemic in normal or immunosuppressed mice, and their continued growth *in vitro* is *absolutely* dependent upon HCGF – they do not respond to other haemopoietic growth factors such as GM–CSF or M–CSF. When re-plated in soft agar, in the presence of HCGF plus erythropoietin and appropriate culture medium, the cells have a plating efficiency of between 1 and 10 % and a majority of the colonies produced contain cells of several lineages, e.g. erythrocytes, neutrophils, macro-phages, megakaryocytes. Therefore, the permanently growing cell lines consist of multipotent cells and for this reason we denote them as FDC–Mix (Factor Dependent Cells – Mixed). We now have several such cell lines available for study, and they show also the following characteristics. (1) When initially isolated, all the cell lines show an ability to form spleen colonies in irradiated mice: the spleen colonies contain mixed myeloid cells. With further time in culture, we have noticed that this spleen colony forming ability may be lost (Spooncer & Dexter, un-published). (2) All the cell lines show an ability to reconstitute *in vitro* haemopoiesis on irradiated marrow stromal cells. The FDC–Mix cells infiltrate the stroma, and produce foci of developing haemopoietic cells that can be induced, in such cultures, to undergo erythroid and neutrophil development. Unlike the spleen colony forming ability, this is a stable characteristic that is not lost with time in culture.

src(MoMuLV) infection of marrow culture, then, has provided us with a powerful tool to investigate further self-renewal and differentiation of stem cells. The FDC–Mix cells can be expanded in liquid culture to any desired cell number required for appropriate biochemical and molecular analysis. What is the role of *src* in the emergence and development of these multipotent cells? It seems that the effect has been indirect. Collaborative work in progress, with Drs Wyke and Stoker (ICRF, London), has shown that the FDC–Mix cells do not express v-*src* kinase activity and using molecular probes, we have been unable to demonstrate integration of the *src*(MoMuLV) in the cell lines. Thus, neither integration nor expression of the *src* oncogene is required for the maintenance of the stem cell lines. It seems probable then, that the original change occurred in the *src*(MoMuLV)-infected primary culture. Our working model suggests that *src*(MoMuLV) infection and trans-formation of the stromal cells led to a disturbance in the normal regulatory environment. As a consequence of this, there then occurred a selection for multipotent cells with (a) an ability to survive and grow in this environment and (b) an increased probability for self-renewal that is intrinsic to the cells. We do not know, of course, if this represents a selection of a subpopulation of stem cells normally present in long-term culture or if the cells arise as a consequence of an independent mutation event. However, several points are worthy of comment. Firstly, cells with this enhanced capacity for self-renewal occur with a high frequency and this would tend to rule out virus 'hit and run' models, or 'transformation' by virus promoter insertion. It seems probable, therefore, that the cells arise as a consequence of an independent mutation event conferring a stable change in self-renewal ability. If this is the case, it must be a highly mutable 'gene' because of the frequency with which such cells arise. Nonetheless, the results are important conceptually in terms of an understanding of leukaemogenesis.

Conventionally, leukaemic cells are thought to arise as a consequence of 'oncogene' expression in the haemopoietic cell (Fig. 3A). As a result, the cell responds aberrantly to the normal stromal regulatory influences and expands inappropriately. Work with the *src*(MoMuLV) long-term cultures now suggests an alternative model (Fig. 3B): oncogene expression in the regulatory cells, leading to an inbalance in the normal growth and developmental signals and a selection for cells that can survive and grow in this unfavourable environment. These cells may not be leukaemic (they can still respond to differentiation-inducing signals like the FDC–Mix cells). However, they do have a selective advantage over their normal counterparts and the altered clone may then take over much of the haemopoietic system (consider, e.g., human chronic myeloid leukaemia and the advantage of the Ph positive stem cells). Leukaemia may then arise when the cells undergo a further change, which makes them unresponsive to differentiation inducing signals, i.e. an 'uncoupling' of growth and development as suggested by Sachs (1980, 1982). In other words, for leukaemogenesis *two* independent changes may often be necessary: one of them affecting the process of self-renewal (giving clonal advantage) and the other affecting differentiation (leading to

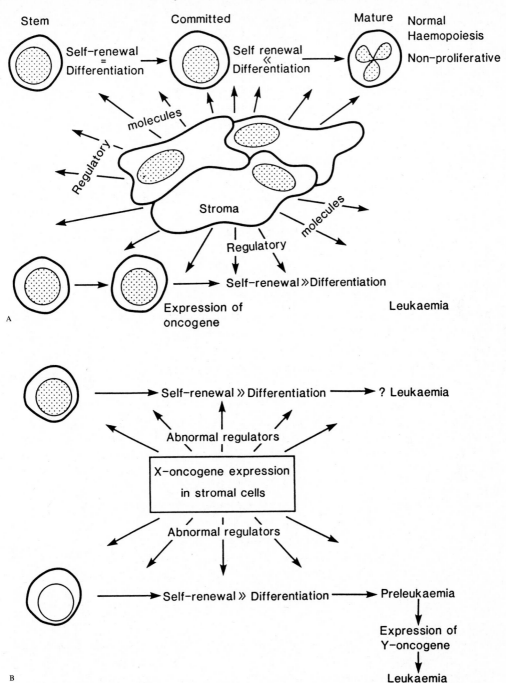

Fig. 3. Under the influence of stromal cells and regulatory molecules the balance between stem cell self-renewal and differentiation is maintained and the appropriate output of cells into the mature cell compartment is achieved (A, top line). Expression of an oncogene in a primitive haemopoietic cell leads to disturbed haemopoiesis and (possibly) leukaemia (B, bottom line). In this case the regulatory signals remain unaltered; it is the response of the haemopoietic cell to those signals that is abnormal. Oncogene expression by the stromal cells (B) may lead to disturbed haemopoiesis or leukaemia due to presentation of inappropriate regulatory signals to the (unaltered) haemopoietic cells.

inhibition of maturation). One or both of these changes may be mediated indirectly by a disturbance in the normal regulatory influences.

This leads on to the next question: what is the mechanism underlying differentiation driven by the stromal cells and haemopoietic cell growth factors? Again, using marrow culture systems some intriguing data are emerging. We were interested in the several reports demonstrating that inhibitors of poly(ADP)-ribosylation of chromatin proteins could 'block' differentiation in certain *in vitro* cell systems (Farzaneh, Zalin, Brill & Shall, 1982; Johnstone & Williams, 1982). The most effective inhibitor was 3-aminobenzamide and subsequent work with this compound showed that it could modulate the development of the GM–CFC (Francis *et al.* 1983). No studies were reported on its effect on stem cells. To investigate this aspect, we added 3-aminobenzamide to long-term marrow cultures and measured the numbers of CFU–S, GM–CFC and mature cells that were produced. The results were disappointing in that continuous treatment with a low concentration of 3-aminobenzamide did not influence stem cell growth or differentiation and higher doses of the compound were generally inhibitory for all stages of development – the stem cells, committed cells and mature cells. At least in long-term marrow cultures, therefore, the compound did not influence differentiation. At this time, we were also interested in examining the importance of ADP-ribosylation of cell membrane-associated proteins, particularly since changes in ribosylation have been shown to be important features of the regulatory subunits of adenylate cyclase in response to insulin, and various toxins (Coulson, Nassau & Tait, 1983; Tait & Nassau, 1984). Moreover, a series of compounds had been synthesized that could act as artificial substrates for ADP-ribosylation by cholera toxin and that, therefore, had the potential to act as modulators of ADP-ribosylation '*in vivo*'.

Two of these agents were examined in detail: compounds 115 and 117 in Tait & Nassau (1984). When added to long-term marrow cultures, the effects were dramatic, in that both caused a reduction in the production of mature cells to less than 1 % of control values. At the same time, there was no inhibition in the growth of CFU–S, which remained at control values even after several weeks continuous treatment. In many respects, therefore, the effects seen with compounds 115 and 117 on haemopoiesis resemble those seen after infection of long-term cultures with the *src*(MoMuLV) virus. To determine where the developmental block had occurred in cultures treated with compounds 115 and 117, we then measured the *in vitro* colony forming efficiency of cells in the presence of HCGF or CSF–1. HCGF is a multi-lineage stimulating factor that can recruit colony development from multipotent stem cells as well as committed progenitor cells. CSF–1 on the other hand, is a lineage restricted growth factor that recruits only the committed progenitor cells, the GM–CFC. Using these growth factors, it was therefore possible to determine where the maturation block had occurred. The results showed that compounds 115 and 117 led to a reduction of CSF–1-responsive cells to levels less than 1 % of control, while there was *no* reduction in the production of HCGF responsive cells (Dexter, Whetton & Heyworth, 1985). Clearly, the block seen in the treated long-term cultures occurs at the level of the primitive multipotent cells.

Obviously, much further work is required before we can state with some certainty that the effects are due to modulation of ADP-ribosylation of membrane proteins. Nonetheless, the data demonstrate that the cells are blocked at the multipotent stem cell level and that HCGF 'overcomes' the block when the cells are plated in soft agar. This infers that part of the transition from multipotential to committed progenitor cells may well involve an ADP-ribosylation event.

In conclusion, many problems still remain to be solved. However, the last few years have seen the development of model systems for the growth and development of stem cells and of committed progenitor cells. The growth factors required for these cells have been purified to homogeneity and some of them have been molecularly cloned. Oncogenes are present in vectors suitable for incorporation into the various stromal cells and haemopoietic cells. As indicated in this article, this has provided the means for obtaining 'stem cell' lines as models for self-renewal/differentiation controls. Furthermore, stem cell differentiation can now be blocked using synthetic compounds and a combination of the various systems should encourage significant progress to be made in the next few years.

This work was supported by the Cancer Research Campaign. T.M.D. is a Fellow of the Cancer Research Campaign.

REFERENCES

ALLEN, T. D. & DEXTER, T. M. (1984). The essential cells of the haemopoietic micro-environment. *Expl Haem.* **12**, 517–521.

BAZILL, G. W., HAYNES, M., GARLAND, J. M. & DEXTER, T. M. (1983). Characterisation and partial purification of a haemopoietic factor in WEHI-3B cell conditioned medium. *Biochem. J.* **210**, 747–759.

BEARD, J. W. (1963). Avian virus growths and their etiologic agents. *Adv. Cancer Res.* **7**, 1–127.

BOETTIGER, D. B., ANDERSON, S. & DEXTER, T. M. (1984). Effect of *src* infection on long-term marrow cultures. Increased self-renewal of hemopoietic progenitor cells without leukaemia. *Cell* **36**, 767–773.

BURGESS, A. W., METCALF, D., RUSSELL, S. H. M. & NICOLA, N. A. (1980). Granulocyte/macrophage, megakaryocyte, eosinophil, and erythroid colony stimulating factors produced by mouse spleen cells. *Biochem. J.* **185**, 301–314.

CARTWRIGHT, J. E., ATHENS, J. W. & WINTROBE, M. M. (1964). The kinetics of granulopoiesis in normal man. *Blood* **24**, 780.

COULSON, C. J., NASSAU, P. M. & TAIT, R. M. (1983). The ADP-ribosyltransferase activity of cholera toxin and *Escherichia coli* heat labile toxin. *Biochem. Soc. Trans.* **12**, 184–187.

DANCEY, J. T., DEUBELBEISS, K. A., HARKER, L. A. & FINCH, C. A. (1976). Neutrophil kinetics in man. *J. clin. Invest.* **58**, 705.

DEXTER, T. M. (1982). Stromal cell associated haemopoiesis. *J. cell. Physiol. (suppl.)* **1**, 87–94.

DEXTER, T. M., ALLEN, T. D. & LAJTHA, L. G. (1977). Conditions controlling the proliferation of haemopoietic stem cells *in vitro*. *J. cell. Physiol.* **91**, 335–344.

DEXTER, T. M., BOETTIGER, D. & SPOONCER, E. (1985). Self-renewal of haemopoietic stem cells. The roles of the environment of growth factors and of the *src* oncogene. In *Modern Trends in Human Leukaemia,* VI (ed. R. Neth, R. Gallo, M. Greaves & T. Janka), pp. 363–371. Berlin, Heidelberg: Springer-Verlag.

DEXTER, T. M. & LAJTHA, L. G. (1981). Self-renewal factors for haemopoietic progenitor cells and their potential relevance in Leukaemogenesis – a possibility to consider. In *Advances in Comparative Leukaemia Research* (ed. D. S. John & J. R. Blakesee), pp. 73–79. Amsterdam: Elsevier North-Holland.

DEXTER, T. M., SCOTT, D. & TEICH, N. M. (1977). Infection of bone marrow cells *in vitro* with FLV: Effects on stem cell proliferation, differentiation and leukaemogenic capacity. *Cell* **12**, 355–564.

DEXTER, T. M., WHETTON, A. D. & HEYWORTH, C. M. (1985). Inhibitors of cholera-toxin-induced adenosine diphosphate ribosylation of membrane associated proteins blocks stem cell differentiation. *Blood* **65**, 1544–1548.

DOWNWARD, J., YARDEN, Y., MAYES, E., SCARCE, J., TOTTY, N., STOCKWELL, P., ULLRICH, A., SCHLESSINGER, J. & WATERFIELD, M. D. (1984). Close similarity of epidermal growth factor receptor and v-erb B oncogene protein sequences. *Nature, Lond.* **307**, 521–527.

EAVES, A. C. & EAVES, C. J. (1984). Erythropoiesis in culture. *Clin. Haem.* **13**, 371–391.

FARZANEH, F., ZALIN, R., BRILL, D. & SHALL, S. (1982). DNA strand breaks and ADP ribosyl transferase activation during cell differentiation. *Nature, Lond.* **300**, 362–366.

FRANCIS, G. E., GRAY, D. A., BERNEY, J. J., WING, M. A., GUIMARAES, J. E. T. & HOFFBRAND, A. V. (1983). Role of ADP-ribosyl transferase in differentiation of human granulocyte – macrophage progenitors to the macrophage lineage. *Blood* **62**, 1055–1062.

GREAVES, M. F. (1982). Leukaemogenesis and differentiation. Commentary on recent progress and ideas. *Cancer Surveys* **1**, 189–204.

GUALTIERI, R. J., SHADDUCK, R. K., BAKER, D. G. & QUESENBERRY, P. J. (1984). Hematopoietic regulatory factors produced in long-term murine bone marrow cultures and the effect of *in vitro* radiation. *Blood* **64**, 516–525.

HODGSON, J. S. & BRADLEY, T. R. (1984). *In vivo* kinetic status of hematopoietic stem and progenitor cells as inferred from labelling with bromodeoxyuridine. *Expl Haem.* **12**, 683–687.

IHLE, J. N., KELLER, J., OROSZLAND, S., HENDERSON, L. E., COPELAND, T. D., FITCH, F., PRYSTOWSKY, M. B., GOLDWASSER, E., SCHRADER, J. W., PALASZYNSKI, E., DY, M. & LEBEL, B. (1983). Biologic properties of homogenous Interleukin 3. I. Demonstration of WEHI-3 growth factor activity, mast cell growth activity, P Cell-stimulating factor activity. *J. Immun.* **131**, 282–287.

ISCOVE, N. N., TILL, J. E. & MCCULLOCH, E. A. (1970). The proliferative states of mouse granulopoietic progenitor cells. *Proc. Soc. exp. Biol. Med.* **134**, 33.

JOHNSTONE, A. P. & WILLIAMS, G. W. (1982). Role of DNA breaks and ADP-ribosyl transferase activity in eukaryotic differentiation demonstrated in human lymphocytes. *Nature, Lond.* **300**, 368–370.

LAJTHA, L. G., POZZI, L. V., SCHOFIELD, R. & FOX, M. (1969). Kinetic properties of haemopoietic stem cells. *J. Cell Tiss. Kinet.* **2**, 39–49.

METCALF, D. (1977). *Hemopoietic Colonies.* pp. 227. Berlin, Heidelberg, New York: Springer-Verlag.

METCALF, D. & MERCHAV, S. (1982). Effects of GM–CSF deprivation on precursors of granulocytes and macrophages. *J. cell. Physiol.* **112**, 411–418.

MIYAKE, T., KUNG, C. K. H. & GOLDWASSER, E. (1977). Purification of human erythropoietin. *J. biol. Chem.* **252**, 5558–5564.

NICOLA, N. A., BURGESS, A. W. & METCALF, D. (1979). Similar molecular properties of granulocyte – macrophage colony-stimulating factors produced by different mouse organs *in vitro* and *in vivo*. *J. biol. Chem.* **254**, 5290–5299.

NICOLA, N. A., METCALF, D., JOHNSON, G. R. & BURGESS, A. W. (1979). Separation of functionally distinct human granulocyte – macrophage colony stimulating factors. *Blood* **54**, 614–627.

NICOLA, N. A., METCALF, D., MATSUMOTO, M. & JOHNSON, G. R. (1983). Purification of a factor inducing differentiation in murine myelomonocytic leukemia cells. Identification as granulocyte colony-stimulating factor. *J. biol. Chem.* **258**, 9017–9023.

SACHS, L. (1980). Constitutive uncoupling of pathways of gene expression that control growth and differentiation in myeloid leukaemia: a model for the origin and progression of malignancy. *Proc. natn. Acad. Sci. U.S.A.* **77**, 6152–6156.

SACHS, L. (1982). Normal developmental programmes in myeloid leukaemia. Regulatory proteins in the control of growth and differentiation. *Cancer Surveys* **1**, 321–342.

SCHOFIELD, R. & DEXTER, T. M. (1985). Studies on the self-renewal ability of CFU–s which have been serially transferred in long-term culture or *in vivo*. *Leukemia Res.* **9**, 305–313.

SCHRADER, J. W. & CRAPPER, R. (1983). Autogenous production of a hemopoietic growth factor, P cell stimulating factor, as a mechanism for transformation of bone marrow derived cells. *Proc. natn. Acad. Sci. U.S.A.* **80**, 6892–6896.

SPOONCER, E., BOETTIGER, D. B. & DEXTER, T. M. (1984). Continuous *in vitro* generation of multipotential stem cells from src infected cultures. *Nature, Lond.* **310**, 228–230.

STANLEY, E. R., GUILBERT, L. J., TUSHINSKI, R. J. & BARTELMEZ, S. H. (1983). *J. cell. Biochem.* **21**, 151–159.

SUGIMOTO, Y., WHITMAN, M., CANTLEY, L. C. & ERIKSON, R. L. (1984). Evidence that the Rous sarcoma virus transforming gene product phosphorylates phosphatidylinositol. *Proc. natn. Acad. Sci. U.S.A.* **81**, 2117–2121.

TAIT, R. M. & NASSAU, P. M. (1984). Artificial low-molecular-mass substrates of cholera toxin. *Eur. J. Biochem.* **143**, 213–219.

TEICH, N. M., ROWE, J., TESTA, N. G. & DEXTER, T. M. (1981). Retrovirus infection of murine bone marrow cultures as a system for studying differentiation. In *Cellular Controls in Differentiation* (ed. C. W. Lloyd & D. A. Rees), pp. 149–169. New York, London: Academic Press.

TILL, J. E. & McCULLOCH, E. A. (1961). A direct measurement of the radiation sensitivity of normal mouse bone marrow cells. *Rad. Res.* **14**, 213–222.

TILL, J. E. & McCULLOCH, E. A. (1980). Hemopoietic stem cell differentiation. *Biochim. biophys. Acta* **605**, 431–459.

WHETTON, A. D., BAZILL, G. W. & DEXTER, T. M. (1984). Haemopoietic cell growth factor mediates cell survival via its action on glucose transport. *EMBO J.* **3**, 409–413.

WHETTON, A. D. & DEXTER, T. M. (1983). Effect of haematopoietic cell growth factor on intracellular ATP levels. *Nature, Lond.* **303**, 629–631.

WICKRAMASINGHE, S. N. & WEATHERALL, D. J. (1982). The pathophysiology of erythropoiesis. In *Blood and its Disorders*, 2nd edn (ed. R. M. Hardisty & D. J. Weatherall). Oxford: Blackwell Scientific.

J. Cell Sci. Suppl. 3, 97–106 (1985)
Printed in Great Britain © The Company of Biologists Limited 1985

THE HUMAN INTERLEUKIN-2 RECEPTOR

WARNER C. GREENE, JOEL M. DEPPER, MARTIN KRÖNKE AND
WARREN J. LEONARD

*Metabolism Branch, National Cancer Institute, National Institutes of Health, Bethesda,
MD 20205, U.S.A.*

SUMMARY

Complementary DNAs corresponding to the human receptor for interleukin-2 (IL-2) have been molecularly cloned, sequenced, and expressed in both COS-1 and L cells. The human genome appears to contain a single structural gene for this receptor located on the short arm of chromosome 10 (band 14–15). However, when transcribed, at least two families of mRNAs are produced, which vary in length due to the use of at least three different polyadenylation signals. Sequence analysis of the cloned cDNAs and S_1 nuclease protection assays indicate an alternative pathway of mRNA processing for this receptor whereby a 216 base-pair segment contained within the protein coding region is spliced, resulting in an mRNA unable to encode a functional IL-2 receptor. In contrast, cDNAs corresponding to mRNA retaining this 216 base-pair region code membrane receptors that bind both IL-2 and anti-Tac (monoclonal anti-IL-2 receptor antibody). Analysis of the deduced amino acid sequence reveals that the receptor is composed of 272 amino acids including a signal peptide 21 amino acids in length. Hydrophobicity analysis suggests a single, 19 amino acid transmembrane domain. A short intracytoplasmic domain composed of 13 amino acids is present and contains two potential phosphate acceptor sites (serine and threonine but not tyrosine) as well as positively charged residues presumably involved in cytoplasmic anchoring. Two sites for N-linked glycosylation sites and numerous extracytoplasmic O-linked glycosylation sites are present.

INTRODUCTION

Interleukin-2 (IL-2 or T-cell growth factor) is a 15 000 M_r glycoprotein that is required for the growth of human T cells (Morgan, Ruscetti & Gallo, 1976; Smith, 1980). Complementary DNAs for this lymphokine have been isolated and expressed in both prokaryotic and eukaryotic cells (Taniguchi *et al.* 1983; Devos *et al.* 1983). Furthermore, the human IL-2 gene has been cloned, sequenced and localized to human chromosome 4 (Fujita, Takaoka, Matsui & Taniguchi, 1983; Holbrook *et al.* 1984; Siegel *et al.* 1984). As with other polypeptide hormones, IL-2 exerts its biological effects through binding to specific high-affinity membrane receptors (Robb, Munck & Smith, 1981). However, neither IL-2 nor IL-2 receptors are produced by resting T cells (Robb *et al.* 1981; Greene & Robb, 1985). Instead, after exposure to antigen, T cells that have bound antigen enter a programme of cellular activation leading to *de novo* synthesis and secretion of IL-2 and expression of IL-2 receptors. The interaction of IL-2 with its high-affinity cellular receptor then triggers cellular proliferation resulting in the growth and development of helper, suppressor and cytotoxic effector T cells. Following the initial increase in IL-2 receptor expression, a decline in receptor expression occurs and is paralleled by diminished proliferation (Cantrell & Smith, 1983; Depper *et al.* 1984a;

Robb, 1984). Thus, IL-2 receptor expression is the principal mechanism by which the specificity, magnitude and duration of human T-cell response is regulated.

While IL-2 receptors are not present in most human leukaemic T-cell lines, these receptors are uniformly expressed in large numbers in adult T-cell leukaemia (ATL) cells infected with human T-lymphotrophic virus-I (HTLV-I) (Gootenberg *et al.* 1981; Depper *et al.* 1984*b*). While not proven, it is possible that these receptors are involved in the malignant growth of these leukaemic cells.

We have previously demonstrated that monoclonal anti-Tac antibody, prepared by Uchiyama, Broder & Waldmann (1981), recognizes the human IL-2 receptor (Leonard *et al.* 1982, 1983; Robb & Greene, 1983). We have characterized the IL-2 receptor on normal activated T cells as a sulphated glycoprotein containing intrachain disulphide bonds with an apparent M_r of 55 000 (Leonard *et al.* 1983, 1985).

These receptors are composed of a peptide precursor (M_r 33000), which is cotranslationally processed by N-linked glycosylation to yield two intermediate forms (M_r 35000 and 37000). The N-glycosylated precursors undergo further post-translational processing involving the addition of O-linked carbohydrate, sialic acid and sulphate. We now describe the isolation of cDNAs encoding the IL-2 receptor and further analysis of the structure of this receptor. These studies have been reported in greater detail (Leonard *et al.* 1984) and also similar results found by others (Nikaido *et al.* 1984; Cosman *et al.* 1984).

MATERIALS AND METHODS

Human T lymphotrophic virus (HTLV-I)-infected HUT 102B2 cells were used for IL-2 receptor protein purification and isolation of RNA. mRNA was prepared from these cells using guanidine isothiocyanate and isopycnic centrifugation in caesium chloride followed by selection of poly(A)$^+$ mRNA with oligo(dT)-cellulose. A HUT 102B2 cDNA library was constructed in lambda gt10 according to the method of St John (unpublished) except that size-fractionated, double-stranded cDNA was purified by absorption to glass silica mesh. The resultant cDNA library contained $2\cdot4\times10^6$ recombinant phage clones with inserts ranging in size from 500 base-pairs (bp) to several thousand bases. Following amplification, 200 000 phage clones were screened by Benton & Davis (1977) plaque hybridization with a 17-nucleotide-long synthetic probe prepared on the basis of the protein sequence of the receptor (see Results). Candidate clones were evaluated by selective hybridization of mRNA and complete sequencing using the dideoxy chain termination method of Sanger (1975) in M13 bacteriophage. DNA sequence data were analysed and compared on an IBM system 370 using the programme described by Queen & Korn (1980). cDNAs were expressed by ligating each into the *Eco*RI site of pcEXV-1 (generously provided by Drs James Miller and Ron Germain). This vector places the cDNA inserts under the control of the early simian virus 40 (SV40) promoter and enhancer sequences. These constructs were subsequently transfected into COS-1 cells or murine L-cell fibroblasts by precipitation with calcium phosphate and evaluated for IL-2 receptor expression in binding assays with purified radiolabelled IL-2 and anti-Tac.

RESULTS AND DISCUSSION

Purification of the human IL-2 receptor

The IL-2 receptor was purified from NP-40 detergent extracts of HUT 102B2 cells by immunoaffinity chromatography with anti-Tac antibody. The extract was first passed over a control UPC 10 monoclonal antibody column and then over the anti-Tac column. Following serial washes at varying ionic strengths, the receptor was eluted with 2·5% acetic acid. Following lyophilization, the receptor was found to retain biological activity (capacity to bind IL-2) and was > 95% pure as judged by silver staining of sodium dodecyl sulphate (SDS)/polyacrylamide gels (Fig. 1). The sequence of the N-terminal 29 amino acids was determined by gas-phase micro-sequencing (100–250 pm per analysis) and selected positions identified or confirmed by sequencing receptor biosynthetically labelled with radioactive amino acids (Table 1).

Molecular cloning of cDNAs corresponding to the human IL-2 receptor

On the basis of the protein sequence of amino acids 3–8, an oligonucleotide probe 17 nucleotides in length with 64-fold degeneracy was synthesized. This oligo-nucleotide probe was used to screen 200 000 recombinant phages from the amplified

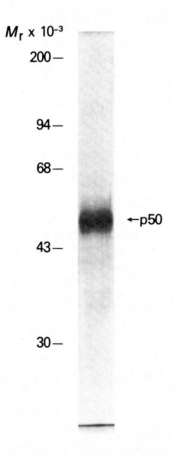

Fig. 1. Silver staining of the HUT 102B2 human IL-2 receptor purified by immuno-affinity chromatography with anti-Tac antibody. Migration of known M_r markers is indicated. (Presented with the permission of the publishers of *Nature*.)

HUT 102B2 cDNA library. Following sequential screening, 11 candidate phage clones containing cDNA inserts that hybridized to the 17-mer were identified. Clone 2 (900 bp), clone 3 (2400 bp) and clone 4 (1700 bp) were chosen for further analysis and subcloned into pBR322. Each of these clones was evaluated for the capacity to hybridize selectively to mRNA, which when translated and immunoprecipitated with a rabbit anti-IL-2 receptor heteroantiserum would produce the primary translation product of the IL-2 receptor. As shown in Fig. 2, each of three clones, but neither pBR327 nor filters without DNA, selectively hybridized to IL-2 receptor mRNA. These data strongly suggested an association between these cDNAs and the human IL-2 receptor.

Each of the inserts or appropriate restriction fragments from clones 2, 3 and 4 were subcloned into M13 bacteriophage and their complete DNA sequences were determined. A complete listing of these sequences is given by Leonard *et al.* (1984). Each of the sequences contained a long, open reading frame including a region of 87 nucleotides encoding the 29 amino acids determined by protein sequencing, thus confirming their relationship to the IL-2 receptor. Comparison of the sequence of clones 3 and 4, however, revealed that clone 4 lacked a 216 bp segment within the protein coding region, which was present in clone 3. Further, this segment was flanked on each side by the sequence T-T-C-C-A-G-G-T indicative of a typical mRNA donor and acceptor splicing site. Thus, the presence of this internally truncated cDNA suggested that an alternative pathway of mRNA processing existed for the IL-2 receptor. S_1 nuclease protection assays revealed that mRNA corresponding to this differently spliced mRNA was present in both normal activated T cells as well as five different HTLV-I-infected leukaemic T cell lines (Krönke, Leonard & Greene, unpublished data). Since the predicted protein from the spliced cDNA (clone 4) was 72 amino acids shorter than that encoded by the unspliced cDNA (clone 3), but otherwise identical, it was unclear which cDNA corresponded to the true IL-2 receptor mRNA. To address this issue, the cDNA inserts from clones 3 and 4 were ligated into an expression vector, pcEXV-1, which contains SV40 promoter and enhancer sequences. Plasmids with the cDNAs in the correct

Table 1. *N-terminal amino acid sequence of the human IL-2 receptor*

1	2	3	4	5	6	7	8
glutamic-	leucine-	cysteine-	aspartic-	aspartic-	aspartic-	proline-	proline

9	10	11	12	13	14	15
glutamic-	isoleucine-	proline-	histidine-	alanine-	threonine-	phenylalanine-

16	17	18	19	20	21	22	23
lysine-	alanine-	methionine-	alanine-	tyrosine-	lysine-	glutamic-	glycine-

24	25	26	27	28	29
threonine-	methionine-	leucine-	asparagine-	cysteine-	glutamic

The human IL-2 receptor from HUT 102B2 was sequenced by automated Edman degradation on a gas-phase sequenator followed by analysis of samples by high performance liquid chromatography. The positions of leucine, cysteine, aspartic acid, proline and methionine were determined or confirmed by sequencing of receptor biosynthetically labelled with the respective radioactive amino acid.

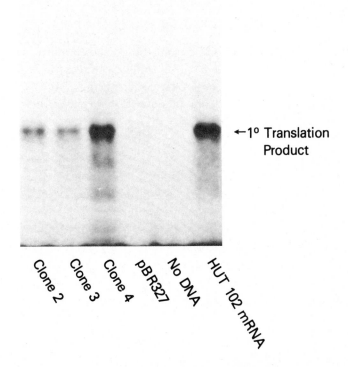

Fig. 2. Selective hybridization of IL-2 receptor mRNA. The cDNA inserts of phage clones 2, 3 and 4 were subcloned into the *Eco*RI site of pBR322. Approximately 5 μg of plasmid DNA containing these inserts or pBR327 were linearized with *Sal*I and bound to nitrocellulose. Nitrocellulose filters were then hybridized with HUT 102B2 mRNA, and the mRNA selectively retained was eluted and translated in a wheat-germ lysate cell-free translation system. Translations were immunoprecipitated with an anti-IL-2 receptor heteroantibody and analysed by SDS/PAGE. As shown, clones 2, 3 and 4, but not pBR327 or filters lacking DNA, selectively hybridized to mRNA, which when translated generated the same primary (1°) translation product as obtained with HUT 102B2 mRNA. (This figure is presented with the permission of the publishers of *Nature*.)

orientation were then transfected into COS-1 cells by precipitation with calcium phosphate and analysed for directed synthesis of the IL-2 receptor. As shown in Fig. 3, radiolabelled binding of IL-2 and anti-Tac occurred only when the unspliced cDNA was transfected (clone 3). Further, cell surface iodination and immuno-precipitation with anti-Tac confirmed the presence of the 50000 M_r receptor characteristic of HUT 102B2 cells. In contrast, the spliced cDNA, while effectively transcribed, did not result in the production of receptors capable of binding either IL-2 or anti-Tac. Essentially identical results were obtained in stable transfection studies performed with thymidine kinase-deficient mouse L cells. These L cell transfectants, however, expressed only low-affinity IL-2 receptors and did not respond to IL-2 with increased proliferation.

Analysis of the IL-2 receptor gene

Southern blots of *Eco*RI-restricted genomic DNA probed with the IL-2 receptor cDNA demonstrated five fragments of size 10, 6, 2·4 and 0·7×10³ base-pairs. Furthermore, there was no evidence for rearrangement or amplification of this receptor gene in HTLV-I-infected ATL cells (Leonard & Greene, unpublished observations). *In situ* hybridization studies have localized the IL-2 receptor gene to the chromosome 10p band 14–15 (Leonard, Donlan, Lebo & Greene, unpublished data). Sequence analysis of the IL-2 receptor gene indicates the presence of eight exons and seven introns. The amino acid sequence of the normal and HUT102B2 receptors appears to be identical.

Analysis of IL-2 receptor mRNA

Northern blot analysis of mRNA expession from several cellular sources demonstrated the presence of two differently sized mRNA families (3500 and 1500 bases) (Fig. 4). These mRNAs were present in activated normal T cells as well as HTLV-I-infected T and B cells and phorbol diester-induced, Tac-positive, acute lymphocytic leukaemic T cells but not in resting T cells.

Further study of the molecular basis for the difference in size of the two mRNAs has revealed that use of different polyadenylation signal sequences is involved. A proximal A-A-T-A-A-A sequence is apparently disregarded to generate the large mRNA (3500 nucleotides) while the smaller mRNA (1500 nucleotides) is produced

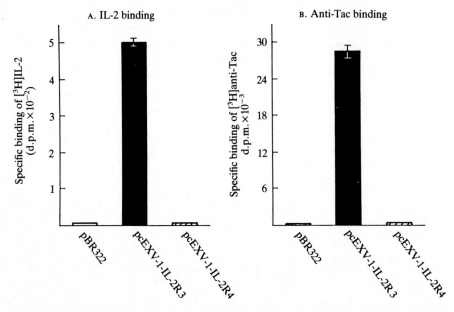

Fig. 3. DNA from pCEXV-1 expression vector constructs containing clone 3 and clone 4 cDNA inserts in the proper orientation or pBR322 were transfected into COS-1 cells by precipitation with calcium phosphate. Specific binding of purified radiolabelled JURKAT IL-2 (A) and purified radiolabelled anti-Tac (B) were measured after 48 h of culture.

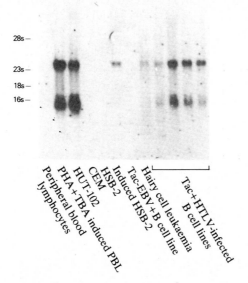

Fig. 4. Northern blot analysis of poly(A)$^+$ mRNA from varying lymphoid cell lines hybridized with IL-2 receptor cDNA. (This figure is presented with the permission of the publishers of *Nature*.)

when the proximal polyadenylation signal sequence is used (Leonard *et al.* 1984). S_1 nuclease protection assays also indicated the use of a third polyadenylation site (A-T-T-A-A-A) approximately 200 bases upstream from the proximal A-A-T-A-A-A sequence. Each of the mRNAs appears functional since size separation of HUT 102B2 mRNA on a methylmercuric hydroxide gel, translation of mRNA from different slices of the gel and immunoprecipitation of the resultant proteins demonstrate the primary translation product for the receptor from fractions corresponding to both the small and large families of mRNAs. The cellular strategy for multiple mRNAs of different sizes that encode the same protein remains unclear; however, differences in mRNA stability and translatability have not been excluded.

Analysis of the primary structure of the human IL-2 receptor

The availability of the cDNA sequence permitted complete deduction of the primary amino acid sequence of the IL-2 receptor (Fig. 5). The receptor is composed of 272 amino acids including a signal peptide of 21 amino acids. The length of the signal peptide has been confirmed by sequencing the primary translation product after labelling with [^{35}S]methionine (Leonard, Rudikoff & Greene, unpublished data). The protein contains 13 cysteine residues, suggesting potential extensive intrachain disulphide bonding, confirmed in immunoprecipitates electrophoresced under reducing and non-reducing conditions (Leonard *et al.* 1983). Two N-linked glycosylation sites are present and, since two N-glycosylated precursors have been identified, we believe it is likely that both sites are used. Hydrophobicity analysis suggests the presence of a single transmembrane domain near the carboxy terminus and a short intracytoplasmic domain (13 amino acids). The intracytoplasmic domain contains several basic amino acids, which form a charge cluster and presumably serve as a cytoplasmic anchoring region. Further, serine and threonine residues are present within the putative intracytoplasmic domain and could serve as potential phosphate acceptor sites. We and others have demonstrated that this receptor may be phosphorylated (Leonard *et al.* 1985; Shackelford & Trowbridge, 1984; Wano & Uchiyama, unpublished data).

In view of the exceedingly short intracytoplasmic tail predicted by the DNA sequence, it seems unlikely that signal transduction by the receptor involves an enzymic activity in this domain. In [^{35}S]methionine-labelled immunoprecipitates, we have previously observed coprecipitation of two larger proteins (M_r 113000 and 180000) (Leonard *et al.* 1982). These proteins appear to be located on the inner face of the membrane as they are not glycosylated or labelled by cell surface iodination techniques. Each, however, is constitutively phosphorylated. It is possible, though unproven, that these proteins form a receptor complex with the IL-2 receptor and thus might be involved in signal transduction following IL-2 binding.It is also possible that this complex binds IL-2 with a much greater affinity than p55 alone. Recent studies have delineated both high- ($K_d = 5$ pM) and low- ($K_d = 30$ nM) affinity IL-2 receptors on activated T cells (Robb *et al.* 1984). The growth-promoting effects of IL-2 appear to be mediated by the high-affinity receptors. The lack of these

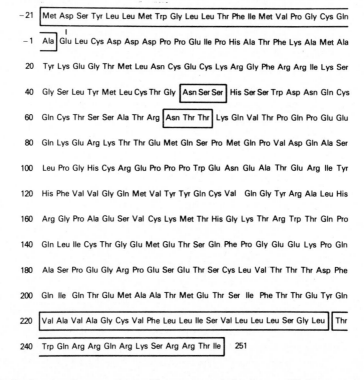

Fig. 5. Deduced primary amino acid sequence of the human IL-2 receptor. Signal peptide, two potential N-glycosylation sites, transmembrane domain and intracytoplasmic region are indicated.

proteins in the L-cell transfectants could explain the failure of these cells to bind IL-2 with high affinity as well as to respond to IL-2. Notwithstanding, we have not completely excluded the possibility that the high- and low-affinity forms of the IL-2 receptor are different proteins sharing reactivity with anti-Tac. Given the preponderance of low-affinity receptors on HUT 102B2 the sequence we obtained would almost certainly have been derived from the low-affinity receptor protein.

The availability of cDNA probes to the IL-2 receptor, hopefully, will aid in studies related to IL-2 receptor structure, function and regulation. Further, these cDNAs should be useful in further defining the intriguing relationship between HTLV-I-induced transformation of T cells and expression of IL-2 receptors.

REFERENCES

BENTON, W. D. & DAVIS, R. W. (1980). *Science* **196**, 180.

CANTRELL, D. A. & SMITH, K. A. (1983). Transient expression of interleukin 2 receptors; consequences for T cell growth. *J. exp. Med.* **158**, 1895–1911.

COSMAN, D., CERRETTI, D. P., LARSEN, A., PARK, L., MARCH, C., DOWER, S., GILLIS, S. & URDAL, D. (1984). Cloning, sequence and expression of human interleukin 2 receptor. *Nature, Lond.* **312**, 768–771.

DEPPER, J. M., LEONARD, W. J., KRÖNKE, M., NOGUCHI, P., CUNNINGHAM, R. E., WALDMANN, T. A. & GREENE, W. C. (1984*a*). Regulation of interleukin 2 receptor expression: effects of phorbol diester, phospholipase c, and reexposure to lectin and antigen. *J. Immun.* **133**, 3054–3061.

DEPPER, J. M., LEONARD, W. J., KRÖNKE, M., WALDMANN, T. A. & GREENE, W. C. (1984*b*). Augmented T cell growth factor receptor expression in HTLV infected human leukemic T cells. *J. Immun.* **133**, 1691–1695.

DEVOS, R., PLAETINCK, G., CHEROUTRE, H., SIMONS, G., DEGRAVE, W., TAVERNIER, J., REMAUT, E. & FIERS, W. (1983). Molecular cloning of human interleukin 2 cDNA and its expression in *E. coli*. *Nucl. Acids Res.* **11**, 4307–4322.

FUJITA, T., TAKAOKA, C., MATSUI, H. & TANIGUCHI, T. (1983). Structure of the human interleukin-2 gene. *Proc. natn. Acad. Sci. U.S.A.* **80**, 7437–7441.

GOOTENBERG, J. E., RUSCETTI, F. W., MIER, J. W., GAZDAR, A. & GALLO, R. C. (1981). Human cutaneous T cell lymphoma and leukemia cell lines produce and respond to T cell growth factor. *J. exp. Med.* **154**, 1403–1417.

GREENE, W. C. & ROBB, R. J. (1985). Receptors for T-cell growth factor: structure, function and expression on normal and neoplastic cells. In *Contemporary Topics in Molecular Immunology*, vol. 10 (ed. S. Gillis & F. P. Inman), pp. 1–34. New York: Plenum.

HOLBROOK, N., SMITH, K. A., FORNACE, A. J., COMEAN, C., WISKOCIL, R. L. & CRABTREE, G. R. (1984). T-cell growth factor: complete nucleotide sequence and organization of the gene in normal and malignant cells. *Proc. natn. Acad. Sci. U.S.A.* **81**, 1634–1638.

LEONARD, W. J., DEPPER, J. M. & CRABTREE, G. R. (1984). Molecular cloning and expression of cDNAs for the human interleukin-2 receptor. *Nature, Lond.* **311**, 626–631.

LEONARD, W. J., DEPPER, J. M., KRÖNKE, M., ROBB, R. J., WALDMANN, T. A. & GREENE, W. C. (1985). The human receptor for T-cell growth factor: evidence for variable post translational processing, phosphorylation, sulfation and the ability of precursor forms of the receptor to bind TCGF. *J. biol. Chem.* **260**, 1872.

LEONARD, W. J., DEPPER, J. M., ROBB, R. J., WALDMANN, T. A. & GREENE, W. C. (1983). Characterization of the human receptor for T cell growth factor. *Proc. natn. Acad. Sci. U.S.A.* **80**, 6957–6961.

LEONARD, W. J., DEPPER, J. M., UCHIYAMA, T., SMITH, K. A., WALDMANN, T. A. & GREENE, W. C. (1982). A monoclonal antibody that appears to recognize the receptor for human T cell growth factor: partial characterization of the receptor. *Nature, Lond.* **300**, 267–269.

MORGAN, D. A., RUSCETTI, F. W. & GALLO, R. C. (1976). Selective *in vitro* growth of T lymphocytes from normal human bone marrows. *Science* **193**, 1007–1008.

NIKAIDO, T., SHIMIZU, N., ISHIDA, N., SABE, H., TESHIGAWASA, K., MAEDA, M., UCHIYAMA, T., YODOI, J. & HONJO, T. (1984). Molecular cloning of cDNA encoding human interleukin 2 receptor. *Nature, Lond.* **311**, 631–635.

QUEEN, C. L. & KORN, C. J. (1980). *Meth. Enzym.* **65**, 595–609.

ROBB, R. J. (1984). Interleukin 2: the molecule and its function. *Immun. Today* **5**, 203–209.

ROBB, R. J. & GREENE, W. C. (1983). Direct demonstration of the identity of T-cell growth factor binding protein and the Tac antigen. *J. exp. Med.* **158**, 1332–1337.

ROBB, R. J., MUNCK, A. & SMITH, K. A. (1981). T-cell growth factors: quantification, specificity, and biological relevance. *J. exp. Med.* **154**, 1455–1474.

ROBB, R. J., GREENE, W. C. & RUSK, C. M. (1984). Low and high affinity cellular receptors for interleukin 2: implications for the level of Tac antigen. *J. exp. Med.* **160**, 1126–1146.

SANGER, F. & COULSON, A. R. (1980). *J. molec. Biol.* **94**, 414–418.

SHACKELFORD, D. A. & TROWBRIDGE, I. S. (1984). Induction of expression of the human interleukin 2 receptor by a phorbol diester. *J. biol. Chem.* **259**, 11706–11712.

SIEGEL, L. J., HARPER, M. E., WONG-STAAL, F., GALLO, R. C., NASH, W. G. & O'BRIEN, S. J. (1984). Gene for T-cell growth factor: location on human chromosome 4q and feline chromosome B1. *Science* **223**, 175–178.

SMITH, K. A. (1980). T-cell growth factor. *Immun. Rev.* **51**, 337–357.

TANIGUCHI, T., MATSUI, H., FUJITA, T., TAKAOKA, C., KASHIMA, N., YOSHIMOTO, R. & HAMURO, J. (1983). Structure and expression of a cloned cDNA for human interleukin 2. *Nature, Lond.* **302**, 305–310.

UCHIYAMA, T., BRODER, S. & WALDMANN, T. A. (1981). A monoclonal antibody (anti-Tac) reactive with activated and functionally mature human T cells. *J. Immun.* **126**, 1393–1397.

J. Cell Sci. Suppl. 3, 107–113 (1985)
Printed in Great Britain © The Company of Biologists Limited 1985

NERVE GROWTH FACTORS AND MOLECULES OF THE EXTRACELLULAR MATRIX IN NEURONAL DEVELOPMENT

DAVID EDGAR

Department of Neurochemistry, Max-Planck-Institute for Psychiatry, D-8033 Martinsried, Federal Republic of Germany

SUMMARY

The survival of developing neurons is epigenetically regulated by trophic factors. Only one such protein, the nerve growth factor (NGF) has been shown to act *in vivo*, where it supports the survival of neural-crest-derived sensory and sympathetic neurons. Recently, however, other proteins have been isolated and shown to support the survival of cultured neurons. Furthermore, in addition to the effects of soluble trophic factors, proteins of the extracellular matrix are also able to modulate neuronal survival. Analysis of the basal lamina protein, laminin, shows that when used as a culture substrate it stimulates neurite outgrowth and potentiates neuronal survival *via* a site associated with its heparin binding domain. On proteolytic cleavage of laminin, however, a cryptic site is unmasked that can also promote neuronal survival and neurite growth. The properties of this cryptic site indicate that it may be similar to that of the laminin-like molecule synthesized by Schwann cells, which although recognized by anti-laminin antibodies is not inhibited by them.

THE ROLE OF NERVE GROWTH FACTORS

It is ironic that the first protein to be isolated, characterized and named as a growth factor, the nerve growth factor (NGF), does not act to stimulate the rate of division of its responsive nerve cells: thus the action of NGF is fundamentally different from those of subsequently discovered growth factors – EGF, PDGF etc. – which are stimulators of mitosis. While essentially nothing is known about the molecules and mechanisms that regulate the division of neurons or their precursor cells, the role of NGF to promote the survival of developing neurons and to maintain the differentiated properties of mature neurons is well established (for a review, see Thoenen & Barde 1980).

NGF is still the only molecule that has been shown to act *in vivo* as a trophic factor exerting a retrograde survival-promoting effect from target tissue to innervating neurons, the evidence until very recently being indirect: administration of anti-NGF antibodies to embryonic or young animals resulted in the death of peripheral sensory and sympathetic neurons. Direct evidence that target tissues determine the numbers of their innervating neurons by the production of NGF has, however, now been provided by showing that organs densely innervated by the sympathetic nervous system have higher levels of NGF than those with a meagre innervation (Korsching & Thoenen, 1983a). The amounts of NGF and its mRNA are correlated with the density of sympathetic innervation (Heumann, Korsching, Scott & Thoenen, 1984; Shelton & Reichardt, 1984), indicating that target organs do indeed synthesize

NGF, although it is not clear which cells are responsible. As NGF levels have now been shown to be able to determine the extent of sympathetic axonal ramification (Campenot, 1982), then endogenous NGF production is indeed most probably responsible for the extent of sympathetic innervation.

The mechanism of action of NGF to promote neuronal survival during development and to maintain levels of neurotransmitter-synthesizing enzymes and neuropeptides in the adult is still unclear; endogenous NGF has been shown to be transported retrogradely along axons to the neuronal cell bodies situated in peripheral ganglia (Korsching & Thoenen, 1983b). This retrograde accumulation thus explains the high levels of NGF found in sympathetic ganglia although the low levels of its mRNA indicate that it is not synthesized there (Heumann et al. 1984). Interruption of retrograde transport by axotomy or colchicine treatment leads to the death of young neurons showing that the retrograde transport to the cell body of either NGF itself or of some unknown second messenger is necessary for the survival promoting effect. It is clear that the specific uptake of NGF is due to the presence of high-affinity NGF receptors (K_D 10^{-11} M) on the neuronal membrane, and once internalized the NGF remains in membrane-bound compartments (Schwab, Heumann & Thoenen, 1982). Details of the molecular mechanism of action of NGF after receptor binding, internalization and transport, however, remain unknown.

Although NGF is the only protein that has been demonstrated to have the role of a neurotrophic factor in vivo, it is most unlikely that it is the only protein with this function: the epigenetic control of neuronal survival has been demonstrated throughout the nervous system, whereas NGF has only been shown to affect the survival of peripheral sensory and sympathetic neurons derived from the neural crest (see Lindsay et al. 1985). Indeed recent experiments in vitro using tissue culture

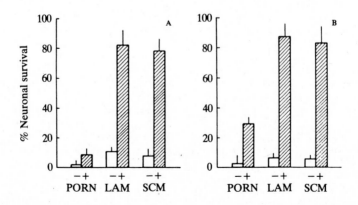

Fig. 1. Potentiation of neuronal survival by laminin and mouse Schwann cell matrix molecules. Sympathetic neurons from: A, 8-day-old and B 12-day-old embryonic chicks were cultured on a polyornithine culture (PORN) substrate previously coated with 10 μg mouse EHS sarcoma laminin (LAM) (Edgar et al. 1984) or conditioned medium taken from cultured mouse Schwann cells (SCM) (Edgar & Thoenen, 1982). Where shown (+), 20 ng ml^{-1} NGF was added to the culture medium (F14+10% horse serum). Means ± S.E.M. ($n = 4$) are shown.

techniques have shown that a variety of tissue extracts and molecules produced by cultured cells are able to support the survival of neurons that are unresponsive to NGF (for reviews, see Barde, Edgar & Thoenen, 1983; Lindsay *et al.* 1985). At the time of writing only two of these molecules have been isolated: ciliary neurotrophic factor CNTF from embryonic eye tissues (Barbin, Manthorpe & Varon, 1984) and a brain-derived neurotrophic factor, BDNF (Barde, Edgar & Thoenen, 1982). CNTF supports the survival of not only ciliary (parasympathetic) neurons but also of sensory and sympathetic neurons in the peripheral nervous system and is a protein of M_r 20000, pI 5·0. BDNF, on the other hand, supports the survival only of those neurons that project into the central nervous system, i.e. primary sensory neurons derived from both neural crest and placodes, and retinal ganglion cells derived from the neural tube (unpublished observation). It is a protein of M_r 12000, pI > 10 (Barde *et al.* 1982). Establishment of the physiological roles for CNTF and BDNF awaits the production of antibodies against them in order to determine the consequences of their neutralization, *in vivo* (Edgar & Barde, 1983).

THE TROPHIC EFFECT OF MOLECULES OF THE EXTRACELLULAR MATRIX

It has recently become apparent from tissue culture experiments that not only 'classical' soluble neurotrophic molecules but also the extracellular matrix plays a decisive role in neuronal survival and maturation *in vitro*. A number of different cell types have been shown to produce molecules that when attached to the culture

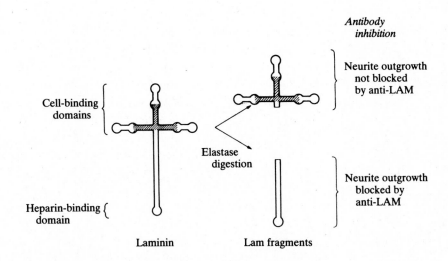

Fig. 2. Cartoon summary of laminin fragmentation and antibody inhibition studies. Proteolysis was by mild digestion with elastase (4h at 4°C). While antisera against the whole laminin molecule or purified antibodies against the heparin binding domain blocked the neurite outgrowth due to both laminin or the fragment containing the heparin binding domain neither antisera nor antibodies blocked the neurite promoting activity of the fragment containing the cell binding domains. For details see Timpl *et al.* (1983*b*) and Edgar *et al.* (1984).

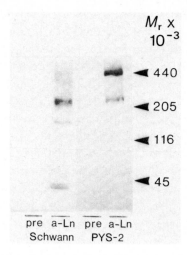

Fig. 3. Immunoprecipitation of PYS-2 cell laminin (for comparison) and Schwann cell molecules with anti-laminin (a-Ln) antisera. PYS-2 cells and mouse Schwann cells were labelled for 18 h with 10 μCi [^{35}S]methionine in Dulbecco's minimal essential culture medium containing 10% foetal calf serum. The labelled proteins released into 500 μl medium were precipitated with Pansorbin (Calbiochem). Conditions of precipitation were as described in the legend to Table 1. After washing the Pansorbin pellets the proteins were eluted by boiling in sodium dodecyl sulphate/polyacrylamide gel electrophoresis sample buffer containing mercaptoethanol and electrophoresed on a 3% to 10% polyacrylamide gradient gel. ^{35}S-labelled proteins were detected by fluorography.

substrate evoke a very rapid outgrowth of neurites from a variety of neurons (Collins, 1978; Adler, Manthorpe, Skaper & Varon, 1981; Barde *et al.* 1983). Additionally, although such substrates alone do not support neuronal survival, they do potentiate survival in response to a classical neurotrophic factor such as NGF (Edgar & Thoenen, 1982: see also Fig. 1).

Some progress has been made with the partial purification of the neurite-promoting activities indicating that they are proteins, possibly associated with a heparin sulphate proteoglycan (see, e.g., Lander, Fujii, Gospodarowicz & Reichardt, 1982). Recently, however, it was found that the basement membrane protein laminin, when used as a tissue culture substrate was both able to stimulate rapid neurite outgrowth (Baron van Evercooren *et al.* 1982) and potentiate neuronal survival in response to NGF (Edgar, Timpl & Thoenen, 1984; and Fig. 1). Because laminin is a well-defined molecule (Fig. 2) it lends itself to an analysis of how molecules fixed in the extracellular matrix can interact with neurons to stimulate neurite outgrowth and potentiate survival. It was thus shown that although antisera against laminin block its effects on neurons, when purified antibodies against specific domains of the laminin molecule were used only those against the heparin binding globular domain at the end of the long arm of the molecule were inhibitory (Edgar *et al.* 1984). This indirect evidence implicating the heparin binding domain in laminin's interaction with neurons is supported by the observation that a proteolytic fragment of laminin containing the heparin-binding domain (but not the previously characterized non-neuronal cell binding domains (Timpl, Engel & Martin, 1983*b*), also stimulated neurite outgrowth and potentiated survival. Thus laminin has at least two distinct cellular binding sites, for neuronal and non-neuronal cells, respectively (Edgar *et al.* 1984). Fragmentation of laminin also lead to the exposure of a previously cryptic site on the molecule, as a neuronal binding site was detected in a fragment comprising the short arms of the molecule that could not be blocked by anti-laminin antibodies (Edgar *et al.* 1984). This observation is of interest because, while the effects of the various undefined extracellular matrix molecules on neurons are apparently identical to those of laminin (see below), they cannot be blocked by anti-laminin antisera (see Edgar *et al.* 1984, for references). So the neurite-promoting and survival-potentiating effects of the extracellular matrices produced by cultured cells may be due to molecules analogous to the fragment consisting of the laminin short arms produced by partial proteolysis.

COMPARISON OF THE EFFECTS OF LAMININ AND SCHWANN CELL EXTRA-CELLULAR MATRICES ON NEURONS IN CULTURE

As reported for the extracellular matrix produced by chick embryo heart cells (Edgar & Thoenen, 1982), both laminin and the matrix produced by mouse Schwann cells (SCM) potentiated the survival of embryonic sympathetic neurons in response to NGF (Fig. 1). The extent of potentiation was found to be dependent upon the age of the neurons and this was most clearly illustrated in the case of young (E8) neurons (Fig. 1A) where they displayed an absolute requirement for the laminin or Schwann cell matrix in order to survive in the presence of NGF.

Anti-laminin antiserum was able specifically to immunoprecipitate two polypeptides from the molecules produced and secreted by the Schwann cells, of 230 000 and

Table 1. *Immunoprecipitation of neurite promoting activity*

	Neurite promoting activity remaining in solution (U/ml)	
Antiserum	Laminin	Schwann cell matrix
−(Starting activity)	120	180
Preimmune	120	160
Anti-laminin	<2·5	<2·5

F14H10 culture medium was either supplemented with 10 μg EHS tumour laminin or conditioned by being previously used to culture mouse Schwann cells. Samples of 500 μl were then supplemented with 350 mM-NaCl, 0·05 % sodium deoxycholate, 0·1 % Nonidet P40 and 2 μl rabbit pre-immune or anti-laminin antiserum (a gift from Dr R. Timpl). After 30 min incubation at room temperature, 150 μl Pansorbin (Calbiochem) suspension in culture medium was added and the mixtures were shaken for a further 2 h. After centrifugation the supernatants were tested for neurite promoting activity by assessing the ability of serial dilutions to coat polyornithine-treated multiwell dishes and stimulate neurite outgrowth from cultured chick sympathetic neurons (Edgar *et al.* 1984). One unit (U) is defined as the minimum volume of culture medium that evoked a detectable neurite-outgrowth response after 2 h culture.

150 000 M_r (Fig. 3). These bands correspond in molecular wieght to the laminin B chains and entactin or nidogen, respectively (Hogan, Taylor & Cooper, 1982; Timpl *et al*. 1983*a*). Significantly, although the anti-laminin antisera do not block the activity of the Schwann cell medium (see Edgar *et al*. 1984, for references) the activity was effectively removed from the medium by immunoprecipitation (Table 1), indicating that either laminin B chains or entactin/nidogen are responsible for the neuron-stimulatory effects of the Schwann cell matrix, or alternatively that the activity is due to a minor protein not seen on the fluorogram, but which nevertheless is associated with the laminin B chains and, or, entactin.

CONCLUSIONS

Both the extracellular matrix provided by cultured Schwann cells and the purified basement membrane protein laminin stimulate neurite outgrowth and potentiate neuronal survival in response to the neurotrophic factor, NGF. Although the molecules produced by Schwann cells are clearly different from the classical form of laminin, in having no A chain and not being blocked by anti-laminin antibodies, they also have striking similarities. Thus anti-laminin antibodies do precipitate polypeptides synthesized by the Schwann cells that correspond in molecular weight to the B chains of laminin and also entactin/nidogen, proteins known to form a non-covalent complex with authentic laminin (Hogan *et al*. 1982; Timpl *et al*. 1983*a*). It is therefore tempting to speculate that the form of laminin synthesized by Schwann cells, and responsible for the effects of their matrix on neurons, is analogous to the short arm fragment of laminin, generated by proteolysis and whose effects on neurons are also not blocked by anti-laminin antibodies (Edgar *et al*. 1984).

REFERENCES

ADLER, R., MANTHORPE, M., SKAPER, S. D. & VARON, S. (1981). Polyornithine neurite promoting factors. *Brain Res*. **206**, 129–144.

BARBIN, G., MANTHORPE, M. & VARON, S. (1984). Purification of the chick eye ciliary neurotrophic factor. *J. Neurochem*. **43**, 1468–1478.

BARDE, Y.-A., EDGAR, D. & THOENEN, H. (1982). Purification of a new neurotrophic factor from mammalian brain. *EMBO J*. **1**, 549–553.

BARDE, Y.-A., EDGAR, D. & THOENEN, H. (1983). New neurotrophic factors. *A. Rev. Physiol*. **45**, 601–612.

BARON VAN EVERCOOREN, A., KLEINMAN, H. K., OHNO, S., MARANGOS, P., SCHWARTZ, J. P. & DUBOIS-DALCO, M. E. (1982). *J. Neurosci. Res*. **8**, 179–193.

CAMPENOT, R. B. (1982). Development of sympathetic neurons in compartmentalized cultures. *Devl Biol*. **93**, 1–21.

COLLINS, F. (1978). Induction of neurite outgrowth by a conditioned medium factor bound to the culture substratum. *Proc. natn. Acad. Sci. U.S.A*. **75**, 5210–5213.

EDGAR, D. & BARDE, Y.-A. (1983). Neuronal growth factors. *Trends Neurosci*. **6**, 260–262.

EDGAR, D. & THOENEN, H. (1982). Modulation of NGF-induced survival of chick sympathetic neurons. *Devl Brain Res*. **5**, 89–92.

EDGAR, D., TIMPL, R. & THOENEN, H. (1984). The heparin-binding domain of laminin is responsible for its effects on neurite outgrowth and neuronal survival. *EMBO J*. **3**, 1463–1468.

HEUMANN, R., KORSCHING, S., SCOTT, J. & THOENEN, H. (1984). Relationship between the levels of NGF and its mRNA in sympathetic ganglia and peripheral target tissues. *EMBO J*. **3**, 3183–3189.

HOGAN, B. M. L., TAYLOR, A. & COOPER, A. R. (1982). Murine parietal endoderm cells synthesize heparan sulfate and 170 and 145K glycoproteins as components of Reichert's membrane. *Devl Biol.* **90**, 210–214.

KORSCHING, S. & THOENEN, H. (1983a). NGF in sympathetic ganglia and corresponding target tissues of the rat. *Proc. natn. Acad. Sci. U.S.A.* **80**, 3513–3516.

KORSCHING, S. & THOENEN, H. (1983b). Quantitative demonstration of the retrograde axonal transport of endogenous NGF. *Neurosci. Lett.* **39**, 1–4.

LANDER, A. D., FUJII, D. K., GOSPODAROWICZ, D. & REICHARDT, L. F. (1982). A heparan sulfate proteoglycan induces rapid neurite outgrowth *in vitro. J. Cell Biol.* **94**, 574–582.

LINDSAY, R. M., BARDE, Y.-A., DAVIES, A. M. & ROHRER, H. (1985). Differences and similarities in the neurotrophic growth factor requirements of sensory neurons derived from neural crest and neural placode. *J. Cell Sci. Suppl. 3*, 115–129.

SCHWAB, M., HEUMANN, R. & THOENEN, H. (1982). Communication between target organs and nerve cells. *Cold Spring Harbor Symp. quant. Biol.* **46**, 125–134.

SHELTON, D. L. & REICHARDT, L. F. (1984). Expression of β-nerve growth factor gene correlates with the density of sympathetic innervation in effector organs. *Proc. natn. Acad. Sci. U.S.A.* **81**, 7951–7955.

THOENEN, H. & BARDE, Y.-A. (1980). Physiology of nerve growth factor. *Physiol. Rev.* **60**, 1284–1335.

TIMPL, R., DZIADEK, M., FUJIWARA, S., NOWAK, H. & WICK, G. (1983a). Nidogen, a new self-aggregating basement membrane protein. *Eur. J. Biochem.* **137**, 455–465.

TIMPL, R., ENGEL, J. & MARTIN, G. R. (1983b). Laminin. *Trends Biochem. Sci.* **8**, 207–209.

J. Cell Sci. Suppl. 3, 115–129 (1985)
Printed in Great Britain © The Company of Biologists Limited 1985

DIFFERENCES AND SIMILARITIES IN THE NEUROTROPHIC GROWTH FACTOR REQUIREMENTS OF SENSORY NEURONS DERIVED FROM NEURAL CREST AND NEURAL PLACODE

RONALD M. LINDSAY[1],*, YVES-ALAIN BARDE[2], ALUN M. DAVIES[3] AND HERMANN ROHRER[2]

[1] *Laboratory of Neurobiology, National Institute for Medical Research, The Ridgeway, Mill Hill, London NW7 1AA, U.K.*

[2] *Department of Neurochemistry, Max-Planck Institute for Psychiatry, D-8033 Planegg-Martinsried, Federal Republic of Germany*

[3] *Department of Anatomy, St George's Hospital Medical School, Tooting, London SW17 0RE, U.K.*

SUMMARY

This article reviews recent studies that have examined differences and similarities in the neurotrophic growth factor requirements of neural crest- and neural placode-derived sensory neurons of the developing chick embryo. From *in vitro* experiments using both explant and dissociated, neuron-enriched cultures of spinal and cranial nerve sensory neurons, it has been established that only sensory neurons of neural crest origin are responsive, at least in terms of survival and neurite outgrowth, to mouse submandibular gland nerve growth factor (NGF). Sensory neurons derived from neural placodes (neurons of the ventrolateral portion of the trigeminal ganglion and the entire neuronal population of the vestibular, geniculate, petrosal and nodose ganglia) are largely unresponsive to NGF throughout embryonic development, but do respond to neurotrophic activity present in extracts of brain and various peripheral 'end-organs', such as heart or liver. By incubation of neuron-enriched cultures with radiolabelled $[^{125}I]NGF$, followed by autoradiographic exposure, it has been demonstrated that placode-derived neurons, in marked contrast to those of neural crest origin, are completely devoid of specific cell surface receptors for NGF. In contrast to differences in their requirement and responsiveness to NGF, both placode- and crest-derived sensory neurons are responsive to the survival and neurite-promoting activity of a recently purified brain-derived neurotrophic factor (BDNF). It is postulated that all primary sensory neurons have a dual growth factor requirement during development; their survival being dependent on a supply of both a peripheral and a central 'target'-derived neurotrophic factor. It appears that BDNF may act as common 'central target-derived' neurotrophic factor for both placode- and crest-derived sensory neurons, but that within peripheral tissues there are specific neurotrophic factors for each of these two classes of primary sensory neurons.

INTRODUCTION

Sensory neurons of peripheral nerve ganglia arise from either of two distinct, transient embryological structures: the neural crest and neural placodes. Of these

---

* Present address for all correspondence: Sandoz Institute for Medical Research, 5 Gower Place, London WC1E 6BN, U.K.

two contributory sources to the formation of the peripheral nervous system, that of the neural crest has been the more extensively studied (for a review, see Le Douarin, 1982), especially in birds where it is now well established that the neural crest gives rise to both the neurons and the satellite cells of autonomic ganglia and spinal nerve sensory ganglia (dorsal root ganglia, DRG). More recently, the precise contribution of the neural crest and neural placodes to the formation of cranial nerve sensory ganglia has been elucidated (Noden, 1978; Narayanan & Narayanan, 1980; Ayer-Le Lievre & Le Douarin, 1982; D'Amico Martel & Noden, 1983; and see Lindsay & Rohrer, 1985, for a review of earlier studies) using the quail-chick chimera transplantation paradigm devised by Le Douarin (1973). It is now concluded, at least for birds, that neurons of the distal ganglia of the VIIth, IXth and Xth cranial nerves (geniculate, petrosal and nodose ganglia, respectively) and neurons of the vestibuloacoustic complex of the VIIIth cranial nerve are exclusively of neural placode origin. The trigeminal ganglion of the Vth cranial nerve contains neurons of both crest and placode origin (the placode-derived neurons being predominant in the ventrolateral pole of the maxillo–mandibular lobe) while the satellite cells of all cranial ganglia are entirely of neural crest origin.

It is now well established that during embryonic development the survival and subsequent maturation of certain classes of peripheral neurons is vitally dependent upon specific neurotrophic growth factor molecules. Until recently the vast majority of evidence supporting such a crucial role for neurotrophic growth factors in development and maintenance of the nervous system had come almost entirely from studies with nerve growth factor (NGF) isolated from the submandibular glands of mice (for a review of NGF, see Thoenen & Barde, 1980). Studies *in vitro* and *in vivo* have led to the present view that sympathetic neurons require NGF for survival and maintenance during embryonic and post-natal development. Spinal sensory neurons have also been shown to require NGF for survival, but their dependence on NGF appears to be limited to a fixed period of embryonic development.

In contrast to extensive information on the role of NGF in promoting survival and neurite outgrowth from neural crest-derived sensory neurons, there have been very few studies that have addressed in any detail the neurotrophic growth factor requirements of neural placode-derived sensory neurons. Whilst studies on the development of mammalian cranial nerve ganglia *in vivo* suggest that placode-derived sensory neurons are insensitive to NGF (Johnson, Gorin, Brandeis & Pearson, 1980; Pearson, Johnson & Brandeis, 1983), evidence from *in vitro* studies on the responsiveness of placode-derived sensory neurons to NGF is both scant and conflicting. Published and unpublished studies by Levi-Montalcini (1966; personal communication; see also, Hamburger, 1962) suggest that NGF does not promote the survival or outgrowth of neurites from placode-derived ganglia such as the nodose ganglion or ventrolateral pole of the trigeminal ganglion of the chick. This view is also supported by more recent studies on the chick trigeminal and nodose ganglia in culture (Ebendal & Hedlund, 1974, 1975; Lindsay, 1979; Lindsay *et al.* 1982; Davies & Lumsden, 1983). However, explants of the chick embryo nodose ganglia and dissociated cultures of perinatal rat nodose ganglia have been reported to be responsive to NGF, in terms of the survival and neurite promoting activity of NGF (Hedlund & Ebendal, 1980; Baccaglini & Cooper, 1982).

This report summarizes recent studies (Davies & Lindsay, 1985; Lindsay & Rohrer, 1985; Lindsay, Thoenen & Barde, 1985) comparing the effect of NGF as a neurotrophic growth factor upon explant and dissociated neuron-enriched cultures of neural crest and neural placode-derived sensory neurons. In addition the response of these two classes of sensory neurons to BDNF, a novel neurotrophic factor recently purified from pig brain (Barde, Edgar & Thoenen, 1982), has been examined using cultures of nodose and spinal DRG ganglia as representatives of neural placode and neural crest-derived sensory neurons, respectively.

MATERIALS AND METHODS

Cultures

Dorsal root ganglia and cranial nerve sensory ganglia (trigeminal, jugular, vestibular, geniculate, petrosal and nodose ganglia) were taken from chick embryos of ages between E4 and E16, as described previously in detail (Davies & Lindsay, 1985; Lindsay & Rohrer, 1985). For explant cultures five or six ganglia of each type were embedded in 1 ml of collagen gel in 35 mm Nunc tissue culture dishes (Lindsay & Tarbit, 1979). After gelation, each culture was overlaid with 1·5 ml of growth medium (Eagle's minimum essential medium supplemented with 10% heat-inactivated horse serum) containing, as appropriate, NGF, tissue extract or other additives. In explant cultures the magnitude of neurite outgrowth scored at 24 and, or, 48 h was taken as a measure of responsiveness to NGF or other neurotrophic factor activity. All measurements were made under phase-contrast microscopy at ×125 magnification with neurite outgrowth being rated on an arbitrary scale of 0 to 5+, or 0 to 10+ as before (Lindsay & Peters, 1984; Davies & Lindsay, 1985, respectively).

Dissociated, neuron-enriched cultures of placode- or neural crest-derived sensory neurons were established from ganglia taken from chick embryos of ages between E5 and E12, as before (Lindsay & Rohrer, 1985). Neuron-enriched cell suspensions were plated at densities between 5×10^3 and 12×10^3 cells per 35 mm culture dish. For most bioassays using dissociated neuron-enriched cultures, culture dishes were pre-coated either with a thin film native collagen gel, or with poly-L-lysine (50 μg ml^{-1}) or both. In studies on the responsiveness of sensory neurons to BDNF, culture dishes were coated sequentially with poly-D,L-ornithine (500 μg ml^{-1}) and the basement membrane protein laminin as described previously (Edgar, Timpl & Thoenen, 1984). The response of dissociated neurons to NGF, tissue extracts or BDNF was assessed by determining the percentage of the cells originally plated that survived as process-bearing neurons (phase-bright cells with neurites at least 4–5 cell diameters in length) at a minimum of 48 h after plating. In the absence of any exogenous neurotrophic activity the percentage of process-bearing cells that survived beyond 24 h was never more than 3–5%.

Tissue extracts

Extracts of chick tissues (E18–E20 chick embryo heart and brain, 1 week post-hatching chick liver) were prepared as described previously (Lindsay & Peters, 1984; Lindsay & Rohrer, 1985).

[^{125}I]NGF binding and autoradiography

Dissociated, neuron-enriched cultures of nodose and DRG ganglia taken from E5–E12 chick embryos were cultured on polyornithine-coated 4-well 35 mm dishes as before (Rohrer & Barde, 1982; Lindsay & Rohrer, 1985). Cultures were grown in F-14 medium supplemented with 10% horse serum, 15% chick liver extract and 5 ng ml^{-1} NGF.

The preparation of [^{125}I]NGF, labelling of cultures, fixation, dipping and autoradiographic exposure was carried out as described before (Rohrer & Barde, 1982; Lindsay & Rohrer, 1985).

RESULTS AND DISCUSSION

Response of ganglion explants to NGF

In explant culture the most extensive comparisons were made between the response of E4–E16 chick embryo nodose and DRG ganglia to NGF concentrations over the range 0·5 to 50 ng ml^{-1}. As shown in Fig. 1 some spontaneous neurite outgrowth was observed in control cultures of nodose ganglia at the earliest ages studied (E4–E5). This spontaneous neurite outgrowth in the absence of any exogenous neurotrophic activity seems to be peculiar to the nodose, and to a lesser extent to the petrosal ganglion, as it has not been observed to any substantial degree with other cranial nerve ganglia or DRG (Davies & Lindsay, 1985; Lindsay & Rohrer, 1985). In addition to the spontaneous fibre outgrowth from E4–E5 explants, it is clear that neurite outgrowth from nodose ganglia at this stage is stimulated by NGF (Figs 1, 2), although the density of the fibre halo never reaches that seen with older DRG (Fig. 1H). A slight response to NGF was still observed at E7 but by E9 nodose ganglion explants appeared to be refractory to the neurite-promoting activity of NGF. This pattern of responsiveness of cultured nodose ganglia to NGF is in complete contrast to that observed with DRG. The latter show little neurite outgrowth in response to NGF at embryonic ages below E6, but exhibit increasingly dense fibre outgrowth in response to NGF at chick embryo ages above E7.

Our initial observations with the nodose ganglion were later extended to a comparison of the NGF responsiveness of all other chick embryo sensory ganglia of either neural crest or neural placode (Davies & Lindsay, 1985). As predicted, the neurite promoting activity of NGF was confined, except at very early embryonic ages, to sensory ganglia of neural crest origin (DRG, dorsomedial portion of the trigeminal ganglion and the jugular ganglion) as shown for explant cultures of E11 ganglia in Fig. 3. Whilst modest neurite outgrowth was observed from E4–E6 geniculate and petrosal ganglion in response to NGF, the ventrolateral pole of the trigeminal ganglion and the vestibular ganglion were refractory at all ages to NGF (Davies & Lindsay, 1985). In all the above experiments increasing the NGF concentration above 50 ng ml^{-1} (up to 1 μg ml^{-1}) had no further effect in promoting neurite outgrowth from placode or crest-derived ganglia.

Response of dissociated neurons to NGF

As studied over the developmental range E6 to E12, dissociated neuron-enriched cultures of nodose ganglia were refractory to NGF in terms of enhanced survial or

---

Fig. 1. Phase-contrast micrographs of E5, E7 and E9 chick embryo nodose ganglia (A–F) and E9 dorsal root ganglia, DRG (G,H), explants after 24 h in culture. The left-hand panels (A,C,E,G) show control cultures and the right-hand panels show explants grown in the presence of NGF at 25 ng ml^{-1}. Explants were cultured in collagen gel as described in Materials and Methods. Bar, 100 μm.

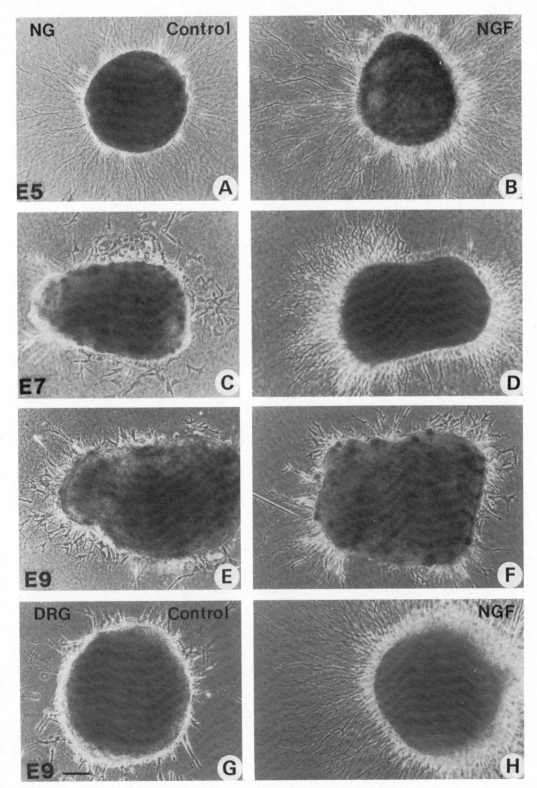

R. M. Lindsay and others

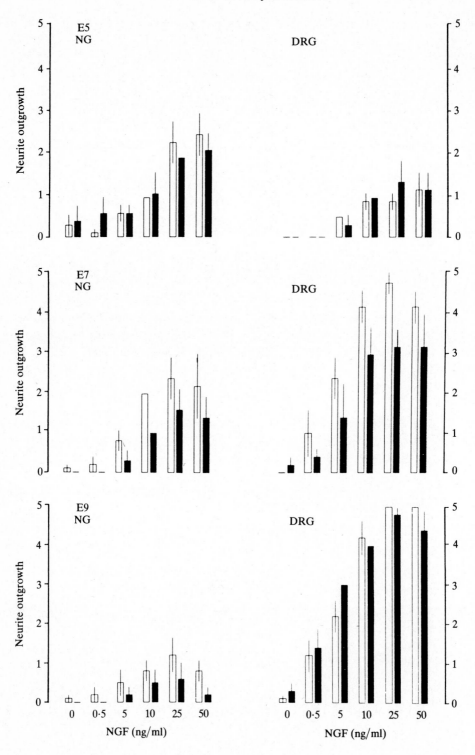

Fig. 2

neurite outgrowth (Fig. 4). Whilst in previous studies with DRG neurons alone we have routinely used the term neuronal survival (defined as 'phase-bright cells with neurites at least 4 to 5 cell diameters in length') as a measure of the responsiveness of neurons to NGF or other trophic activity, it is clear that this definition must be modified when dealing with nodose (and perhaps other) neurons. With highly enriched cultures of DRG neurons, at least of the chick embryo, cultured on dishes coated with either collagen, polylysine or polyornithine, we have invariably found that in control cultures all of the neurons die in the absence of exogenously added neurotrophic growth factor. However, with chick nodose ganglion neurons, especially from older (E12) embryos, we have observed both on collagen- and laminin-coated dishes (Lindsay & Rohrer, 1985; Lindsay *et al.* 1985) that a small percentage of neurons survive and extend neurites without added neurotrophic factor and quite a high percentage of phase-bright neuronal cells survive but do not extend processes even after 1 week in culture. Thus, although it makes no difference to previous or present results, the response of dissociated, neuron-enriched cultures to NGF, tissue extracts or BDNF is now defined in terms of 'process-bearing' neurons rather than 'surviving' neurons.

Although less detailed than our studies with dissociated cultures of the nodose ganglion, a comparative study of the response to NGF of dissociated, neuron-enriched cultures of either E6 or E9 vestibular, petrosal, jugular or DRG indicated again that NGF only elicits fibre outgrowth from sensory neurons of neural crest origin as neurons of the two placodal ganglia (vestibular and petrosal) tested were refractory to NGF (Davies & Lindsay, 1985).

Response of placode-derived neurons to tissue extracts

Although NGF does not appear to influence the survival or outgrowth of neurites from placode-derived sensory neurons, it has previously been shown that nodose ganglion neurons do survive and elaborate extensive neurites *in vitro* when co-cultured with astroglial cells from adult rat brain (Lindsay, 1979; Lindsay *et al.* 1982). In more recent studies (Davies & Lindsay, 1985; Lindsay & Rohrer, 1985) we have shown that nodose and other placode-derived neurons are also responsive to neurotrophic activity in extracts of various peripheral organs. For example, liver extract from 1-week-old chicks was found to elicit neurite outgrowth from both nodose (Fig. 4) and petrosal neurons, although, interestingly the same extract had no effect on vestibular neurons of the same developmental age. Nodose ganglion neurons from E12 chick embryos were found to be the most responsive (50–60%) to

---

Fig. 2. Bar charts comparing the magnitude of neurite outgrowth from E5, E7 and E9 chick embryo nodose and DRG explants grown in the presence of NGF concentrations of 0–50 ng ml^{-1} as indicated under the pairs of bars. The open bars represent scores at 24 h, and the filled bars scores of the same cultures made at 48 h. Neurite outgrowth was scored on an arbitrary scale of 0 to 5+, as described before (Lindsay & Peters, 1984). Apart from a minimum positive score of 0·5, all responses were scored as whole integers. Results are means+S.E.M. ($n = 6$).

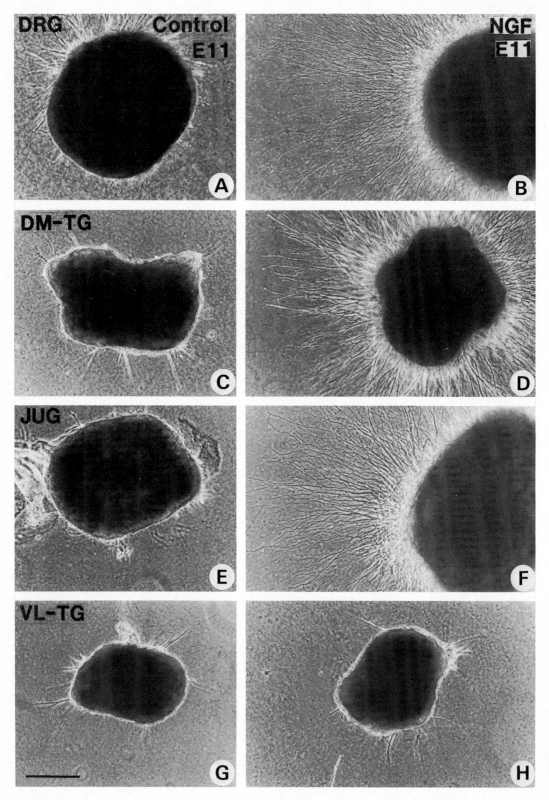

Fig. 3. For legend see p. 124

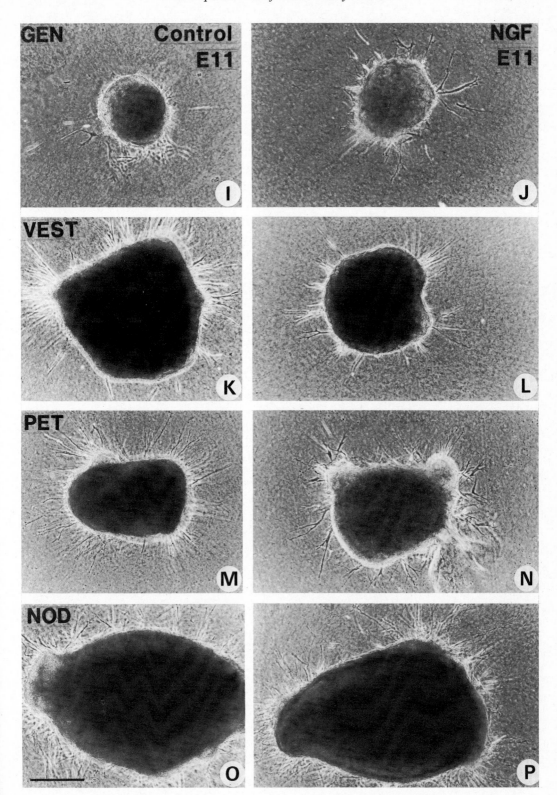

Fig. 3. For legend see p. 124

the neurite promoting activity of chick liver extract, but even at embryonic age E5 chick liver extract elicited neurite outgrowth from 25–30% of nodose ganglion neurons. The neurotrophic activity in chick liver extract has been shown to be dose dependent and is not blocked by antiserum to mouse NGF, at least as far as neurite promoting activity towards placode-derived sensory neurons is concerned.

Receptors for NGF on sensory neurons

Cultures of DRG and nodose ganglion neurons from E6–E12 chick embryos were maintained in culture with either chick liver extract, NGF (5 ng ml^{-1}), or both, and after 2 days in culture the percentage of cells that were labelled with [^{125}I]NGF was determined as described previously (Rohrer & Barde, 1982; Lindsay & Rohrer, 1985). Regardless of whether they had been cultured in the presence of liver extract alone or with liver extract plus NGF, more than 90% of process-bearing E6–E10 DRG neurons were heavily labelled with [^{125}I]NGF, as shown by the heavy accumulation of silver grains observed on neurites and cell bodies after auto-radiographic exposure (Fig. 5A,B). Over this age range the percentage of DRG neurons that survived and produced neurites in response to exogenous neurotrophic activity (NGF or liver extract) ranged from 25–30% at E6 to 50–60% at E10.

In marked contrast to DRG neurons, cultures of nodose ganglion neurons from chick embryos of all ages between E6 and E12 were found to be virtually devoid of specific cell surface receptors for NGF as assessed by incubation with [^{125}I]NGF and autoradiography. As shown in Fig. 5C,D the density of silver grains on cultured nodose ganglion neurons was not above background. This observation was the same regardless of whether nodose ganglion neurons were cultured in the presence of liver extract alone or with liver extract plus NGF. The only age at which there was any indication of specific NGF receptors on nodose ganglion neurons was at E5, where in a limited number of experiments up to 35% of process-bearing nodose ganglion cells were labelled with silver grains after incubation with [^{125}I]NGF.

Response of DRG and nodose ganglion neurons to BDNF

In addition to their requirement for NGF, it has recently been suggested that DRG neurons may be dependent on a second neurotrophic factor (Barde, Lindsay, Monard & Thoenen, 1978; Lindsay, 1979; Lindsay & Tarbit, 1979; Barde *et al.* 1980, 1982; Lindsay *et al.* 1982; Lindsay & Peters, 1984). These studies have led to the recent isolation and complete purification from pig brain of a novel neurotrophic growth factor: brain-derived neurotrophic factor or BDNF (Barde *et al.* 1982).

Fig. 3. Phase-contrast micrographs of E11 chick embryo spinal (DRG) and cranial nerve sensory ganglia cultured as explants in the absence (left-hand panels: A,C,E,G,I,K,M,O) and presence of NGF at 20 ng ml^{-1} (right-hand panels: B,D,F,H,J,L,N,P). DRG, dorsal root ganglion; DM-TG, dorsomedial pole of the maxillomandibular lobe of the trigeminal ganglion; JUG, jugular ganglion; VL-TG, ventrolateral pole of the maxillomandibular lobe of the trigeminal ganglion; GEN, geniculate ganglion; VEST, vestibular portion of the vestibuloacoustic ganglionic complex; PET, petrosal ganglion; NOD, nodose ganglion. Bar, 200 μm.

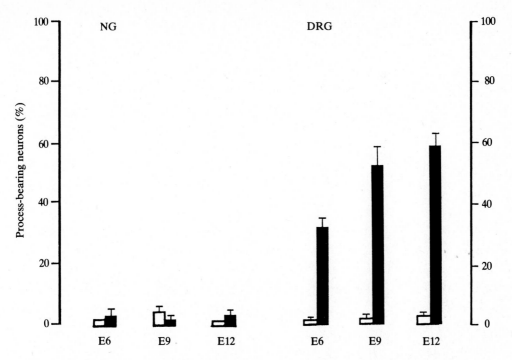

Fig. 4. Bar chart showing the mean percentage of process-bearing neurons in dissociated, neuron-enriched cultures of E6, E9 and E12 chick embryo nodose and DRG after 48 h incubation in the absence (first bar at each age, control cultures) or presence of a saturating level of NGF, 50 ng ml^{-1} (second bar at each age). Cells were cultured on collagen gel-coated 35 mm tissue culture dishes at a density of 6×10^3 to 10^4 cells per dish.

Given that nodose ganglion neurons are refractory to NGF, as reported here, but exhibit enhanced survival and neurite outgrowth when cultured with adult rat brain astroglial cells (Lindsay, 1979; Lindsay *et al.* 1982), it was of interest to compare the response of DRG and nodose ganglion neurons to BDNF.

When cultured on laminin-coated tissue culture dishes (Edgar *et al.* 1984), we have found that 40–50% of nodose ganglion neurons from chicks of embryonic ages between E6 and E12 survive and extend neurites in the presence of BDNF (10–20 ng ml^{-1}). At younger ages (E6) BDNF promotes survival and neurite outgrowth from nodose ganglion neurons, whilst at older embryonic stages (E12), at least on a laminin substrate, nodose ganglion neurons can survive (without processes) for a week or more without the addition of exogenous neurotrophic activity, but do extend neurites in response to BDNF (Lindsay *et al.* 1985). The addition of NGF to cultures of nodose ganglion neurons had no additive or synergistic effect with BDNF. Over the same age range (E6–E12) on laminin-coated dishes, BDNF supported survival and neurite outgrowth from 40–70% of DRG neurons. In the case of DRG neurons, however, the combination of NGF with BDNF was additive such that almost all (85–100%) of the cells plated survived and produced neurites when both neurotrophic factors were present.

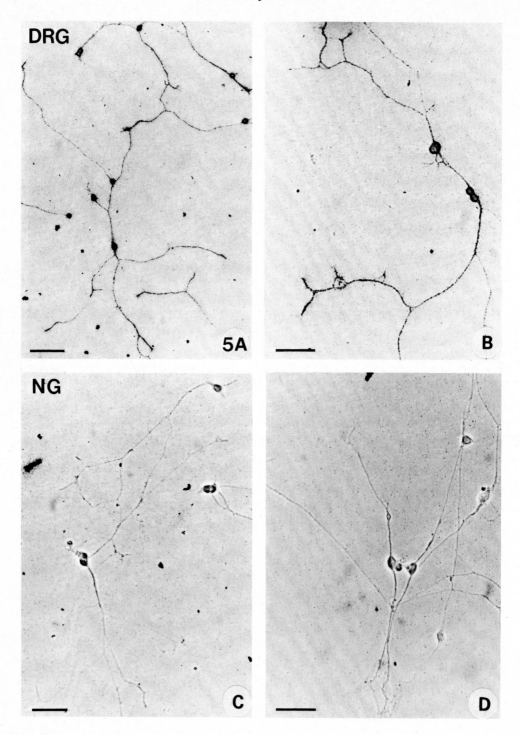

CONCLUSIONS

In this article summarizing our recent studies in which we compared the neurotrophic growth factor requirements of neural crest and neural placode-derived sensory neurons, we have suggested that NGF has little or no effect in promoting either the survival or outgrowth of neurites from placode-derived neurons. We have shown, at least with the nodose ganglion, that placode-derived sensory neurons are devoid of NGF receptors even at very early embryonic stages (E6).

We are, however, left with the anomalous result that explants of E4–E6 geniculate, petrosal or nodose ganglia do exhibit modest fibre outgrowth in response to NGF, although at all stages in dissociated, neuron-enriched cultures we have not observed any neurotrophic effect of NGF towards these placode-derived neurons. In the light of our own bias, it is tempting to speculate that the NGF-induced neurite outgrowth from the above three placodal ganglia in explant culture is not in fact fibre outgrowth from placodal neurons but is rather a peculiar *in vitro* phenomenon whereby neural crest-derived cells within these otherwise placodal ganglia express neuronal potentials (neurite outgrowth) that are not normally expressed, or indeed are actively repressed *in vivo*. As we have recently outlined (Davies & Lindsay, 1985; Lindsay *et al.* 1985) this suggestion arises from quail-chick transplantation studies by Ayer-Le Lievre & Le Douarin (1982). These authors have shown by construction of a chimeric nodose ganglion, which was subsequently transplanted back into the neural crest migration pathway of a young host, that neural crest-derived precursor cells, which normally only give rise to satellite cells of placode-derived ganglia, can express neuronal potentialities (autonomic neuron phenotype) when exposed to a different environment than usual.

Finally, we have shown (Lindsay *et al.* 1985) that both neural crest and neural placode-derived sensory neurons are responsive, at least *in vitro*, to a neurotrophic factor (BDNF) derived from the central nervous system. We interpret this observation, although still preliminary, as indicating that within their central 'target' most, if not all, primary sensory neurons of both crest and placode origin share a common neurotrophic factor. This is obviously in contrast to the situation in the periphery, in which we interpret the differential response of DRG and nodose ganglion neurons to NGF as indicative of there being distinct growth factors in peripheral tissues for these two classes of peripheral neurons. It remains to be established whether a peripheral and a central neurotrophic factor are required simultaneously by developing sensory neurons or whether, as previously suggested

Fig. 5. Autoradiographic detection of NGF receptors on E6 and E9 chick embryo DRG sensory neurons (A,B) and contrasting lack of NGF receptors on placode-derived nodose ganglion sensory neurons of similar ages (C,D). Dissociated, neuron-enriched cultures of each type of ganglion were maintained for 2 days in the presence of chick liver extract (150 μl ml^{-1}) and NGF (5 ng ml^{-1}) on polyornithine (500 μg ml^{-1}) coated dishes before incubation with [^{125}I]NGF and autoradiographic exposure as described previously (Rohrer & Barde, 1982). Note dense silver grains over all DRG neurites, even at E6 (A), and complete absence of grains over similarly treated nodose ganglion cultures. Bar, 100 μm.

(Barde *et al.* 1980), there is an ontogenic shift from dependence upon a peripheral to a central 'target'-derived neurotrophic factor.

We thank Janice Wilson and Caroline Peters for excellent technical help in the course of these studies. The collaborative aspect of this study was made possible by a twinning grant from the European Science Foundation, to the Laboratory of Neurobiology, N.I.M.R., London, and the Department of Neurochemistry, Max-Planck-Institute for Psychiatry, Munich.

REFERENCES

AYER-LE LIEVRE, C. S. & LE DOUARIN, N. M. (1982). The early development of cranial sensory ganglia and the potentialities of their component cells studied in quail-chick chimeras. *Devl Biol.* **94**, 291–310.

BACCAGLINI, P. I. & COOPER, E. (1982). Electrophysiological studies of newborn rat nodose neurones in cell culture. *J. Physiol.* **324**, 429–439.

BARDE, Y.-A., EDGAR, D. & THOENEN, H. (1980). Sensory neurons in culture: changing requirements for survival factors during embryonic development. *Proc. natn. Acad. Sci. U.S.A.* **77**, 1199–1203.

BARDE, Y.-A., EDGAR, D. & THOENEN, H. (1982). Purification of a new neurotrophic factor from mammalian brain. *EMBO J.* **1**, 549–553.

BARDE, Y.-A., LINDSAY, R. M., MONARD, D. & THOENEN, H. (1978). New factor released by cultured glioma cells supporting survival and growth of sensory neurones. *Nature, Lond.* **274**, 818.

D'AMICO-MARTEL, A. & NODEN, D. (1983). Contributions of placodal and neural crest cells to avian cranial peripheral ganglia. *Am. J. Anat.* **166**, 445–468.

DAVIES, A. M. & LINDSAY, R. M. (1985). The cranial sensory ganglia in culture: Differences in the response of placode-derived and neural crest-derived neurons to nerve growth factor. *Devl Biol.* (in press).

DAVIES, A. & LUMSDEN, A. (1983). Influence of nerve growth factor on developing dorso-medial and ventrolateral neurons of chick and mouse trigeminal ganglia. *Int. J. Neurosci.* **1**, 171–177.

EBENDAL, T. & HEDLUND, K.-O. (1974). Histology of the chick embryo trigeminal ganglion and initial effects of its cultivation with and without nerve growth factor. *Zoon* **2**, 25–35.

EBENDAL, T. & HEDLUND, K.-O. (1975). Effects of nerve growth factor on the chick trigeminal ganglion in culture. *Zoon* **3**, 33–47.

EDGAR, D., TIMPL, R. & THOENEN, H. (1984). The heparin binding domain of laminin is responsible for its effects on neurite outgrowth and neuronal survival. *EMBO J.* **3**, 1463–1468.

HAMBURGER, V. (1962). Specificity in neurogenesis. *J. cell. comp. Physiol.* **60**, 581–592.

HEDLUND, K.-O. & EBENDAL, T. (1980). The chick embryo nodose ganglion: effects of nerve growth factor in culture. *J. Neurocytol.* **9**, 665–682.

JOHNSON, E. M., GORIN, P. D., BRANDEIS, L. D. & PEARSON, J. (1980). Dorsal root ganglion neurons are destroyed by exposure in utero to maternal antibody to nerve growth factor. *Science* **210**, 916–918.

LE DOUARIN, N. M. (1973). A biological cell labelling technique and its use in experimental embryology. *Devl Biol.* **20**, 217–222.

LE DOUARIN, N. M. (1982). *The Neural Crest.* Cambridge University Press.

LEVI-MONTALCINI, R. (1966). The nerve growth factor: its mode of action on sensory and sympathetic nerve cells. *The Harvey Lectures* **60**, 217–259.

LINDSAY, R. M. (1979). Adult rat brain astrocytyes support survival of both NGF-dependent and NGF-insensitive neurones. *Nature, Lond.* **282**, 80–82.

LINDSAY, R. M., BARBER, P. C., SHERWOOD, M. R. C., ZIMMER, J. & RAISMAN, G. (1982). Astrocytes from adult rat brain. Derivation, characterization and neurotrophic properties of pure astroglial cells from corpus callosum. *Brain Res.* **243**, 329–343.

LINDSAY, R. M. & PETERS, C. (1984). Spinal cord contains neurotrophic activity for spinal nerve sensory neurons. Late developmental appearance of a survival factor distinct from nerve growth factor. *Neuroscience* **12**, 45–51.

LINDSAY, R. M. & ROHRER, H. (1985). Placodal sensory neurons in culture. Nodose ganglion neurons are unresponsive to NGF, lack NGF receptors but are supported by a liver-derived neurotrophic factor. *Devl Biol.* (in press).

LINDSAY, R. M. & TARBIT, J. (1979). Developmentally regulated induction of neurite outgrowth from immature chick sensory neurons (DRG) by homogenates of avian and mammalian heart, liver and brain. *Neurosci. Lett.* **12**, 195–200.

LINDSAY, R. M., THOENEN, H. & BARDE, Y.-A. (1985). Placode and neural crest-derived sensory neurons are responsive at early developmental stages to brain-derived neurotrophic factor (BDNF). *Devl Biol.* (in press).

NARAYANAN, C. H. & NARAYANAN, Y. (1980). Neural crest and placodal contributions in the development of the glossopharyngeal–vagal complex in the chick. *Anat. Rec.* **196**, 71–82.

NODEN, D. M. (1978). The control of avian cephalic neural crest cytodifferentiation. *Devl Biol.* **67**, 313–329.

PEARSON, J., JOHNSON, E. M. & BRANDEIS, L. (1983). Effects of antibodies to nerve growth factor on intrauterine development of derivatives of cranial neural crest and placode in the guinea pig. *Devl Biol.* **96**, 32–36.

ROHRER, H. & BARDE, Y.-A. (1982). Presence and disappearance of nerve growth factor receptors on sensory neurons in culture. *Devl Biol.* **89**, 309–315.

THOENEN, H. & BARDE, Y.-A. (1980). Physiology of nerve growth factor. *Physiol. Rev.* **60**, 1284–1335.

J. Cell Sci. Suppl. 3, 131–137 (1985)
Printed in Great Britain © The Company of Biologists Limited 1985

THE LDL RECEPTOR AND THE REGULATION OF CELLULAR CHOLESTEROL METABOLISM

JOSEPH L. GOLDSTEIN* AND MICHAEL S. BROWN

Departments of Molecular Genetics and Internal Medicine, University of Texas Health Science Center at Dallas, Southwestern Medical School, 5323 Harry Hines Blvd, Dallas, TX 75235, U.S.A.

INTRODUCTION

Cholesterol is a structural component of the plasma membrane that surrounds animal cells. It is absolutely essential for cell growth and survival. Yet, excessive amounts of cholesterol can also be lethal – as when massive amounts of cholesterol deposit in cells of the artery wall producing atherosclerosis. Thus, animal cells have evolved a highly ordered mechanism for regulating their cholesterol content. In this article, we review some of the recent studies that have been carried out by our group on the cellular and molecular biology of the cell surface receptor for low density lipoprotein, or LDL, the major transport protein for cholesterol in human plasma.

The LDL receptor has turned out to be an exciting system in several ways. First, the LDL receptor has served as a prototype for the study of receptor-mediated endocytosis, a general biological process in which cells bind hormones and other macromolecules at the surface and take them into the cell for nutritional and regulatory processes. And second, the LDL receptor studies have taught us a great deal about how genes regulate cholesterol metabolism. Mutations occurring in the gene for the receptor disrupt the regulation of blood cholesterol levels, producing hypercholesterolaemia and atherosclerosis.

The LDL receptor is a member of a class of membrane glycoproteins called lipoprotein receptors (Goldstein & Brown, 1977). These receptors remove cholesterol-carrying lipoproteins from the circulation through the process of receptor-mediated endocytosis (Goldstein, Anderson & Brown, 1979). They are present on the surface of essentially all cultured mammalian cells, where they mediate the uptake of plasma LDL, thereby providing cells with the cholesterol that they need for growth. In the body, most LDL receptors are expressed in the liver, where they supply cholesterol for secretion into bile, for conversion to bile acids, and for re-secretion into the plasma in newly synthesized lipoproteins (Brown & Goldstein, 1983; Mahley & Innerarity, 1983). LDL receptors are also present in high concentrations in the adrenal cortex and the ovarian corpus luteum, where they function to provide cholesterol for steroid hormone formation (Brown, Kovanen & Goldstein, 1979).

---

* Author for correspondence.

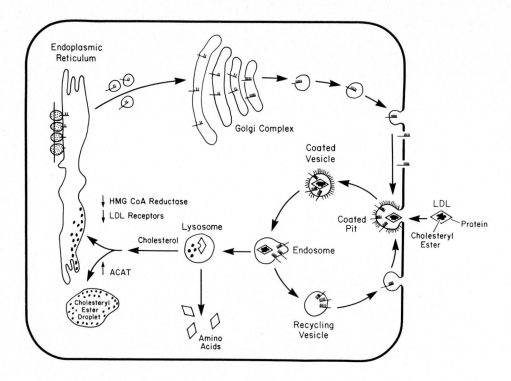

Fig. 1. The LDL receptor pathway in mammalian cells. The receptor undergoes a circuitous itinerary, beginning life as a newly synthesized protein on the endoplasmic reticulum. The remainder of the itinerary is discussed in the text. HMG CoA reductase denotes 3-hydroxy-3-methylglutaryl CoA reductase; ACAT denotes acyl-CoA: cholesterol acyltransferase. Vertical arrows indicate regulatory effects.

STRUCTURE AND FUNCTION

The human LDL receptor is a glycoprotein of 839 amino acids that spans the plasma membrane one time with its NH_2 terminus facing the extracellular environment and its COOH terminus facing the cytoplasm (Schneider, Beisiegel, Goldstein & Brown, 1982; Schneider *et al.* 1983; Russell *et al.* 1984; Yamamoto *et al.* 1984). The external domain contains a cysteine-rich region that bears the binding site for LDL. It also contains amino acid sequences that serve as the sites of attachment for asparagine-linked (N-linked) and serine/threonine-linked (O-linked) carbohydrate chains. The cytoplasmic domain contains 50 amino acid residues that direct the receptor to its proper sites of function in the cell.

Fig. 1 illustrates the itinerary followed by the LDL receptor as it carries LDL into cells. The receptor is synthesized in the rough endoplasmic reticulum. Here the high mannose precursor of the N-linked carbohydrate is added, apparently co-translationally (Tolleshaug, Hobgood, Brown & Goldstein, 1983; Cummings *et al.* 1983). The receptor precursor also contains the core sugar (i.e. *N*-acetylgalacto-samine) of each O-linked tetrasaccharide chain, which is added to the protein at the earliest time point that can be studied (approximately 10 min after synthesis) (Tolleshaug *et al.* 1983; Cummings *et al.* 1983). These O-linked core sugars are added before the mannose residues of the N-linked chains are trimmed, i.e. while the receptor is still in the endoglycosidase H-sensitive stage. Thus, the O-linked core sugars must be added either in the endoplasmic reticulum, or in the transitional zone between the endoplasmic reticulum and the Golgi apparatus.

Within 30 min after its synthesis, the receptor decreases in mobility on sodium dodecyl sulphate (SDS)-containing gels from a mobility corresponding to 120 000 M_r to a mobility corresponding to 160 000 M_r (Tolleshaug *et al.* 1983; Cummings *et al.* 1983). This change is coincident with the enzymic reactions that modify the high-mannose N-linked oligosaccharide chains to the complex, sialic acid-containing, endoglycosidase H-resistant type. At the same time, the core N-acetylgalactosamine of each O-linked chain is elongated by the addition of one galactose and two sialic acid residues. The net amount of carbohydrate that is added is not sufficient to account for a true increase of 40 000 in the M_r, and so we believe that the bulk of the change is due to conformational alterations in the protein and changes in the amount of SDS binding that retard its mobility in SDS-containing gels.

About 45 min after its synthesis, the LDL receptor appears on the surface, where it clusters together with other receptors in indented regions of the plasma membrane that are coated on the cytoplasmic surface with a protein called clathrin. These are the so-called 'coated pits' that are responsible for the receptor-mediated endocytosis of a variety of receptor-bound molecules (Goldstein *et al.* 1979). While in the coated pit, the receptor binds LDL by attaching to the protein component of the lipo-protein. Within 3–5 min of their formation, the coated pits invaginate to form coated endocytic vesicles that pinch off from the plasma membrane and exist for a brief moment (less than 2 min) as free structures in the cytoplasm. Very quickly, the clathrin coat dissociates from the surface of the coated vesicle, which now appears as a smooth-surfaced structure. Multiple endocytic vesicles fuse with each other to create larger membrane-enclosed sacs of irregular contour called endosomes (Brown, Anderson & Goldstein, 1983). The pH of the endosomes is lower than that of the surrounding cytoplasm, owing to the presence of proton pumps in the membrane of the endosome that acidify its contents (Helenius, Mellman, Wall & Hubbard, 1983). Under the influence of the acid pH, the LDL dissociates from the receptor. The receptor can then return to the surface, apparently by clustering together with other receptors in a segment of the endosome membrane that pinches off to form a recycling vesicle that carries the receptors back to the surface (Brown *et al.* 1983). Once it reaches the surface the receptor binds another LDL particle and initiates another cycle of endocytosis and recycling. Each receptor makes one round-trip every 10 min in a continuous fashion.

The LDL that dissociates from the receptor remains within the lumen of the endosome and is eventually delivered to a lysosome when the membranes of the endosome and lysosome fuse. The LDL is now exposed to a variety of acid hydrolases. Its protein component is hydrolysed to amino acids and its cholesteryl esters are hydrolysed by an acid lipase, liberating cholesterol for use in the synthesis of new membranes (Goldstein & Brown, 1977). After leaving the lysosome, the cholesterol liberated from LDL regulates the cell's cholesterol metabolism, thereby assuring a steady level of cholesterol within the cell (Goldstein & Brown, 1977). To accomplish this regulation, the incoming cholesterol modulates several reactions (Goldstein & Brown, 1977), the most important of which involves the receptor itself. In this reaction, the build-up of cholesterol within the cell causes the cell to shut off the synthesis of new LDL receptors (Goldstein & Brown, 1977). Through this 'feedback' mechanism, cells adjust the production of receptors to supply sufficient cholesterol to meet their varying demands, but not enough to overload themselves with cholesterol. When cells are growing actively and producing new membranes, they synthesize a maximal number of LDL receptors (approximately 40 000 per cell) to supply the necessary amounts of cholesterol. On the other hand, when cells cease to grow, they have little demand for cholesterol. Consequently, the cholesterol begins to build up in the cell, and the production of LDL receptors is suppressed to levels as low as 10 % of the maximum. In this way, intracellular accumulation of excessive cholesterol is prevented.

GENETICS

The importance of the LDL receptor in normal physiology was first appreciated when its absence was shown to produce a severe disease, in this case familial hypercholesterolaemia (FH). FH exists clinically in two forms: the less severe heterozygous form and the more severe homozygous form (Goldstein & Brown, 1983). Heterozygotes, who inherit one mutant gene, are quite common, accounting for one out of every 500 persons among most ethnic groups throughout the world. These heterozygotes have plasma LDL levels that are twofold above normal even before birth, and they begin to have heart attacks as early as age 35 years. Among people under age 60 who suffer heart attacks, 5 % have the heterozygous form of FH – 25-fold more than in the general population.

Ordinarily, each FH heterozygote passes a single copy of the mutant gene to half of his or her offspring, and these offspring then have heterozygous FH. If two FH heterozygotes marry, as occurs in one out of 250 000 marriages, each offspring has a one in four chance of inheriting two doses of the mutant gene, one from each parent. Such an offspring is an FH homozygote. FH homozygotes number about one in a million persons in the population. They have LDL levels that are more than six times above normal. Heart attacks can occur as early as age 2 and are almost inevitable by age 20. It is notable that these children have no risk factors for atherosclerosis other than an elevated level of LDL. They have normal blood pressure, they do not smoke, and they do not have an elevated blood glucose level. The homozygous form of FH is a vivid experiment of nature that demonstrates unequivocally the causal relationship between elevated LDL levels and atherosclerosis.

Eleven years ago, we began to study FH with the hope of learning the mechanism for the elevation of LDL in these patients (Goldstein & Brown, 1973; Brown & Goldstein, 1974). We soon discovered that cultured skin fibroblasts and circulating blood cells from FH homozygotes produce few or no functional LDL receptors. They are therefore unable to bind, internalize and degrade LDL with normal efficiency. The receptor deficiency arises because FH homozygotes inherit two defective copies of the gene for the LDL receptor, one from each parent. They have no copy of the normal gene and therefore can produce no normal LDL receptors.

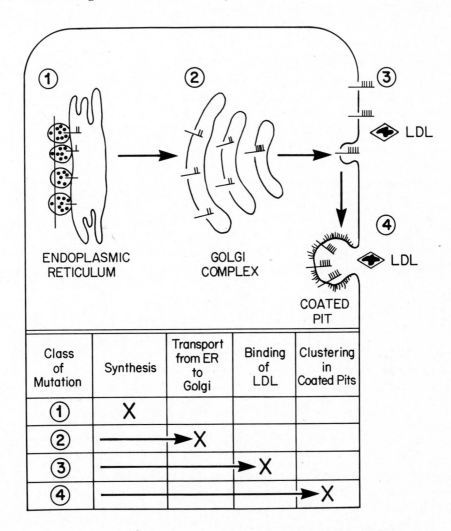

Fig. 2. Four classes of mutations in the structural gene for the LDL receptor have been identified in patients with familial hypercholesterolaemia. Each mutation affects a different region in the gene and thus interferes with a different step in the normal process by which the receptor is synthesized, processed in the Golgi complex, and transported to coated pits where it is available to bind LDL. Each class of mutation can be further subdivided into different mutant alleles that have been reviewed by Goldstein & Brown (1984). (Reprinted from *Journal of Lipid Research*, with permission.) ER, endoplasmic reticulum.

Cells from their parents (and from other FH heterozygotes) have one normal gene and one mutant gene for the receptor. They synthesize half the normal number of LDL receptors and are therefore able to bind, internalize and degrade LDL at half the normal rate. All individuals with FH studied so far have mutations in the gene encoding the LDL receptor, but the mutations are not all the same. The mutations fall into four different classes, depending on the site in the gene at which the mutation has occurred (Tolleshaug *et al.* 1983; Goldstein & Brown, 1973).

Fig. 2 presents a summary of the four classes of LDL receptor mutations that have been identified in patients with FH. One class of mutant genes produces no detectable receptors (so-called 'null' alleles). The second class produces receptors that are synthesized in the rough endoplasmic reticulum, but cannot be transported to the cell surface and therefore cannot perform their normal function. The third class of mutations produces receptors that move to the cell surface normally, but are unable to bind LDL owing to an abnormality in the binding site. The fourth class of mutations produces receptors that are transported to the surface and bind LDL, but are unable to enter coated pits and therefore cannot carry LDL into cells (so-called 'internalization defective' alleles) (Tolleshaug *et al.* 1983; Cummings *et al.* 1983; Brown *et al.* 1983; Goldstein & Brown, 1983).

Studies of the molecular basis of the mutations in the LDL receptor are beginning to reveal those parts of the protein that signal transport to the plasma membrane and those that signal the incorporation into coated pits. Thus, these mutations are providing new insights into fundamental cell biology (Goldstein & Brown, 1984; Lehrman *et al.* 1985).

The authors' research is supported by grants from the National Institutes of Health (HL 20948) and the Moss Heart Fund.

REFERENCES

BROWN, M. S., ANDERSON, R. G. W. & GOLDSTEIN, J. L. (1983). Recycling receptors: The round-trip itinerary of migrant membrane proteins. *Cell* **32**, 663–667.

BROWN, M. S. & GOLDSTEIN, J. L. (1974). Familial hypercholesterolemia: Defective binding of lipoproteins to cultured fibroblasts associated with impaired regulation of 3-hydroxy-3-methylglutaryl coenzyme A reductase activity. *Proc. natn. Acad. Sci. U.S.A.* **71**, 788–792.

BROWN, M. S. & GOLDSTEIN, J. L. (1983). Lipoprotein receptors in the liver: Control signals for plasma cholesterol traffic. *J. clin. Invest.* **72**, 743–747.

BROWN, M. S., KOVANEN, P. T. & GOLDSTEIN, J. L. (1979). Receptor-mediated uptake of lipoprotein-cholesterol and its utilization for steroid synthesis in the adrenal cortex. *Recent Prog. Hormone Res.* **35**, 215–257.

CUMMINGS, R. D., KORNFELD, S., SCHNEIDER, W. J., HOBGOOD, K. K., TOLLESHAUG, H., BROWN, M. S. & GOLDSTEIN, J. L. (1983). Biosynthesis of the N- and O-linked oligosaccharides of the low density lipoprotein receptor. *J. biol. Chem.* **258**, 15 261–15 273.

GOLDSTEIN, J. L., ANDERSON, R. G. W. & BROWN, M. S. (1979). Coated pits, coated vesicles and receptor-mediated endocytosis. *Nature, Lond.* **279**, 679–685.

GOLDSTEIN, J. L. & BROWN, M. S. (1973). Familial hypercholesterolemia: Identification of a defect in the regulation of 3-hydroxy-3-methylglutaryl coenzyme A reductase activity associated with overproduction of cholesterol. *Proc. natn. Acad. Sci. U.S.A.* **70**, 2804–2808.

GOLDSTEIN, J. L. & BROWN, M. S. (1977). The low-density lipoprotein pathway and its relation to atherosclerosis. *A. Rev. Biochem.* **46**, 897–930.

GOLDSTEIN, J. L. & BROWN, M. S. (1983). Familial hypercholesterolemia. In *The Metabolic Basis of Inherited Disease* (ed. J. B. Stanbury, J. B. Wyngaarden, D. S. Fredrickson, J. L. Goldstein & M. S. Brown) chap. 33, 5th edn, pp. 672–712. New York: McGraw-Hill Book Co.

GOLDSTEIN, J. L. & BROWN, M. S. (1984). Progress in understanding the LDL receptor and HMG CoA reductase, two membrane proteins that regulate the plasma cholesterol. *J. Lipid Res.* **25**, 1450–1461.

HELENIUS, A., MELLMAN, I., WALL, D. & HUBBARD, A. (1983). Endosomes. *TIBS* **8**, 245–250.

LEHRMAN, M. A., SCHNEIDER, W. J., SUDHOF, T., BROWN, M. S., GOLDSTEIN, J. L. & RUSSELL, D. W. (1985). Mutation in LDL receptor: Alu–Alu recombination deletes exons encoding transmembrane and cytoplasmic domains. *Science* **227**, 140–146.

MAHLEY, R. W. & INNERARITY, T. L. (1983). Lipoprotein receptors and cholesterol homeostasis. *Biochim. biophys. Acta* **737**, 197–222.

RUSSELL, D. W., SCHNEIDER, W. J., YAMAMOTO, T., LUSKEY, K. L., BROWN, M. S. & GOLDSTEIN, J. L. (1984). Domain map of the LDL receptor: Sequence homology with the epidermal growth factor precursor. *Cell* **37**, 577–585.

SCHNEIDER, W. J., BEISIEGEL, U., GOLDSTEIN, J. L. & BROWN, M. S. (1982). Purification of the low density lipoprotein receptor, an acidic glycoprotein of 164,000 molecular weight. *J. biol. Chem.* **257**, 2664–2673.

SCHNEIDER, W. J., SLAUGHTER, C. J., GOLDSTEIN, J. L., ANDERSON, R. G. W., CAPRA, D. J. & BROWN, M. S. (1983). Use of anti-peptide antibodies to demonstrate external orientation of NH$_2$-terminus of the LDL receptor in the plasma membrane of fibroblasts. *J. Cell Biol.* **97**, 1635–1640.

TOLLESHAUG, H., HOBGOOD, K. K., BROWN, M. S. & GOLDSTEIN, J. L. (1983). The LDL receptor locus in familial hypercholesterolemia: Multiple mutations disrupting the transport and processing of a membrane receptor. *Cell* **32**, 941–951.

YAMAMOTO, T., DAVIS, C. G., BROWN, M. S., SCHNEIDER, W. J., CASEY, M. L., GOLDSTEIN, J. L. & RUSSELL, D. W. (1984). The human LDL receptor: A cysteine-rich protein with multiple Alu sequences in its mRNA. *Cell* **39**, 27–38.

J. Cell Sci. Suppl. 3, 139–149 (1985)
Printed in Great Britain © The Company of Biologists Limited 1985

MOLECULAR DISSECTION OF THE HUMAN TRANSFERRIN RECEPTOR

CLAUDIO SCHNEIDER

EMBL, Heidelberg, West Germany

AND J. G. WILLIAMS

ICRF Laboratories, Mill Hill, London, U.K.

SUMMARY

Transferrin is the major iron carrier protein in vertebrates and is required for maintenance of cell viability. To deliver iron, transferrin binds to its receptor, the complex is internalized and directed into acidic vacuoles where iron is dissociated and the ligand–receptor complex is recycled back to the plasma membrane. The transferrin receptor is a transmembrane glycoprotein, composed of two disulphide-bonded subunits (each of apparent M_r 90 000). It contains three N-linked glycan units and is post-translationally modified with both phosphate and fatty-acyl groups. The primary structure of the receptor consists of 760 amino acids divided into three domains. Starting from the N-terminal residue the cytoplasmic domain consists of 62 amino acids, followed by 26 predominantly non-polar residues, which constitute the transmembrane domain, and 672 residues form the C-terminal extracellular domain. It does not contain an N-terminal cleavable signal sequence.

INTRODUCTION

Iron is an essential trace element for cell growth and metabolism in both prokaryotes and eukaryotes. Despite its abundance in Nature, under normal physiological conditions the stable state of iron is Fe(III) and its equilibrium concentration cannot exceed 10^{-17} M (Aisen & Listowsky, 1980). To maintain the element in soluble form, for transport into the cell, vertebrates have evolved high-affinity iron-binding serum proteins, the transferrins.

Transferrin binds two Fe(III) ions per molecule in association with a small anion (Aisen & Listowsky, 1980). For transport of iron into the cell, transferrin first binds to a high-affinity receptor and the receptor–ligand complex is then internalized via coated pits (Octave *et al.* 1982; Karin & Minz, 1981; Hopkins & Trowbridge, 1983). The binding of the two iron atoms to transferrin is pH-dependent: at a pH of less than 5 complete dissociation occurs (Princiotto & Zapolsky, 1975; Lestas, 1976). It has been shown that receptor-bound transferrin maintains this pH-dependent characteristic (Dautry-Versat, Chiechanover, & Lodish, 1983). Moreover, in contrast to many other ligands, apotransferrin (iron free transferrin) does not dissociate from its receptor at an acidic pH, but at a neutral pH (Dautry-Versat *et al.* 1983; Klausner *et al.* 1983). These results suggest that internalization of diferric transferrin, followed by exposure to the acidic environment of intracellular organelles, is the mechanism by which cells obtain iron. Following release of iron in an acidic vesicle, apotransferrin recycles to the plasma membrane and is released to the

TRANSFERRIN PATHWAY

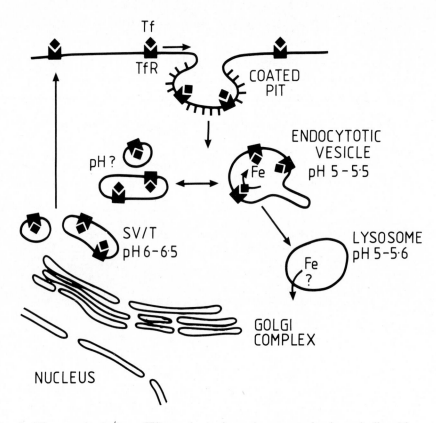

Fig. 1. The transferrin/iron (Tf) uptake pathway is presented schematically. After internalization through coated pits and passage through an acidic compartment (pH 5·0) where iron is released, the transferrin/receptor complex (TfR) is routed to a small para-Golgi vesicular/tubular system (SV/T) in its travel back to the plasma membrane. The whole process takes about 15–20 min. The iron released in the acidic compartment is processed in lysosomes to be transported into the cytoplasm.

extracellular medium (Chiechanover, Scwartz & Lodish, 1983; Klausner *et al.* 1983). In this way, transferrin bypasses the degradative environment of lysosomes (Fig. 1; and Hopkins, 1985).

STRUCTURE OF THE TRANSFERRIN RECEPTOR

The human transferrin receptor, isolated from placenta (Seligman, Schleicher & Allen, 1979), has been shown to be a disulphide-bounded dimer consisting of two similar subunits of apparent molecular weight 90 000.

The availability of monoclonal antibodies (Trowbridge & Omary, 1981; Sutherland *et al.* 1981) has permitted a more detailed biochemical analysis of the molecule to be performed (Schneider, Sutherland, Newman & Greaves, 1982). The general structural features that emerge from such studies are illustrated schematically in Fig. 2.

The molecule is a transmembrane glycoprotein, containing three N-linked glycan units and it is post-translationally modified with both phosphate (Schneider *et al.* 1982) and fatty-acyl groups (Omary & Trowbridge, 1984).

The extracellular domain represents the bulk of the transferrin receptor and it can be cleaved from intact cells with a low concentration of trypsin to yield a soluble fragment of apparent molecular weight 70 000. Each external domain, released by trypsin, contains the three glycan units and the transferrin binding site, leaving the region of the molecule containing the intersubunit disulphide bridge associated with the membrane. Chemical crosslinking experiments (Schneider *et al.* 1982) and sedimentation analysis (Enns & Sussman, 1981) have shown that each receptor monomer can bind one transferrin molecule. No apparent interaction between the

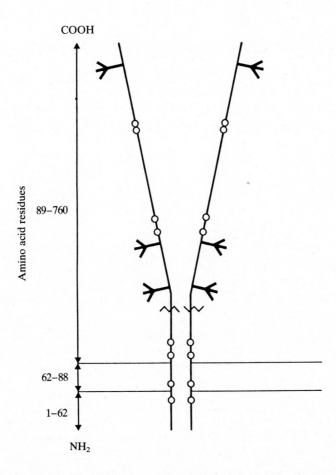

Fig. 2. Structure of the transferrin receptor. The receptor is depicted as spanning the plasma membrane close to its N-terminal end, exposing it in the cytoplasm. It contains three glycan units linked to asparagine. The positions of the cysteine residues (O) and the trypsin cleavage site(s) ($\wedge\wedge$) are indicated.

two subunits seems to be necessary since the trypsin-cleaved monomeric subunit can bind the ligand equally well (Schneider, unpublished). Both *in vivo* (Schneider *et al.* 1982) and *in vitro* (Schneider, Asser, Sutherland & Greaves, 1983) studies show there to be a cytoplasmic domain, and also a membrane spanning region in the transferrin receptor. Protease K digestion of the endoplasmic reticulum-protected newly synthesized transferrin receptor reduces the molecular weight by 5000, the cleaved fragment being the cytoplasmic tail. The *in vitro* biosynthesis results provided clear evidence for the lack of a cleavable signal sequence, since the primary translation product has the same molecular weight as the *in vivo* synthesized molecule after treatment with endoglycosidase.

CLONING OF THE TRANSFERRIN RECEPTOR

The strategy used for cloning relied mainly on an antiserum raised against the affinity-purified human transferrin receptor (TR) (Schneider *et al.* 1983*a*). With this reagent it proved possible to immuno-select polysomes engaged in the synthesis of the TR and thus greatly enrich the TR mRNA (Schneider *et al.* 1983*a*).

This mRNA was used in differential screening of a cDNA library made from partially enriched TR mRNA prepared by sucrose gradient sedimentation of placental mRNA. The fractions with the highest amount of TR mRNA, as detected by *in vitro* translation and immunoprecipitation, were in the 28 S region of the gradient. Once a cDNA clone was isolated, Northern transfer analysis confirmed that the mRNA coding for the receptor was 5 kb (1 kb = 10^3 bases) in length, almost twice the length required to code for a protein of 80 000 M_r (Fig. 3). Sequence analysis of the longest clone available (2 kb in size) showed that it was derived entirely from within the 3' non-coding region and this comprised about half of the length of the mRNA. In order to obtain the remaining 3 kb, containing the coding region, a new cDNA library was made from immunoselected mRNA. A set of five overlapping clones was isolated from this library, containing a total of 5 kb of sequence (Schneider *et al.* 1984). Inspection of the sequence obtained predicts a polypeptide of 760 amino acids, in good agreement with the molecular weight estimated from the primary *in vitro* translation product (Fig. 4).

The N-terminal cytoplasmic domain consists of 62 amino acids, containing four serine residues, which may act as phosphate acceptors. It is followed by a stretch of 26, predominantly non-polar, amino acids, this segment being the only potential transmembrane region. Thus the amino terminus of the transferrin receptor contains no obvious signal sequence. This confirms the observation made in the *in vitro* translation experiments (Schneider, Kurkinen & Greaves, 1983*b*). The lack of an N-terminal cleavable signal sequence is not, however, uncommon. No such signal sequence has been identified in the Ia-associated invariant polypeptide (Claesson *et al.* 1983) and the rat liver asialoglycoprotein receptor (Drickemer, Mamon, Binns & Leung, 1984), which also have the reverse orientation in the plasma membrane. It is thus possible that the transbilayer sequence performs the dual role of acting as a signal sequence and of anchoring the protein in the plasma membrane.

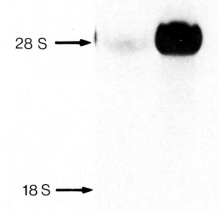

28 S ⟶

18 S ⟶

Fig. 3. Northern transfer analysis of the transferrin receptor (TR) mRNA. Equal amounts of total (left lane) and poly(A)$^+$ (right lane) RNA from human placenta were run on a glyoxal gel and blotted onto nitrocellulose. The blot was probed with nick-translated TR cDNA clone.

```
   1
 125   GGCGGCTCGGGACGGAGGACGCGCTAGTGTGAGTGCGGGC
       TAGGGAGCCGCACGGGAGCGGGAAAGCGGTCGGCGCCCAGGCGGGCCCCAGCCCGGCCGCAGCCTGTGGGAGGGCCTGGCTGGGAGGCGGCCGCCTCCGGTGCCTGTCTCCCTTCATCCTGCGGCGGCCGCCTCCGGTGCTGTCCAGCAGCCA
                                                                 AGAACTACACCGACCCTCGTGTCCCTT [ATG] GAGCGGGCCGCGCCGAGCCGCTGGCCGCCGCCGCCT

 264   ATG ATG GAT CAA GCT AGA TCA GCA TTC TCT AAC TTG TTT GGT GGA GAA GAA TTC TCA TAT ACC CGG TTC AGC CTG CAA GTA GAT GGC GAT AAC AGT CAT
       MET MET Asp Gln Ala Arg Ser Ala Phe Ser Asn Leu Phe Gly Gly Glu Glu Phe Ser Tyr Thr Arg Phe Ser Leu Gln Val Asp Gly Asp Asn Ser His   35

 369   GTG GAG ATG AAA CTT GCT GTA GAT GAA GAA AAT GCT AAC ACA AAG GCC AAT AAC AAG CCA AAA CCA AAT GTC GTA GGG GTA CCA AAA GAA ACT GAA GAA ACT GTT
       Val Glu MET Lys Leu Ala Val Asp Glu Glu Asn Ala Asn Thr Lys Ala Asn Asn Lys Pro Lys Pro Asn Val Val Gly Val Pro Lys Glu Thr Glu Glu Thr Val   70

 474   ATT GCT GTG ATC TTT TTG TTG ATT GGA TTT ATG ATT GGC TAC TTG GGC TAT GAG (TGC) GAG ACC GGA
       Ile Ala Val Ile Phe Leu Leu Ile Gly Phe MET Ile Gly Tyr Leu Gly Tyr Glu ⊙Cys Glu Thr Gly   105

 579   TCT CCA GTG GTG AGG GAG GAG CCA GGA TTC CCT GCA GCA CGT TTA TAT GAT GAC TTG
       Ser Pro Val Val Arg Glu Glu Pro Gly Phe Pro Ala Ala Arg Leu Tyr Asp Asp Leu   140

 684   ACC AGC ACC ATC CTG CTG AAT GAA AAT TCA CTA TCA CCT GGA TCT GAA GAT AAT CTT GCG TTG TAT CAA TTT CGT GAA
       Thr Ser Thr Ile Leu Leu Asn Glu Asn Ser Leu Ser Pro Gly Ser Glu Asp Asn Leu Ala Leu Tyr Gln Phe Arg Glu   175

 789   TTT AAA CTC AGC GTC AAA GTC TGG CGT GAT CAT CAA GTT GTT AAG AGC GCT GCA ACA ATC ACC TTT GGA AAT GTG GTT GAT CTT GTT
       Phe Lys Leu Ser Val Lys Val Trp Arg Asp His Gln Val Val Lys Ser Ala Ala Thr Ile Thr Phe Gly Asn Val Val Asp Leu Val   210

 894   TAC CTG GTG GAG AAT CCT GGG TAT GTG GCG TAT AGT GCA ACA ACC ATC GGA AAA AAT GCA ATT GGT GTG GAT
       Tyr Leu Val Glu Asn Pro Gly Tyr Val Ala Tyr Ser Ala Thr Thr Ile Gly Lys Asn Ala Ile Gly Val Asp   245

 999   TTA TAC ACT CCT GTG AAT GGA TCT AGT ATT GTC AGA GCA GGG AAA ATC ACC TTT GGA GAA GCA AGC TTA AAT GCT GAA TTG
       Leu Tyr Thr Pro Val Asn Gly Ser Ser Ile Val Arg Ala Gly Lys Ile Thr Phe Gly Glu Ala Ser Leu Asn Ala Glu Leu   280

1104   ATA TAC ATG GAC CAG CAG ACT AAA TTT CCC ATT GTT AAC GCA GAA CTT CAA TTC ATA CCT CAT GAC ATC CAG GAA ATC TCC AGA AAT ATG ATG AAA
       Ile Tyr MET Asp Gln Gln Thr Lys Phe Pro Ile Val Asn Ala Glu Leu Gln Phe Ile Pro His Asp Ile Gln Glu Ile Ser Arg Asn MET Glu   315

1209   TTC AAT CAC ACT CAG CAG TTT CCA CCA CCT TCA TCA TTC CCT AAT ATA ATC GTC ACA ATC TCC AAG AAG ATG GAA AGC ATC GGA AAT AAT ATG AAA
       Phe Asn His Thr Gln Gln Phe Pro Pro Pro Ser Ser Phe Pro Asn Ile Ile Val Thr Ile Ser Lys Lys MET Glu Ser Val Phe Gly Asn MET Glu   350

1314   GGA GAC (TGT) CCC TCT GAC TGG AAA ACA GAC TCT ACA TGT (Cys) GTA GAA GCA AAA GAG ATA AAA
       Gly Asp ⊙Cys Pro Ser Asp Trp Lys Thr Asp Ser Thr ⊙Cys Val Glu Ala Lys Glu Ile Lys   385

1419   ATT CTT AAC ATC TTT GGA GTT ATT AAA GGC CCA GAT GTT TTA AAT GAT GTC AGC AGC GCA AAA TCC GGT
       Ile Leu Asn Ile Phe Gly Val Ile Lys Gly Pro Asp Val Leu Asn Asp Val Ser Ser Ala Lys Ser Gly   420

1524   GTA GGC ACA GCT CTC TTA AAA CTT GTC GAT ATG TCA CAG ATG GGG CCT AGA ATT TTT GCC AGT TGG AGT GCT
       Val Gly Thr Ala Leu Leu Lys Leu Val Asp MET Ser Gln MET Gly Pro Arg Ile Phe Ala Ser Trp Ser Ala   455

1629   GGA GAC TTT GGA TCG GTT GGT GCC ACT GGA GGA CTA CTT CTG TCC CTG GCA TAT TAT ATT AAT CTT GGT
       Gly Asp Phe Gly Ser Val Gly Ala Thr Gly Gly Leu Leu Leu Ser Leu Ala Tyr Tyr Ile Asn Leu Gly   490

1734   ACC AGC AAC TTC AAG GTT TCT GCC AGC GCC CTT ATT GAG GAA ACA ATG CAT GTG ACT CCG AAG CAT GGG CAA TTT CTA TAT CAG GAC
       Thr Ser Asn Phe Lys Val Ser Ala Ser Ala Leu Ile Glu Glu Thr MET His Val Thr Pro Lys His Gly Gln Phe Leu Tyr Gln Asp   525
```

```
1839  AGC AAC TGG GCC AGC AAA GTT GAG AAA ACT CTC TTA GAC AAT GCT GCT CCT TTC CTT GGA TAT TCT GGA ATC CCA GCA GTT TCT TTT TGC GAG GAC  560
      Ser Asn Trp Ala Ser Lys Val Glu Lys Thr Leu Leu Asp Asn Ala Ala Pro Phe Leu Gly Tyr Ser Gly Ile Pro Ala Val Ser Phe Cys Glu Asp

1944  ACA GAT TAT CCT TAT TTG GGT ACC ATG GAC ACC TAT AAG GAA CTG ATT GAG AGG ATT CCT GAG TTG GCA CGA GCA GCG GCA GAG GTC GCT GCT  595
      Thr Asp Tyr Pro Tyr Leu Gly Thr MET Asp Thr Tyr Lys Glu Leu Ile Glu Arg Ile Pro Glu Leu Ala Arg Ala Ala Glu Val Ala Gly

2049  CAG TTC GTG ATT CTA ACC CAT GAT GTT GAA TTG AAC CTG GAC TAT GAG AGG TAC AGC CAA CTG CTT TCA TTT GTG CGT GAG GTG GAT CAA TAC AGA GCA  630
      Gln Phe Val Ile Leu Thr His Asp Val Glu Leu Asn Leu Asp Tyr Glu Arg Tyr Asn Ser Gln Leu Leu Ser Phe Val Arg Asp Val Asp Gln Tyr Arg Ala

2154  GAC ATA AAG GAA ATG GGC CTG AGT TTA CAG TGG CTG TAT TCT GCT CGT GGA GAC TTC TTC CGT GCT ACT TCC AGA CTA ACA GAT TTC GGG AAT GCT GAG AAA  665
      Asp Ile Lys Glu MET Gly Leu Ser Leu Gln Trp Leu Tyr Ser Ala Arg Gly Asp Phe Phe Arg Ala Thr Ser Arg Leu Thr Thr Asp Phe Gly Asn Ala Glu Lys

2259  ACA GAC AGA TTT GTC ATG AAG AAA CTC AAT GAT CGT GTC ATG GAG GTG AGA GTG CTC CCC TAC CTC CCA CAA AAA GAG TCT CCT TTC CGA CAT GTC  700
      Thr Asp Arg Phe Val MET Lys Lys Leu Asn Asp Arg Val MET Glu Val Arg Val Leu Pro Tyr Leu Pro Gln Lys Glu Ser Pro Phe Arg His Val

2364  TTC TGG GGC TCC GGC TCT TCA CAC GGC CTG GCT TTA GAG GTT CTG GAA CAA CTT AAT ATT GAA ACG AAC AAT GGT GCT TTC ACA AAC CTG TTC AGA AAC CAG TTG  735
      Phe Trp Gly Ser Gly Ser Ser His Gly Leu Ala Leu Glu Val Leu Glu Gln Leu Asn Ile Glu Thr Asn Asn Gly Ala Phe Thr Asn Leu Phe Arg Asn Gln Leu

2469  GCT CTA GCT ACT ATT CAG GGA GCT GCA AAT GCC CTC TCT GGT GAC ATT GAC GAT GAG TTT TAAATGTGATACCCATAGCTTCCATGAGAACAGCAGGGT  770
      Ala Leu Ala Thr Trp Thr Ile Gln Gly Ala Ala Asn Ala Leu Ser Gly Asp Ile Asp Asp Glu Phe
```

Fig. 4. Primary structure of the transferrin receptor deduced from the mRNA sequence. For clarity only the open reading frame and the 5' untranslated region have been reported. (□) beginning of the putative 28aa peptide coded by the 5' untranslated region; (○) cysteines; (∿) potential trypsin cleavage sites.

The transmembrane region is preceded by a cluster of basic residues Lys-Pro-Lys-Arg, which has been referred to as a 'stop-transfer sequence' for membrane glyco-proteins having the normal orientation with respect to the plane of the membrane. This may act as a cytoplasmic anchor by interacting with the polar phospholipid headgroups (Blobel, 1980).

The extracellular domain comprises 648 amino acids. It contains three of the five possible sites for asparagine-linked glycosylation (Asn-X-Ser/Thr). As endo-glycosidase digestion experiments indicate that the receptor contains three N-linked glycan units, all three of these asparagines must be glycosylated. The likely positions of the trypsin cleavage site, which generates the $70\,000\,M_r$ fragment, are either Arg-Arg at position 121–122 or Lys-Arg-Lys at position 128–130 or, most probably, both. There are other potential cleavage sites for trypsin, proximal to the carboxy terminal, which become apparent at higher trypsin concentrations with the appear-ance of a $50\,000\,M_r$ fragment (Schneider, unpublished) but which seem to be shielded from mild treatment with trypsin. This domain, starting at around residue 150, is therefore predicted to have a more compact tertiary structure, with the part proximal to the membrane being more extended to permit the close contact of the two subunits required for disulphide bridge formation.

CYSTEINE DISTRIBUTION

Eight cysteine residues are distributed throughout the sequence. Four of these are clustered in the region of the transbilayer peptide. Two flank the peptide on each side of the membrane margin. One resides within the transbilayer sequence towards the cytoplasmic face of the membrane and is the putative site of fatty acylation via a thioester bond (Kaufmann, Krangel & Strominger, 1984). The remaining cysteine is located close to the bilayer on the extracellular side. As the trypsin-generated fragment does not contain the intersubunit disulphide bond, the disulphide bridge must be formed by one or both of the cysteines adjacent to the lipid bilayer, since it is unlikely that the cysteine on the cytoplasmic side could form such a bridge, because of the strongly reducing environment in the cytoplasm. The remaining four cysteines are present in two clusters in the extracellular domain. It is not known whether any of these cysteine residues form intrachain disulphide bridges, but as the trypsin-cleaved fragment does not change mobility in polyacrylamide gel electrophoresis in the presence of sodium dodecylsulphate under reducing conditions, it can be argued that if any disulphide bridge is formed, this does not change dramatically the tertiary structure of this domain.

5′ 'UNTRANSLATED?' REGION

The 5′ region (280 nucleotides) of the mRNA is longer than average. Comparison of the sequence with that published by McClelland, Kühn & Ruddle (1984) shows this to be due to a differential splicing resulting in an insertion of 210 nucleotides at position 72 of their sequence. From primer extension experiments (D. Banville, unpublished), it seems that the mRNA with the longer 5′ end is a minor population

(< 5 %) with respect to the 'truncated' form. Interestingly, the sequence insert has the potential of coding for a small peptide of 28 residues, starting from position 189 (ATG) and stopping at position 21 with TGA formed by the doublet of methionine residues that initiate the reading frame encoding the transferrin receptor. The percentage of basic residues in this peptide is fairly high (21 %). It is possible that the small peptide could have a regulatory function, either at the translational or at the transcriptional level and this is under investigation.

HOMOLOGY COMPARISON

The partial protein sequence of the mouse transferrin receptor (van Driel *et al.* 1984) reveals a large degree of homology with the human sequence (> 80 %), except in the region 193–205 where the homology is only 40 %. This region of variability on the extracellular domain situated between the conserved region adjacent to the bilayer and the remaining C-terminal part involved in transferrin binding, could be the most antigenic region of the molecule. There is no homology with proteins in established databases.

IRON, TRANSFERRIN RECEPTOR AND CELL PROLIFERATION

Iron is a cofactor of many proteins involved in essential biochemical reactions, e.g. the flow of electrons through the respiratory chain, the decomposition of activated oxygen derivatives, the transport and storage of oxygen (haemoglobin, myoglobin) and the stabilization of a tyrosyl radical in the key enzyme for deoxyribonucleotide synthesis (ribonucleotide reductase) (Reichard & Ehrenberg, 1983). As the major iron carrier, transferrin appears to be required for maintenance of cell viability rather than as a specific growth factor. When cultured in a serum-free medium, all cells tested require transferrin for optimal cell growth (Barnes & Sato, 1980). It is thus likely that all vertebrate cells (excluding specialized, mature cells, such as erythrocytes) have transferrin receptors. Their concentration appears to be correlated with the proliferation rate, being greatly increased by growth stimulation (Larrick & Cresswell, 1979) or decreased by induction of terminal differentiation (Delia *et al.* 1982). This correlation could simply result from a control on the expression of the transferrin receptor by the intracellular level of iron or one of its metabolites, haem (Louache *et al.* 1984; Ward, Jordan, Kushner & Kaplan, 1984), as is the case for the low density lipoprotein (LDL) receptor where receptor biosynthesis is modulated by the concentration of free cholesterol (Brown *et al.* 1975). It has recently been shown that cell growth in artificial media can be sustained in the absence of transferrin if a highly hydrosoluble iron complex is provided (such as ferric ammonium sulphate or citrate), bypassing the transferrin receptor pathway for iron transport (Titeux *et al.* 1984). It remains true, however, that, although the transferrin/receptor pathway can be artificially bypassed *in vitro*, it is the only mechanism of iron uptake *in vivo* (aside from other mechanisms evolved by specialized cells such as the membrane protein gp97, which is in any event functionally and structurally related to transferrin). Thus, if the transferrin binding site on the receptor is blocked by a monoclonal antibody (Trowbridge & Lopez, 1982) cells will stop dividing. It is therefore possible that the malignant transformation of at least some cell types, such as lymphoid cells (Neckers, Yenodika & James, 1984), may result in (or be the result of) unregulated expression of the transferrin receptor, i.e. constitutive expression of the transferrin receptor in the absence of homeostatic regulation by the cell-specific growth factor. Experiments to address this question are under way, using eukaryotic expression vectors carrying a full-length cDNA for the transferrin receptor.

REFERENCES

AISEN, P. & LISTOWSKY, I. (1980). Iron transport and storage proteins. *A. Rev. Biochem.* **49**, 357–393.

BARNES, D. & SATO, CR. (1980). Serum-free cell culture: a unifying approach. *Cell* **22**, 649–655.

BLOBEL, G. (1980). Intracellular protein topogenesis. *Proc. natn. Aca. Sci. U.S.A.* **77**, 1496–1500.

BROWN, J. P., HEWICK, R. M., HELLSTROEM, I., HELLSTROEM, K. E., DOOLITTLE, R. & DRYER, W. (1982). Human melanoma-associated antigen p97 is structurally related to transferrin. *Nature, Lond.* **296**, 171–173.

CHIECHANOVER, A., SCWARTZ, A. & LODISH, H. (1983). Sorting and recycling of cell surface receptors and endocytosed ligands: the asialoglycoprotein and transferrin receptors. *J. Cell Biochem.* **23**, 107–130.

CLAESSON, L., LARHAMMAR, D., RASK, L. & PETERSON, P. A. (1983). c-DNA clone for the human invariant γ-chain of class 2 histocompatibility antigens of its implication for the protein structure. *Proc. natn. Acad. Sci. U.S.A.* **80**, 7395–7399.

DAUTRY-VERSAT, A., CHIECHANOVER, A. & LODISH, H. (1983). pH and the recycling of transferrin during receptor-mediated endocytosis. *Proc. natn. Acad. Sci. U.S.A.* **80**, 2258–2262.

DELIA, D., GREAVES, M., NEWMAN, R., SUTHERLAND, R., MINOVADA, T., KUNG, P. & GOLDSTEIN, G. (1982). *Int. J. Cancer* **29**, 23–31.

DRICKAMER, K. & MAMON, J. F. (1982). Phosphorylation of a membrane receptor for glycoproteins. *J. biol. Chem.* **257**, 15 156–15 161.

DRICKAMER, K., MAMON, J. F., BINNS, G. & LEUNG, J. O. (1984). Primary structure of the rat liver asialoglycoprotein receptor. *J. biol. Chem.* **259**, 770–778.

ENNS, C. A. & SUSSMAN, H. H. (1981). Physical characterization of the transferrin receptor in human placenta. *J. biol. Chem.* **256**, 9820–9823.

HOPKINS, C. R., MILLER, K. & BEARDMORE, J. M. (1985). Receptor-mediated endocytosis of transferrin and epidermal growth factor receptors: a comparison of constitutive and ligand-induced uptake. *J. Cell Sci. Suppl. 3.* 173–186.

HOPKINS, C. R. & TROWBRIDGE, I. S. (1983). Internalization and processing of transferrin and the transferrin receptor in human carcinoma A431 cells. *J. Cell Biol.* **97**, 508–521.

KARIN, M. & MINTZ, B. (1981). Receptor-mediated endocytosis of transferrin in developmentally totipotent mouse terato-carcinoma stem cells. *J. biol. Chem.* **256**, 3215–3252.

KAUFMAN, J. F., KRANGEL, M. S. & STROMINGER, J. L. (1984). Cysteines in the transmembrane region of major histocompatibility complex antigens are falty acylated via thioester bonds. *J. biol. Chem.* **259**, 7230–7238.

KLAUSNER, R. D., VAN RENSWOUDE, J., ASHWELL, C. T., KEPMF, C., SCHECHTER, A., DEAN, A. & BRIDGES, K. R. (1983). Receptor-mediated endocytosis of transferrin in K562 cells. *J. biol. Chem.* **258**, 4715–4724.

LARRICK, J. W. & CRESWELL, P. (1979). Modulation of cell surface transferrin receptors by cellular density and stock of activation. *J. supramolec. Struct.* **11**, 579–586.

LESTAS, A. N. (1976). The effect of pH upon human transferrin: selective labelling of the two iron-binding sites. *Br. J. Haemat.* **32**, 341–350.

LOUACHE, F., TESTA, U., PELICCI, P., THOMOPOULOU, P., TITEUX, M. & ROCHANT, H. (1984). Regulation of transferrin receptors in human hematopoietic cell lines. *J. biol. Chem.* **259**, 11 576–11 582.

McClelland, A., Kühn, L. C. & Ruddle, F. H. (1984). The human transferrin receptor genomic organization and complete primary structure. *Cell* **39**, 267–274.

Neckers, L. M., Yenodika, Cr. & James, S. P. (1984). The role of the transferrin receptor in human B lymphocyte activation. *J. Immun.* **133**, 2437–2441.

Octave, J. N., Schneider, U. J., Hoffmann, P., Trouet, A. & Crichton, R. R. (1982). Transferrin uptake by cultured rat embryo fibroblasts: the influence of lysosomotropic agents, iron chelators and colchicine on the uptake of iron and transferrin. *Eur. J. Biochem.* **123**, 235–240.

Omary, M. B. & Trowbridge, I. S. (1984). Covalent binding of falty acid to the transferrin receptor in cultured human cells. *J. biol. Chem.* **256**, 4715–4718.

Princiotto, J. V. & Zapolsky, E. J. (1975). Difference between the two iron-binding sites of transferrin. *Nature, Lond.* **255**, 87–88.

Reichard, P. & Ehrenberg, A. (1983). Ribonucleotide reductase – a radical enzyme. *Science* **221**, 514–519.

Schneider, C., Asser, U., Sutherland, R. & Greaves, M. (1983*a*). *In vitro* biosynthesis of the human cell surface receptor for transferrin. *FEBS Lett.* **158**, 259–264.

Schneider, C., Kurkinen, M. & Greaves, M. F. (1983*b*). Isolation of cDNA clones for the human transferrin receptor. *EMBO J.* **2**, 2259–

Schneider, C., Owen, M. J., Banville, D., Schneider, C. & Williams, J. G. (1984). Primary structure of human transferrin receptor deduced from the mRNA sequence. *Nature, Lond.* **311**, 675–678.

Schneider, C., Sutherland, R., Newman, R. A. & Greaves, M. F. (1982). Structural features of the cell surface receptor for transferrin that is recognized by the monoclonal antibody OKT9. *J. biol. Chem.* **251**, 8516–8522.

Seligman, P. A., Schleicher, R. B. & Allen, R. H. (1979). Isolation and characterization of the transferrin receptor from human placenta. *J. biol. Chem.* **254**, 9943–9946.

Sutherland, D. R., Delia, D., Schneider, C., Newman, R. A., Kemshead, J. J. & Greaves, M. F. (1981). Ubiquitous cell-surface glycoprotein on tumor cells is proliferation-associated receptor for transferrin. *Proc. natn. Acad. Sci. U.S.A.* **78**, 4515–4519.

Titeux, M., Testa, U., Louache, F., Thomopoulos, P., Rochent, H. & Breton-Gonius, J. (1984). The role of iron in the growth of human leukemic cell lines. *J. cell. Physiol.* **121**, 251–256.

Trowbridge, I. S. & Lopez, F. (1982). Monoclonal antibody to transferrin receptor blocks transferrin binding and inhibits human tumor cell growth in vitro. *Proc. natn. Acad. Sci. U.S.A.* **79**, 1175–1179.

Trowbridge, I. S. & Omary, B. M. (1981). Human cell surface glycoprotein related to cell proliferation is the receptor for transferrin. *Proc. natn. Acad. Sci. U.S.A.* **78**, 3039–3043.

van Driel, I. R., Stearne, P. A., Grego, B., Simpson, R. J. & Goding, J. W. (1984). The receptor for transferrin on muryne myeloma cells: one step purification based on its physiology and partial aminoacid sequence. *J. Immun.* **133**, 3220–3224.

Ward, J. H., Jordan, I., Kushner, J. P. & Kaplan, J. (1984). Heme regulation of HeLa cell transferrin receptor number. *J. biol. Chem.* **259**, 13 235–13 240.

J. Cell Sci. Suppl. 3, 151–160 (1985)
Printed in Great Britain © The Company of Biologists Limited 1985

THE USE OF ANTI-SYNTHETIC PEPTIDE ANTIBODIES TO STUDY THE v-erb B PROTEIN FROM CHICKEN AND RAT CELLS TRANSFORMED BY AVIAN ERYTHROBLASTOSIS VIRUS

W. J. GULLICK*, J. J. MARSDEN, J. DOWNWARD
AND M. D. WATERFIELD

Imperial Cancer Research Fund Laboratories, Lincoln's Inn Fields, London WC2A 3PX, U.K.

SUMMARY

Two site-specific anti-peptide antisera have been produced that efficiently recognize the native form of the v-erb B protein from avian erythroblastosis virus(AEV)-infected chicken erythroblasts and fibroblasts, and from AEV-transformed mammalian cells. Since the antibodies were generated against synthetic sequences, the immunoprecipitations could be performed in the presence or absence of immunizing peptide, permitting the specifically precipitated proteins to be identified from background non-specifically adsorbed proteins. We confirmed that immobilized v-erb B protein from cell lysates of unlabelled AEV-infected chicken erythroblasts became labelled upon incubation with $[\gamma\text{-}^{32}P]ATP$. In addition we demonstrated for the first time that v-erb B from mammalian cells became labelled under the same conditions. These results suggest that the v-erb B protein may possess intrinsic kinase activity. The reagents described should permit further investigations as to whether this activity plays a role in maintaining cellular transformation.

INTRODUCTION

Avian erythroblastosis virus is an acutely transforming retrovirus that causes erythroleukaemia and sarcomas in chickens (Graf & Beug, 1978). The ES4 and R strains of AEV contain the 5′ region of the viral *gag* gene sequences followed by two acquired cellular genes, designated v-erb A and v-erb B, followed by the 3′ portion of the viral *env* gene sequence (for a brief review, see Graf & Beug, 1983). The provirus is translated into a genome length mRNA, which encodes v-erb A and v-erb B, and also a subgenomic mRNA, which encodes some 5′ sequences and the v-erb B sequence. The v-erb A protein includes some *gag*-specified N-terminal amino acids and the v-erb B molecule (AEV-H) runs on to contain four *env*-specified amino acids at its C terminus. The v-erb A protein has an apparent molecular weight on sodium dodecyl sulphate/polyacrylamide (SDS/PAGE) gels of 75 000 and is found in the cytoplasm of AEV-infected cells. Recently, the viral *erb* A gene has been sequenced (Debuire *et al.* 1984). The predicted protein that it encodes consists of 398 amino acids with a calculated molecular weight of 45 400. The p75$^{gag\text{-}erb}$ A fusion protein however, has a predicted molecular weight of 72 000, similar to that observed experimentally. Inspection of the sequence of v-erb A revealed that its C-terminal

* Author to whom reprint requests should be addressed.

half possessed a limited degree of homology with the carbonic anhydrase gene family of enzymes, which are involved in CO_2 transport in erythrocytes. The v-*erb* B protein is synthesized as a 62 500 M_r protein, which is glycosylated to give 65 000, 68 000 and finally a mature molecule of 74 000 M_r, which is found in the plasma membrane of infected cells (Hayman *et al.* 1983; Hayman & Beug, 1984; Schmidt, Beug & Hayman, 1985).

Mutants of AEV have been constructed that are defective in either the v-*erb* A or v-*erb* B genes and have been used to determine whether both or only one of the gene products is required for cellular transformation (Frykberg *et al.* 1983). Neither of the mutants behaved in an identical fashion to the wild-type virus but whereas v-*erb* B$^-$ mutants lack transforming activity entirely, v-*erb* A$^-$ mutants can still transform erythroblasts and fibroblasts. However, cells transformed in this way require specialized culture conditions and frequently differentiate spontaneously. Yamamoto *et al.* (1983*a*) have isolated a form of AEV called AEV-H, which carries only the v-*erb* B gene but is still capable of transforming cells, confirming that v-*erb* B can act as an oncogene on its own.

The sequence of the human EGF receptor has recently been obtained and was found to have substantial homology with that of the v-*erb* B protein (Downward *et al.* 1984; Ullrich *et al.* 1984). Alignment of the two structures indicated that the v-*erb* B protein lacked the majority of the extracellular domain of the EGF receptor, which is known to be responsible for ligand binding. The v-*erb* B protein (encoded by AEV-H; Yamamoto *et al.* 1983*b*) possesses about 60 amino acids at its N terminus that are homologous to the extracellular domain of the EGF receptor, a putative transmembrane spanning sequence and a cytoplasmic domain. The cytoplasmic v-*erb* B sequences are extensively homologous to those of the human EGF receptor, although towards the C terminus of the molecule the homology decreases. These shared sequences are those conserved between the oncogenes of the *src* gene family of acutely transforming retroviruses (Yamamoto *et al.* 1983*b*; Privalsky, Ralston & Bishop *et al.* 1984; Hunter & Cooper, 1985). Most of the proteins encoded by this gene family, including the human EGF receptor, have been shown to possess intrinsic protein tyrosine kinase activity. It has, however, proved difficult to determine whether the v-*erb* B protein possesses such an activity (see Privalsky *et al.* 1984). It has been proposed that the lack of a ligand binding domain on the v-*erb* B protein renders it in a form that is continuously generating a signal responsible for maintaining cellular transformation (Downward *et al.* 1984). It is thus important to determine: first, whether v-*erb* B is a protein tyrosine kinase; and secondly, whether this potentially unregulated activity is responsible for transformation.

In this paper we describe antibodies to several synthetic peptides from the sequence of v-*erb* B, two of which are capable of precipitating v-*erb* B from AEV-transformed erythroblasts and fibroblasts. Immunoprecipitates were examined for their ability to incorporate ^{32}P into the v-*erb* B protein from added $[\gamma\text{-}^{32}\text{P}]$ATP. v-*erb* B from both erythroblasts (Kris *et al.* 1985) and from mammalian fibroblasts became labelled, suggesting that the transforming protein was capable of auto-phosphorylation and may thus possess protein kinase activity.

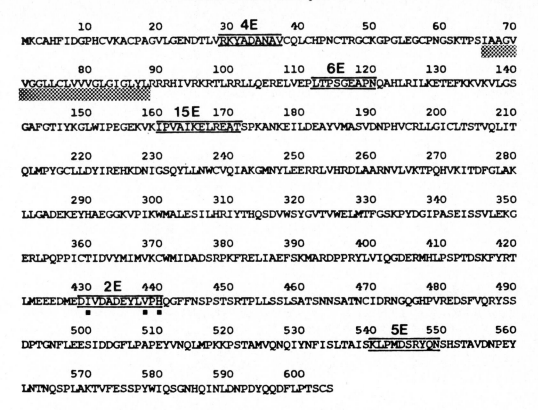

Fig. 1. The complete sequence of the v-*erb* B protein from AEV-H (from Yamamoto *et al.* 1983*b*) showing the position of the synthetic peptides used in this work. The sequences synthesized are indicated by narrow black lines. The putative transmembrane spanning sequence is underlined by a stippled bar. The sequence of peptide 2E synthesized was from the human EGF receptor (DVVDADEYLIPQ) and the different residues in v-*erb* B are indicated by filled squares. The one-letter code for amino acids has been used.

RESULTS AND DISCUSSION

Several peptides from the sequence of the v-*erb* B protein were selected for synthesis (Fig. 1). These were purified and then conjugated to keyhole limpet haemocyanin (KLH) using glutaraldehyde in order to produce an immunogenic structure. Haemocyanin itself is a highly immunogenic molecule (Gullick, Head & Wood, 1981), whereas immunization with short peptides rarely stimulates a humoral immune response. By attaching the peptides to the immunogenic carrier it is possible to obtain high-titre antibody mixtures that can react with both the carrier and the peptide (and also sometimes the cross-linking reagent). In such conjugates it is likely that the peptide becomes attached at many sites on the large ($9 \times 10^6 \ M_r$) haemocyanin molecule. Such structures would exist in conformations influenced by the local surface residues of the carrier. The immune response stimulated would thus be quite varied and reflect the configurations of the peptide in such complexes. These would, however, not necessarily be the same as the conformation that the sequence assumes in the context of the native folded v-*erb* B molecule, particularly since all the sequences used in this work are bordered by contiguous amino acid sequences.

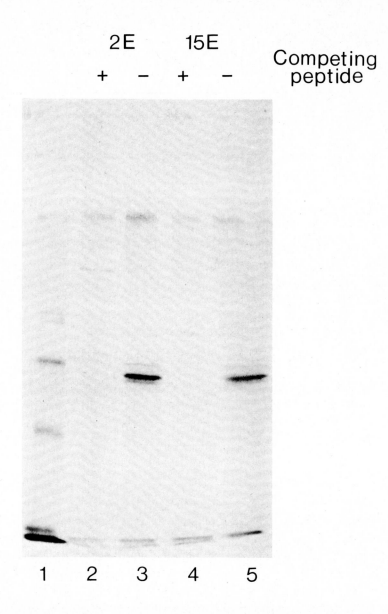

Fig. 2. Immunoprecipitation of the v-*erb* B protein from [^{35}S]methionine-labelled cell lysate from AEV-ES4-infected chicken erythroblasts. Cells were labelled, lysed and immunoprecipitated as described by Gullick *et al.* (1985*b*). Track 1, ^{3}H-labelled molecular weight marker proteins; myosin, 200 000; phosphorylase *b*, 92 500; bovine serum albumin, 69 000; ovalbumin, 46 000; carbonic anhydrase, 30 000 M_r. Tracks 2 and 3, precipitation by antibodies to peptide 2E. Tracks 4 and 5, precipitation by antibodies to peptide 15E. Tracks 2 and 4, precipitations performed in the presence of appropriate competing peptide.

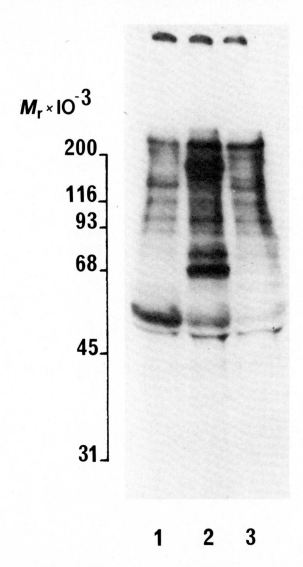

Fig. 3. Phosphorylation of immunoprecipitates of v-*erb* B protein from AEV-ES4-infected chicken erythroblasts. Immunoprecipitations and labelling were as described by Kris *et al.* (1985). Track 1, preimmune serum; track 2, immune serum to peptide 2E; track 3, immunoprecipitation performed in the presence of competing peptide.

In order to ascertain whether such anti-peptide antibodies were produced it was necessary to distinguish anti-peptide response from the background of anti-carrier response. One simple and convenient method that achieves this is an ELISA assay in which the peptide alone is passively adsorbed onto 96-well plastic tissue culture plates (Gullick *et al.* 1985a). Animals immunized with each of the peptides described in Fig. 1 produced antisera that gave a strongly positive reaction in ELISA and were specific for the immunizing sequence (Gullick *et al.* 1985b).

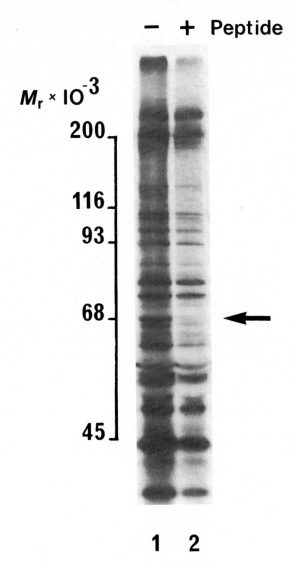

Fig. 4. Immunoprecipitation of the v-*erb* B protein from [³⁵S]methionine-labelled cell lysate from AEV-transformed chick embryo fibroblasts (AEV C23). The cells were labelled as described by Quade *et al.* (1983). Track 1, precipitation by antibodies to peptide 2E; track 2, immunoprecipitation performed in the presence of competing peptide. The arrow indicates the position of the v-*erb* B protein.

The anti-peptide sera were then tested for their ability to immunoprecipitate the v-*erb* B protein. Avian erythroblasts, infected with AEV ES4, were labelled with [³⁵S]methionine and then solubilized with Triton X-100. The antibodies to peptide 2E (Kris *et al.* 1985) and peptide 15E were able to precipitate v-*erb* B protein efficiently (Fig. 2, tracks 3 and 5) from the cell lysate. The reaction was specific, by the criterion that including the immunizing peptide in excess over antibody inhibited the immunoprecipitation (Fig. 2, tracks 2 and 4). Peptide 2E (residues 429–440,

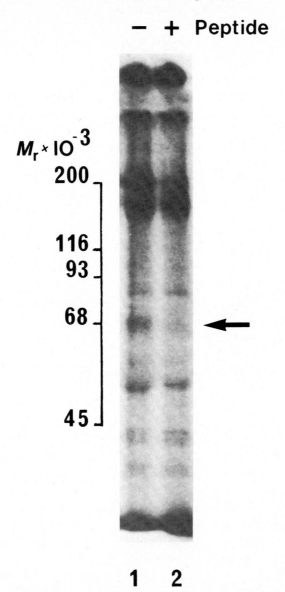

Fig. 5. Phosphorylation of immunoprecipitates of v-*erb* B protein from AEV-transformed rat fibroblasts (AC7). Immunoprecipitations and labelling were as described by Kris *et al*. (1985). Track 1, precipitation by antibodies to peptide 2E; track 2, immunoprecipitation performed in the presence of competing peptide. The arrow indicates the position of the v-*erb* B protein.

Fig. 1) is just C-terminal to the 'protein kinase domain' shared (by definition) by the members of the *src* gene family. Peptide 15E (residues 160–171, Fig. 1) is located within this domain and includes a lysine residue at position 165. This amino acid is likely to contribute to the ATP binding site of v-*erb* B since other homologous protein kinases have been labelled on this residue by a reactive ATP analogue, FSBA (cAMP-dependent protein kinase, residue 71, Zoller, Nelson & Taylor, 1981; v-*src*, residue 295, Kamps, Taylor & Sefton, 1984; EGF receptor, residue 721, Gullick, Downward & Waterfield, unpublished results).

We next determined whether purified unlabelled v-*erb* B protein in an immuno-precipitate became radioactively labelled upon incubation with [γ-^{32}P]ATP. Since the antibodies to the ATP-site peptide 15E inhibit EGF receptor autophosphory-lation and phosphorylation of exogenous substrates (Gullick, Downward & Water-field, unpublished results) they were not used in this experiment. However, EGF receptor immobilized on antibodies to peptide 2E retained some ability to auto-phosphorylate and so these antibodies were used. Immunoprecipitates were pre-pared, using preimmune serum, from unlabelled cell lysates of AEV-infected chicken erythroblasts, which, when run out on SDS/polyacrylamide gels contained some labelled proteins, but no material with the same molecular weight as v-*erb* B (Fig. 3, track 1). However, immunoprecipitates prepared with antibodies to peptide 2E gave strongly labelled material of the appropriate molecular weight (Fig. 3, track 2), which was not present when the precipitation was performed in the presence of competing peptide (Fig. 3, track 3). In addition to the v-*erb* B protein in track 2 there was another band of apparent molecular weight 180 000. This was not, however, the EGF receptor since: (1) AEV cells do not bind [^{125}I]EGF; (2) this material gave a different peptide map to chicken EGF receptor; (3) more extensive washing re-moved it without affecting the subsequent labelling of v-*erb* B (R. Kris, personal communication).

The simplest interpretation of this experiment is that the v-*erb* B protein from AEV-infected chicken erythroblasts possesses a kinase activity which has the ability to autophosphorylate. It is possible, however, that the protein kinase involved is a contaminating protein and that v-*erb* B merely acts as a substrate for this activity. We therefore examined AEV-transformed fibroblast cell lines to establish whether the anti-peptide antibodies could detect v-*erb* B from these cells and whether the purified material also became labelled in immunoprecipitates. We obtained five rat fibroblast cell lines non-productively transformed with AEV (a generous gift from Dr K. Quade; Quade, 1979; Quade *et al.* 1981) and an AEV-transformed chick embryo fibroblast cell line, AEV C-23 (a generous gift from Dr S. Martin; Gilmore, DeClue & Martin, 1985). Cells were labelled with [^{35}S]methionine and then lysates immuno-precipitated with the anti-peptide antibodies. As had been reported previously using tumour-bearing sera (Quade *et al.* 1983), even after extensive washing of immuno-precipitates, high levels of non-specifically adsorbed proteins were invariably found, which were present when the incubation was performed with or without competing peptide. However, material with the predicted molecular weight of the v-*erb* B protein was found in lysates of AEV C-23 cells precipitated with antibodies to peptide 2E (Fig. 4, track 1, arrowed) but was not present when the incubation was performed in the presence of competing peptide (Fig. 4, track 2).

Immunoprecipitates were then prepared from unlabelled lysates of AEV-trans-formed rat fibroblasts using antibodies to peptide 2E. These were then incubated with $[\gamma\text{-}^{32}P]$ATP as described for AEV-infected erythroblast cell lysate. Immuno-precipitates from AC7b cells, which had previously been shown to contain the v-*erb* A protein (Quade *et al.* 1983), contained ^{32}P-labelled material with the predicted molecular weight of the v-*erb* B protein (Fig. 5, track 1, arrowed), which was not present when the incubation was carried out in the presence of competing peptide (Fig. 5, track 2).

These results indicate that antibodies to peptide 2E recognized the v-*erb* B protein from AEV-transformed chicken and rat fibroblasts and have permitted the first demonstration that the v-*erb* B protein, expressed in mammalian cells, becomes labelled with ^{32}P in immunoprecipitates. We are currently using both of the antibody reagents described as immunoaffinity ligands to purify v-*erb* B and then to subject this material to a variety of physical separation techniques to determine more rigorously whether the v-*erb* B protein and the kinase activity copurify, and subsequently to establish whether the v-*erb* B kinase is constitutively activated.

REFERENCES

DEBUIRE, B., HENRY, C., BENAISSA, M., BISERTE, G., CLAVERIE, J. M., SAULE, S., MARTIN, P. & STEHELIN, D. (1984). Sequencing the *erb* A gene of avian erythroblastosis virus reveals a new type of oncogene. *Science* **224**, 1456–1459.

DOWNWARD, J., YARDEN, Y., MAYES, E., SCRACE, G., TOTTY, N., STOCKWELL, P., ULLRICH, A., SCHLESSINGER, J. & WATERFIELD, M. D. (1984). Close similarity of epidermal growth factor receptor and v-*erb* B oncogene protein sequences. *Nature, Lond.* **307**, 521–527.

FRYKBERG, L., PALMIERI, S., BEUG, H., GRAF, T., HAYMAN, M. J. & VENNSTROM, B. (1983). Transforming capacities of avian erythroblastosis virus mutants deleted in the *erb* A or *erb* B oncogenes. *Cell* **32**, 227–238.

GILMORE, T., DECLUE, J. E. & MARTIN, G. S. (1985). Protein phosphorylation at tyrosine is induced by the v-*erb* B gene product *in vivo* and *in vitro*. *Cell* **40**, 609–618.

GRAF, T. & BEUG, H. (1978). Avian leukaemia viruses: interaction with their target cells *in vivo* and *in vitro*. *Biochim. biophys. Acta* **516**, 269–299.

GRAF, T. & BEUG, H. (1983). Role of the v-*erb* A and v-*erb* B oncogenes of avian erythroblastosis virus in erythroid cell transformation. *Cell* **34**, 7–9.

GULLICK, W. J., DOWNWARD, J., PARKER, P. J., WHITTLE, N., KRIS, R., SCHLESSINGER, J., ULLRICH, A. & WATERFIELD, M. D. (1985*a*). The structure and function of the epidermal growth factor receptor studied using antisynthetic peptide antibodies. *Phil. Trans. R. Soc., series B* (in press).

GULLICK, W. J., HEAD, E. J. H. & WOOD, E. J. (1981). Fragmentation of a mollusc haemocyanin with plasmin and immunological identification of the fragments. *Biochem. J.* **197**, 23–29.

GULLICK, W. J., MARSDEN, J. J., WHITTLE, N., WARD, B., BOBROW, L. & WATERFIELD, M. D. (1985*b*). Expression of epidermal growth factor receptors on cervical, ovarian and vulval carcinomas. *Cancer Res.* (in press).

HAYMAN, M. J. & BEUG, H. (1984). Identification of a form of the avian erythroblastosis virus *erb*-B gene product at the cell surface. *Nature, Lond.* **309**, 460–462.

HAYMAN, M. J., RAMSAY, G. M., SAVIN, K., KITCHENER, G., GRAF, T. & BEUG, H. (1983). Identification and characterization of the avian erythroblastosis virus *erb* B gene product as a membrane glycoprotein. *Cell* **32**, 579–588.

HUNTER, T. & COOPER, J. A. (1985). Protein–tyrosine kinases. *A. Rev. Biochem.* **54**, 897–930.

KAMPS, M. P., TAYLOR, S. S. & SEFTON, B. M. (1984). Direct evidence that oncogenic tyrosine kinases and cyclic AMP-dependent protein kinases have homologous ATP-binding sites. *Nature, Lond.* **310**, 589–592.

KRIS, R., LAX, I., GULLICK, W. J., WATERFIELD, M. D., ULLRICH, A., FRIDKIN, M. & SCHLESSINGER, J. (1985). Antibodies against a synthetic peptide as a probe for the kinase activity of the avian EGF receptor and v-*erb* B protein. *Cell* **40**, 619–625.

PRIVALSKY, M. L., RALSTON, R. & BISHOP, J. M. (1984). The membrane glycoprotein encoded by the retroviral oncogene v-*erb* B is structurally related to tyrosine-specific protein kinases. *Proc. natn. Acad. Sci. U.S.A.* **81**, 704–707.

QUADE, K. (1979). Transformation of mammalian cells by avian myelocystomatosis virus and avian erythroblastosis virus. *Virology* **98**, 461–465.

QUADE, K., SAULE, S., STEHELIN, D., KITCHENER, G. & HAYMAN, M. J. (1981). Revertants of rat cells transformed by avian erythroblastosis virus. *Virology* **115**, 322–333.

QUADE, K., SAULE, S., STEHELIN, D., KITCHENER, G. & HAYMAN, M. J. (1983). Virus gene expression in rat cells transformed by avian myelocystomatosis virus strain MC29 and avian erythroblastosis virus. *J. gen. Virol.* **64**, 83–94.

SCHMIDT, J. A., BEUG, H. & HAYMAN, M. J. (1985). Effects of inhibitors of glycoprotein processing on the synthesis and biological activity of the erb B oncogene. *EMBO J.* **4**, 105–112.

ULLRICH, A., COUSSENS, L., HAYFLICK, J. S., DULL, T. J., GRAY, A., TAM, A. W., LEE, J., YARDEN, Y., LIBERMANN, T. A., SCHLESSINGER, J., DOWNWARD, J., MAYES, E. L. V., WHITTLE, N., WATERFIELD, M. D. & SEEBURG, P. H. (1984). Human epidermal growth factor receptor cDNA sequence and aberrant expression of the amplified gene in A431 epidermoid carcinoma cells. *Nature, Lond.* **309**, 418–425.

YAMAMOTO, T., HIHARA, H., NISHIDA, T., KAWAI, S. & TOYOSHIMA, K. (1983*a*). A new avian erythroblastosis virus, AEV-H, carries *erb* B gene responsible for the induction of both erythroblastosis and sarcomas. *Cell* **34**, 225–232

YAMAMOTO, T., NISHIDA, T., MIYAJIMA, N., KAWAI, S., OOI, T. & TOYOSHIMA, K. (1983*b*). The *erb* B gene of avian erythroblastosis virus is a member of the *src* gene family. *Cell* **35**, 71–78.

ZOLLER, M. J., NELSON, N. C. & TAYLOR, S. S. (1981). Affinity labelling of cAMP-dependent protein kinase with *p*-fluorosulfonylbenzoyl adenosine. *J. biol. Chem.* **256**, 10 837–10 842.

J. Cell Sci. Suppl. 3, 161–172 (1985)
Printed in Great Britain © The Company of Biologists Limited 1985

AMPLIFICATION AND OVEREXPRESSION OF THE EGF RECEPTOR GENE IN PRIMARY HUMAN GLIOBLASTOMAS

TOWIA A. LIBERMANN[1], HARRIS R. NUSBAUM[1], NISSIM RAZON[2], RICHARD KRIS[1], IRIT LAX[1], HERMONA SOREQ[3], NIGEL WHITTLE[4], MICHAEL D. WATERFIELD[4], AXEL ULLRICH[5] AND JOSEPH SCHLESSINGER[1,*]

[1]*Department of Chemical Immunology, The Weizmann Institute of Science, Rehovot, Israel*
[2]*Department of Neurosurgery, Ichilov Hospital, Tel Aviv Medical Center, Tel Aviv, Israel*
[3]*Department of Neurobiology, The Weizmann Institute of Science, Rehovot, Israel*
[4]*Protein Chemistry Laboratory, Imperial Cancer Research Fund, Lincoln's Inn Fields, London WC2A 3PX, U.K.*
[5]*Department of Molecular Biology, Genentech, Inc., 460 Point San Bruno Boulevard, South San Francisco, California 94080, U.S.A.*

SUMMARY

The expression of epidermal growth factor (EGF) receptor in brain tumours of glial origin was studied at the protein, mRNA and genomic levels. Four out of 10 glioblastomas that overexpress EGF receptor also have gene amplification. The amplified genes appear to be rearranged, generating an aberrant mRNA in at least one of these tumours. Such receptor defects may be relevant to tumorigenesis of human glioblastomas.

INTRODUCTION

Epidermal growth factor (EGF) is one of a structurally diverse series of polypeptides that, through interaction with specific cell surface receptors, generate a pleiotropic response that by an ill-defined mechanism can induce a mitogenic response in target cells (Carpenter & Cohen, 1979; Schlessinger *et al.* 1983). Subversion of the EGF mitogenic signal through expression of a truncated receptor (Downward *et al.* 1984; Ullrich *et al.* 1984; Yamamoto *et al.* 1983) seems to be involved in transformation by the avian erythroblastosis virus (AEV) oncogene *erb*B, suggesting that similar EGF receptor defects may be found in human neoplasias. Overexpression of EGF receptors has been reported on the epidermoid carcinoma cell line A431 (Fabricant, DeLarco & Todaro, 1977) and in various primary brain tumours (Libermann *et al.* 1984). In A431 cells this is related to amplification of the receptor gene and is accompanied by gene re-arrangement, which causes production of a truncated extracellular EGF binding domain (Ullrich *et al.* 1984; Merlino *et al.* 1984; Weber, Gill & Spiess, 1984; Lin *et al.* 1984).

---

* Author for correspondence.

The target cell specificity for different growth factors is in part governed by the expression of high-affinity cell surface receptors. These receptors transduce the signal generated by ligand binding and, since the expression of altered receptors can in the case of the oncogene *v-erb*B of AEV contribute to the transformation process, the expression of receptors in neoplasias is under investigation. We have obtained cDNA clones that have provided the complete primary structure of the human EGF receptor (Ullrich *et al.* 1984). These probes show that the human A431 epidermoid carcinoma cell line has amplified normal and rearranged receptor genes (Ullrich *et al.* 1984). Amplification of other proto-oncogenes has been recently detected in several tumours and tumour-derived cell lines (Ullrich *et al.* 1984; Brodeur *et al.* 1984; Pelicci *et al.* 1984; Collins & Groudine, 1982). It was proposed that oncogene amplification might play a role in tumorigenesis by leading to excess production of the gene products. Hence, we have used the EGF receptor complementary DNA to examine various neoplasias for abnormal receptor expression at the protein, mRNA and genomic level.

MATERIALS AND METHODS

Cloning of EGF receptor cDNA clone p8

mRNA from A431 cells was isolated with the guanidine thiocyanate/caesium chloride method (Maniatis, Fritsch & Sambrook, 1982). cDNA synthesis, cloning into pUC9 and colony screening were carried out according to published protocols (Helfman *et al.* 1983). Briefly, a 17-mer probe, involving a mixture of 256 oligonucleotides (3′ ATA/G TTA/G GGX TGX TGX AT 5′) based on the amino acid sequence of a tryptic peptide of A431 EGF receptor, was endlabelled with bacteriophage T4 polynucleotide kinase (New England Biolabs) and [γ-^{32}P]ATP (Amersham, 3000 Ci mmol^{-1}). Colony screening hybridization was carried out in 6×SSC (SSC is 0·15 M-NaCl, 0·15 M-sodium citrate, pH 7·0), 5×Denhardt's solution (DS: 0·2% (w/v) Ficoll, 0·2% (w/v) polyvinylpyroliclone, 0·2% (w/v) bovine serum albumin), 1% sodium dodecyl sulphate (SDS), 100 μg ml^{-1} salmon sperm DNA at room temperature for 36 h. Filters were washed at 45 °C with 3×SSC, 0·1% DS. Nucleotide sequence analysis was carried out according to Maxam & Gilbert (1980). p8 is a 2·5×10^3 base-pair (bp) cDNA clone derived from the 2·8×10^3 bp variant mRNA from A431 cells described by Ullrich *et al.* (1984). p8·4 is a *Pst* fragment (399 bp) derived from clone p8.

Southern blot analysis of genomic DNA from tumours and cell lines

High molecular weight chromosomal DNA was isolated as described (Maniatis *et al.* 1982). DNA (15 g) was digested to completion with excess of either *Eco*RI or *Hin*dIII (New England Biolabs), fractionated by electrophoresis through a 0·7% agarose gel and transferred to nitrocellulose paper. EGF-receptor cDNA inserts were radiolabelled with [α-^{32}P]dATP and [α-^{32}P] dCTP (Amersham) by the procedure of Taylor, Illmensee & Summers (1976). Hybridization with 10^7 cts min^{-1} of ^{32}P-labelled probe was performed in 6×SSC, 5×Denhardt's solution, 10% dextran sulphate, 50 mM-sodium phosphate (pH 6·5) and 100 μg ml^{-1} salmon sperm DNA at 65 °C for 16 h. Filters were washed in 0·2×SSC, 0·1% SDS at 65 °C and autoradiographed for 1 day at −70 °C using intensifier screens. Sizes were calculated using phage DNA cleaved with restriction endonuclease *Hin*dIII as standards.

Southern blot analysis (Fig. 2)

High molecular weight DNA (15 μg) of A431 cells (A431), human placenta (HPL), glioblastomas (GM1, GM2) and meningioma (MEN1) was digested with *Eco*RI (a) or *Hin*dIII (b). In

Table 1. *Properties of human brain tumours*

Tissue designation	Source of DNA	No. of EGF receptor gene copies	EGF receptor expression
Controls			
HPL	Human placenta	1	High
A431	Epidermoid vulval carcinoma	15–25	High
Brain tumours			
GM1	Glioblastoma multiforme	20–30	High
GM2 (6)	Glioblastoma multiforme	10–20*/35–45†	High
GM3	Glioblastoma multiforme	1	ND
GM4	Glioblastoma multiforme	1	Low
GM5	Glioblastoma multiforme	1	ND
GM6	Glioblastoma multiforme	50–60	High
GM7 (20)	Glioblastoma multiforme	1	Low
GM8	Glioblastoma multiforme	1	None
GM9	⎰ Glioblastoma multiforme	6–9	ND
	⎱ Adjacent normal brain tissue	1	ND
GM10	Glioblastoma multiforme	1	ND
CGM1 (10)	Cerebellar glioblastoma	1	Low
CGM2	Cerebellar glioblastoma	1	ND
ACII1 (2)	Astrocytoma grade II	1	Medium
ACII2	Astrocytoma grade II	1	ND
ODG1	Oligodendroglioma	1	ND
ODG2	Oligodendroglioma	1	Low
ODG3	Oligodendroglioma	1	Medium
MEN1	Meningioma	1	Medium
MEN2	Meningioma	1	ND
MEN3	Meningioma	1	Medium
PNE	Primitive neurocotodermal tumour	1	ND

Tumour tissue was frozen in liquid nitrogen immediately after removal to avoid degenerative changes. As only small amounts could be obtained, the kinase assay provides the only practical assay for EGF receptor levels in these samples at present. The radioactive content of the ^{32}P-labelled EGF receptor was determined and expressed semi-quantitatively as follows: low, < 2000 c.p.m.; medium, 2000–20 000 c.p.m.; high, > 20 000 c.p.m. For further details see Libermann *et al.* (1984). ND, not determined. Numbers in parentheses refer to tumours analysed previously.

* 5′ probe (II); † 3′ probe (V) (see Fig. 2).

order to exclude technical artifacts due to incomplete digestions, the digestions were repeated several times with large excess of restriction enzymes, producing the same results. The DNAs were electrophoresed and blotted. The blots were hybridized to the nick-translated EGF receptor-specific cDNA inserts isolated from the cDNA clones depicted in Fig. 1A and Fig. 2 under high-stringency conditions. The same blots were reutilized for the different probes without detectable loss of signal. For denaturation of the cDNA–genomic DNA hybrids for reutilization, filters were soaked with slight agitation in 0·5 M-NaOH, 1·5 M-NaCl for 10 min at room temperature, rinsed with water, neutralized twice for 10 min each in 0·5 M-Tris · HCl (pH 7·0), 1·5 M-NaCl and washed in 3×SSC. Filters were kept wet in Saran wrap, preincubated in hybridization buffer and reused as described above. Broken lines in Fig. 2 indicate the regions of the schematically depicted cDNA giving rise to the hybridization patterns shown. Arrowheads indicate the location of DNA fragments in the amplified EGF receptor gene of the glioblastoma tumours, which are undetectable in other DNAs. Roman numerals denote cDNA fragments used as hybridization probes (I, p64·4; II, p8·4; III, p64·1; IV, p64·3; V, p62·3).

Northern blot analysis of mRNA from tumours and cell lines

A431 cells were grown in Dulbecco's modified Eagle's medium containing 10 % foetal calf serum in an atmosphere of 5 % CO_2/95 % air at 37°C. RNA was isolated from frozen tissue of human placenta, and glioblastoma GM1 after pulverization in liquid N_2 and from fresh A431 cells with the guanidine thiocyanate/caesium chloride method as described (Maniatis *et al.* 1982). Samples (10 μg) of poly(A)-selected mRNA were heated at 60°C for 10 min in a solution containing 50 % formamide, 6 % formaldehyde and running buffer (20 mM-MOPS, pH 7·0, 5 mM-sodium acetate, 1 mM-EDTA). The samples were electrophoresed at 100 V for 4 h in 1 % agarose gels containing 6 % formaldehyde at 1× running buffer. The RNA was transferred with 10×SSC to nitrocellulose filters, fixed by heating at 80°C for 2 h and hybridized at 42°C for 2 days with 2×10^6 cts min^{-1} ml^{-1} of nick-translated p64·3 probe in a solution containing 50 % formamide, 5×SSC, 10 % dextran sulphate, 1×Denhardt's solution, 10 mM-sodium phosphate (pH 6·8) and 100 μg ml^{-1} salmon sperm DNA. After washing at 65°C with 0·1×SSC, 0·1 % SDS, the filters were autoradiographed for 2 days at −70°C using intensifier screens.

Immunoprecipitation of functional EGF receptor from tumours and cell lines

Equal amounts (25 mg) of tissue from glioblastomas GM1, GM7 and GM8, meningioma MEN1, oligodendrogliomas ODG2 and ODG3 and human placenta HPL were solubilized as described by Libermann *et al.* (1984). Equal amounts of protein were used for immuno-precipitations with either polyclonal rabbit antibodies TLM, generated against membranes enriched with EGF receptor from the A431 cell line (Libermann *et al.* 1984) or polyclonal rabbit antibodies RK2, generated against a synthetic peptide derived from the C-terminal domain of the EGF receptor (Kris *et al.* 1985). Functional EGF receptor kinase was immunoprecipitated and detected by phosphorylation of the immunoprecipitate using [γ-^{32}P]ATP according to Libermann *et al.* (1984). The immunoprecipitates were dissolved in electrophoresis sample buffer and electrophoresed in a 5 % to 15 % SDS/polyacrylamide gel. The gel was dried and auto-radiographed for 12 h at room temperature. A431 cells were used as a standard source of the EGF receptor.

RESULTS AND DISCUSSION

Brain tumour tissue was obtained from the primary tumours of 21 patients at surgery. Genomic DNA was prepared from these tumours and from human placenta

---

Fig. 1. Southern blot analysis of DNA from primary human brain tumours and human placenta. A. Schematic representation of human EGF receptor cDNA probes from A431 epidermoid carcinoma cells used in this study and a diagram describing the complete cDNA structure. Untranslated sequences are represented by a line, coding sequences are boxed. The open portion represents sequences that encode the signal peptide; hatched regions code for the mature receptor. The filled region demarcates the coding region for the putative transmembrane domain. The probes used for this study are drawn above the diagram. Their construction has been described (Ullrich *et al.* 1984), except for that of probe p8·4, which is derived from the recombinant plasmid p8 (Libermann *et al.* unpublished results). p64·4 and the other probes were previously designated pHER–A64·4, respectively (Ullrich *et al.* 1984). B. Amplification of the EGF receptor gene in glioblastoma and A431 DNA detected by Southern blot analysis of DNA from primary human brain tumours, A431 epidermoid carcinoma cells and human placenta. The DNA from these tumours was digested with *Eco*RI and probed with ^{32}P-labelled p64·1 DNA. kb = 10^3 bp. GM1, GM6, GM7 and GM8 are different primary human glioblastomas, CGM2 is a cerebellar glioblastoma, ACII2 is an astrocytoma grade II, MEN1 is a meningioma, A431 is a human epidermoid carcinoma cell line. HPL is human placenta, which served as a control tissue. PNE is a primitive neuroectodermal tumour; ODG1, ODG2 and ODG3 are oligodendrogliomas.

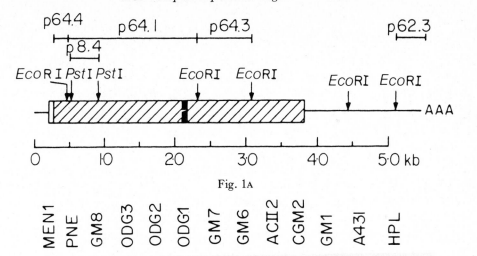

Fig. 1A

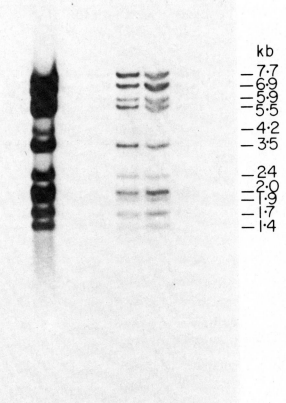

*Eco*RI

Fig. 1B

and A431 cells (Table 1). Southern blot hybridization analysis of equal amounts of *Eco*RI-digested DNA from these tumours using an *Eco*RI fragment of the EGF receptor cDNA (p64·1) as a probe, revealed that four out of ten glioblastomas contain amplified copies of the EGF receptor gene (Fig. 1B and Table 1). None of the more benign brain tumours such as meningioma, oligodendroglioma, astrocytoma grade II (Fig. 1B and Table 1) or other tumours tested (data not shown) showed amplification of the EGF receptor gene. On the basis of densitometric quantification and Southern blot hybridization analysis with varied amounts of DNA, we estimate that the EGF receptor gene is amplified 15- to 25-fold in A431 cells and 6- to 60-fold in four glioblastomas that have gene amplification compared with DNA derived from human placenta.

To characterize in detail the amplification of the EGF receptor gene in these tumours, Southern blots of both *Eco*RI- and *Hind*III-digested DNA were probed

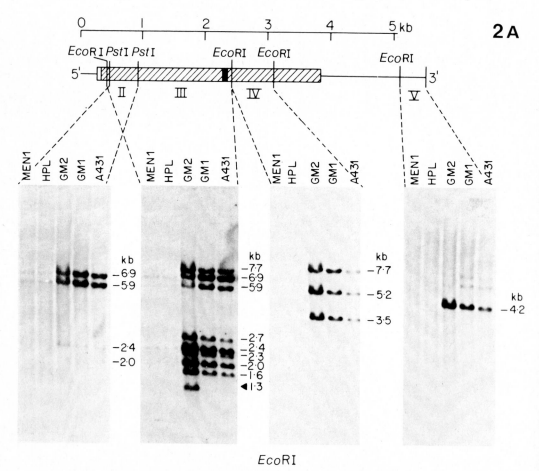

Fig. 2. Southern blot analysis of EGF receptor sequences in human brain tumours, A431 cells and human placenta; 15 µg high molecular weight DNA of A431 cells (A431), human placenta (HPL), glioblastomas (GM1, GM2), and meningioma (MEN1) was digested with *Eco*RI (A) or *Hind*III (B).

with various segments of the cloned EGF receptor cDNA. Fig. 2 shows that different patterns of hybridization were obtained with probes derived from sequences coding for the 5′ end region, the extracellular domain, the intracellular domain and the 3′ untranslated region of the mRNA coding for the EGF receptor. On the basis of more detailed Southern hybridization experiments with different digests of genomic DNA, we estimate that the gene coding for the EGF receptor is larger than 80×10^3 bp (Whittle *et al.* unpublished data). In one of the glioblastomas, GM2, stronger hybridization was observed for the 3′ end probe compared with the hybridization with the 5′ end probe. It was estimated that the 3′ part of the gene is amplified 35- to 45-fold compared to a 10- to 20-fold amplification of the 5′ part of the gene (Fig. 2). Moreover, DNA extracted from GM2 showed an additional strong $9\cdot4\times10^3$ bp band in the *Hind*III digest and a $1\cdot3\times10^3$ bp band in the *Eco*RI digest that was detected by the p64·1 probe derived from the 5′ half of the EGF receptor cDNA (Fig. 2, arrowhead). These bands were not observed in DNA isolated from any other tissue. No additional band could be detected in either digest with any probe derived from the 3′ half of the cDNA. The extra bands are also amplified indicating that they are part of the amplified gene rather than being border sequences

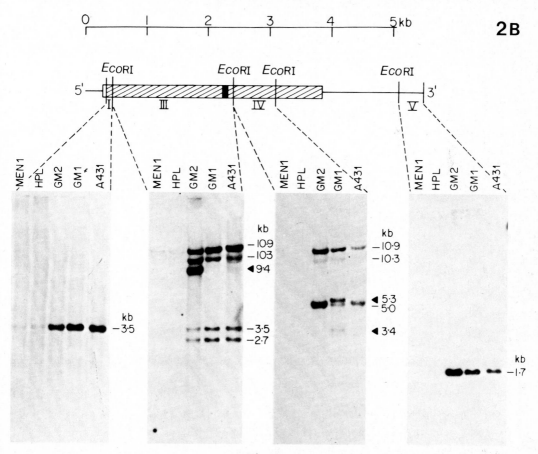

*Hind*III

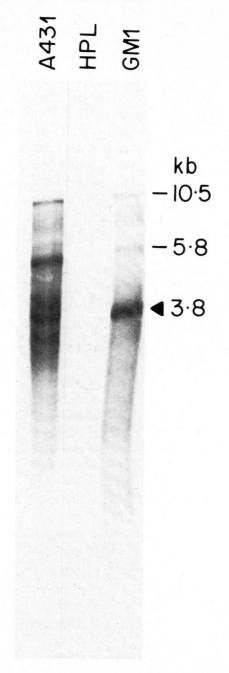

Fig. 3. Northern blot analysis of mRNA from A431 cells, human placenta, and glioblastoma.

flanking the amplified gene. Hence, these results indicate that the amplified EGF receptor gene in this tumour has apparently undergone structural rearrangement involving the 5′ half of the coding region for the EGF receptor.

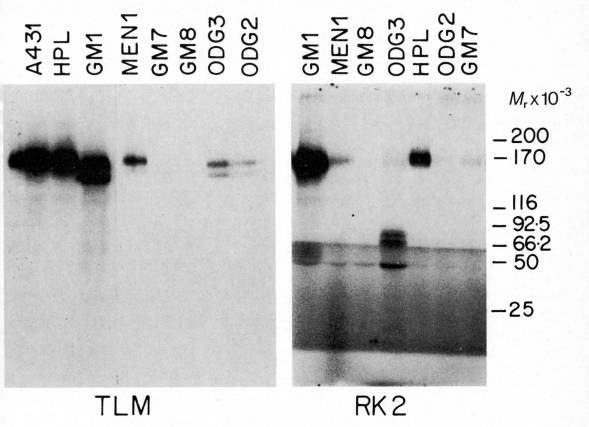

Fig. 4. Immunoprecipitation of functional EGF receptor kinase from human brain tumours, human placenta and A431 cells. Immunoprecipitation experiments of equal amounts (25 mg) of tissue from glioblastomas GM1, GM7 and GM8, meningioma MEN1, oligodendrogliomas ODG2 and ODG3, and human placenta HPL, were performed as described by Libermann *et al.* (1984). 170 M_r indicates the position of the EGF receptor. High molecular weight markers used were: light chain of IgG ($25 \times 10^3 M_r$), heavy chain of IgG ($50 \times 10^3 M_r$), bovine serum albumin ($66 \cdot 2 \times 10^3 M_r$), phosphorylase B ($92 \cdot 5 \times 10^3 M_r$), β-galactosidase ($116 \times 10^3 M_r$) and myosin heavy chain ($200 \times 10^3 M_r$) (Biorad).

The *Hind*III digests of DNA prepared from the glioblastoma designated GM1 showed additional bands of 5·3 and $3 \cdot 4 \times 10^3$ bp hybridizing with the p64·3 probe derived from the cDNA region coding for the intracellular tyrosine kinase domain of the EGF receptor. No additional band was observed when another probe, p64·1 (Fig. 1A), was used in the Southern blot analysis. Altogether, these results suggest that the apparent rearrangement in the gene of EGF receptor in this tumour was limited to the 3′ half of the coding region for the EGF receptor (Fig. 2, arrowheads). The *Eco*RI digests of DNA from this tumour did not show any additional band. Furthermore, when the same blots were hybridized with various other probes, no additional bands could be observed. In DNA from normal human lymphocytes it is possible to detect extra bands, presumably representing EGF receptor gene polymorphism (Whittle *et al.* unpublished data). These polymorphic bands are different from the additional bands detected in the DNA from the tumours.

We explored the possibility that these amplifications and possible rearrangements are associated with enhanced and probably aberrant transcription of the gene leading to enhanced expression of the EGF receptor. Because of the limited amount of tissue available from most of the tumours (normally less than 0·5 g), we were able to extract poly(A) mRNA from only one of the glioblastomas, GM1. The poly(A)-containing RNA fraction was analysed by Northern blot hybridization for the presence of EGF receptor-specific transcripts. Fig. 3 shows that the p64·3 probe, derived from the 3' half of the coding region of the EGF receptor, hybridizes to two transcripts of 5·8 and $10·5 \times 10^3$ bp in A431 cells, in human placenta, and in GM1. The level of these two transcripts was about twofold lower than in A431 cells, but three- to fourfold higher than in human placenta. However, in GM1 an additional major transcript of $3·8 \times 10^3$ bp is observed. This RNA species is approximately 10-fold more abundant than the two normal mRNAs and appears to be derived from the rearranged gene(s). Preliminary experiments with a 5' end probe suggest that it codes for the external domain and at least part of the cytoplasmic domain of the EGF receptor.

EGF receptor expression was further analysed by immunoprecipitation of functional EGF receptor kinase with either polyclonal rabbit antibodies (designated TLM) generated against membranes from A431 cells (Libermann *et al.* 1984), or with polyclonal rabbit antibodies (designated RK2) generated against a synthetic peptide derived from the cytoplasmic region of the EGF receptor (Kris *et al.* 1985). Functional EGF receptor kinase was detected by the addition of $[\gamma\text{-}^{32}P]ATP$ to the immunoprecipitate yielding autophosphorylation of EGF receptor (Libermann *et al.* 1984). Fig. 4 depicts the results of an experiment, in which the phosphorylated receptors from a variety of brain tumours were analysed. High levels of EGF receptor kinase activity were detected in all the glioblastomas with amplified EGF receptor genes (Fig. 4 and Table 1). In contrast, only low or intermediate levels were detected in all the other tumours. Normal brain, as previously described (Libermann *et al.* 1984), expressed only very low levels of EGF receptor. The major phosphorylated protein displayed a molecular weight of about $170\,000\,M_r$ comigrating with the phosphorylated EGF receptor of A431 cells.

Our results suggest a strong correlation between overexpression of the EGF receptor and amplification of the EGF receptor gene (see Table 1). EGF receptor gene amplification was detected in four out of ten glioblastomas examined. Expression of the EGF receptor protein was examined in 20 glioblastomas, including those previously described (Libermann *et al.* 1984), and approximately one third of the glioblastomas were found to express very high levels of EGF receptor. However, in less-malignant brain tumours, such as astrocytoma grade II, meningioma and oligodendroglioma, both the copy number of the EGF receptor gene and the level of the expressed receptor seem to be normal.

In conclusion, we have demonstrated that the EGF receptor gene amplification and elevated expression are frequent events occurring in primary human glioblastomas (Libermann *et al.* 1984, 1985). We suggest that the overexpression of this proto-oncogene may have a role in the development, maintenance and, or, progression of these tumours.

This work was supported by grants from the National Institute of Health, CA-25820 (to J.S.).

REFERENCES

BRODEUR, G. M., SEEGER, R. C., SCHWAB, M., VARMUS, H. E. & BISHOP, J. M. (1984). Amplification of *N-myc* in untreated human neuroblastomas correlated with advanced disease stage. *Science* **224**, 1121–1124.

CARPENTER, G. & COHEN, S. (1979). Epidermal Growth Factor. *A. Rev. Biochem.* **48**, 193–216.

COLLINS, S. & GROUDINE, M. (1982). Amplification of endogenous myc-related DNA sequences in human myeloid leukemia cell line. *Nature, Lond.* **298**, 679–681.

DOWNWARD, J., YARDEN, Y., MAYES, E., SCRACE, G., TOTTY, N., STOCKWELL, P., ULLRICH, A., SCHLESSINGER, J. & WATERFIELD, M. D. (1984). Close similarity of epidermal growth factor receptor and *v-erb*-B oncogene protein sequences. *Nature, Lond.* **307**, 521–527.

FABRICANT, R. N., DeLARCO, J. E. & TODARO, G. J. (1977). Nerve growth factor receptors on human melanoma cells in culture. *Proc. natn. Acad. Sci. U.S.A.* **74**, 565–569.

HELFMAN, D. M., FERAMISCO, J. R., FIDDES, J. C., THOMAS, G. P. & HUGHES, S. H. (1983). Identification of clones that encode chicken tropomyosin by direct immunological screening of a cDNA expression library. *Proc. natn. Acad. Sci. U.S.A.* **80**, 31–35.

KRIS, R., LAX, I., GULLICK, W., WATERFIELD, M. D., ULLRICH, A., FRIDKIN, M. & SCHLESSINGER, J. (1985). Antibodies against a synthetic peptide as a probe for the kinase activity of the avian EGF receptor and *v-erb*-B protein. *Cell* **40**, 619–625.

LIBERMANN, T. A., NUSSBAUM, H. R., RAZON, N., KRIS, R., LAX, I., SOREQ, H., WHITTLE, N., WATERFIELD, M. D., ULLRICH, A. & SCHLESSINGER, J. (1985). Amplification, enhanced expression and possible rearrangement of the EGF-receptor gene in primary human brain tumor, of glial origin. *Nature, Lond.* **313**, 144–147.

LIBERMANN, T. A., RAZON, N., BARTAL, A. D., YARDEN, Y., SCHLESSINGER, J. & SOREQ, H. (1984). Expression of epidermal growth factor receptors in human brain tumours. *Cancer Res.* **44**, 753–760.

LIN, C. R., CHEN, W. S., KRUIGER, W., STOLARSKY, L. S., WEBER, W., EVANS, R. M., VERMA, I. M., GILL, G. N. & ROSENFELD, M. G. (1984). Expression cloning of human EGF-receptor complementary DNA: Gene amplification and three related messenger RNA products in A-431 cells. *Science* **224**, 843–848.

MANIATIS, T., FRITSCH, E. F. & SAMBROOK, J. (1982). *Molecular Cloning*. New York: Cold Spring Harbor Laboratory Press.

MAXAM, A. M. & GILBERT, W. (1980). Sequencing end-labeled DNA with base-specific chemical cleavages. *Meth. Enzym.* **65**, 499–560.

MERLINO, G. T., XU, Y.-H., ISHII, S., CLARK, A. J. L., SAMBA, K., TOYOSHIMA, T., YAMAMOTO, T. & PATTON, I. (1984). Amplification and enhanced expression of the epidermal growth factor receptor gene in A-431 human carcinoma cells. *Science* **224**, 417–419.

PELICCI, P.-G., LANFRANCONE, L., BRATHWAITE, M. D., WOLMAN, S. R. & DALLA-FAVERA, R. (1984). Amplification of the *C-myc* oncogene in a case of human acute myelogenous leukemia. *Science* **224**, 1117–1121.

SCHLESSINGER, J., SCHREIBER, A. B., LEVI, A., LAX, I., LIBERMANN, T. A. & YARDEN, Y. (1983). Regulation of cell proliferation by epidermal growth factor. *CRC Crit. Rev. Biochem.* **14**, 93–111.

TAYLOR, J. M., ILLMENSEE, R. & SUMMERS, J. (1976). Efficient transcription of RNA into DNA by avian sarcoma virus polymerase. *Biochim. biophys. Acta* **4**, 324–330.

ULLRICH, A., COUSSENS, L., HAYFLICK, J. S., DULL, T. J., GRAY, A., TAM, A. W., LEE, J., YARDEN, Y., LIBERMANN, T. A., SCHLESSINGER, J., DOWNWARD, J., MAYES, E. L. V., WHITTLE, N., WATERFIELD, M. D. & SEEBURG, P. H. (1984). Human epidermal growth factor cDNA sequence and aberrant expression of the amplified gene in A-431 epidermoid carcinoma cells. *Nature, Lond.* **309**, 418–425.

WEBER, W., GILL, G. N. & SPIESS, J. (1984). Production of an epidermal growth factor related protein. *Science* **224**, 294–297.

YAMAMOTO, T., NISHIDA, T., MIYAJINA, N., KAWAI, S., OOI, T. & TOYOSHIMA, K. (1983). The *erb-B* gene of avian erythroblastosis virus is a member of the *Src* gene family. *Cell* **35**, 71–78.

J. Cell Sci. Suppl. 3, 173–186 (1985)
Printed in Great Britain © The Company of Biologists Limited 1985

RECEPTOR-MEDIATED ENDOCYTOSIS OF TRANSFERRIN AND EPIDERMAL GROWTH FACTOR RECEPTORS: A COMPARISON OF CONSTITUTIVE AND LIGAND-INDUCED UPTAKE

C. R. HOPKINS, K. MILLER AND J. M. BEARDMORE

Department of Medical Cell Biology, University of Liverpool, Liverpool L69 3BX, U.K.

SUMMARY

The distribution of cell surface receptors for transferrin–iron and epidermal growth factor (EGF) on the surface of cultured epitheloid (A431) cells has been identified by immunocytochemical electron microscopy. The patterns of movement displayed by these two receptor populations as they transfer to their sites of internalization on the cell surface are different. The movement of recycling transferrin receptors over the surface is ligand-independent whereas EGF receptors are more stable residents and remain monodisperse until they bind ligand.

Prior to uptake transferrin receptors cluster, predominantly within existing clathrin-coated pits while the aggregates formed by EGF ligand–receptor complexes induce new membrane invaginations. These results are discussed in relation to receptor populations concerned with constitutive, high capacity uptake processes and receptors involved in signal transduction.

INTRODUCTION

Micropinocytosis and plasma membrane turnover

In most animal cells the turnover of plasma membrane brought about by vesicular transport is thought to be roughly equal to the replacement of the entire cell boundary every hour (Steinman, Silver & Cohn, 1972; Steinman, Mellman, Muller & Cohn, 1983; Haigler, Mckanna & Cohen, 1979). The vesicles involved in the uptake phase of this trafficking are relatively small (50–150 nm diameter) membrane-bound elements, which arise by the inward pinching off of the plasma membrane (van Deurs & Nilausen, 1982; Steinman *et al.* 1983). This process of micropinocytosis, like all other forms of endocytic uptake, requires an ordered series of fusions and fissions within the invaginating lipid bilayer. The inward vesiculation involved in micropinocytosis transfers both plasma membrane and bulk phase solutes derived from the extracellular fluid into the cell and it is the means whereby most soluble macromolecules cross the cell boundary (Steinman *et al.* 1983; Anderson & Kaplan, 1983; Helenius & Marsh, 1982; Pastan & Willingham, 1981).

In most cells a significant proportion of micropinocytic uptake is continuous and independent of stimulus (Steinman *et al.* 1983; Lloyd & Williams, 1984). A steady-state level of cell surface area is nevertheless maintained and this constitutive import of membrane needs, therefore, to be offset by a similar rate of outward, exocytic transport to the plasma membrane. During constitutive endocytosis, the relative density of surface membrane components appears to be maintained and even remains stable for prolonged periods in the absence of protein synthesis (Brown & Goldstein, 1979). It is believed, therefore, that the bulk of the outward bound membrane is membrane that has been internalized by constitutive endocytosis and is now being recycled back to the surface. The best estimates of the rate at which this form of membrane turnover occurs are derived from studies of recycling integral membrane proteins such as transferrin receptors. These proteins spend between 3 and 7 min on the cell surface and between 5 and 20 min inside the cell (Bliel & Bretscher, 1982; Hopkins & Trowbridge, 1983; Ciechanover, Schwartz, Dautry-Varsat & Lodish, 1983).

Large capacity uptake processes

By delivering their content to an intracellular compartment and then returning to the cell surface, endocytic vesicles are capable of internalizing large amounts of exogenous ligand over prolonged periods (Pratten, Williams & Lloyd, 1980). Endocytic uptake probably always includes some transfer of solutes in the bulk phase (Gonatas *et al.* 1984; Helenius & Marsh, 1982), but because these solutes are carried at the concentrations at which they are present in extracellular fluids (of the order of 10^{-5} M) it is of relatively low efficiency. Adsorptive endocytosis, which depends upon extracellular macromolecules binding to integral membrane protein receptors that concentrate within the invaginating membrane, is a much more effective process because it is concentrative. In adsorptive endocytosis uptake efficiency is determined primarily by the high affinity (K_d 10^{-7} to 10^{-9} M) with which the internalizing receptors bind their macromolecular ligand. Some populations of these receptors are capable of unloading their ligand within the cell and then recycling back to the plasma membrane so that they maintain a steady-state availability of unoccupied binding sites on the cell surface (Anderson & Kaplan, 1983; Steinman *et al.* 1983). Constitutive, self-replenishing uptake systems of this kind are not readily saturable and they are ideally suited to large capacity transfer processes such as those involved in the uptake of macromolecular metabolites (e.g. transferrin–iron complexes and LDL (low density lipoproteins)) (Watts, 1984; Anderson, Brown, Beisiegel & Goldstein, 1982) and the removal of end products (e.g. asialoglycoproteins and anti-protease–protease complexes) (Wall & Hubbard, 1981; Hopkins, 1982) from the tissue fluids.

Uptake of effector ligands

Endocytosis is also responsible for internalizing effector ligands such as polypeptide hormones and growth factors. The uptake of these ligands is also receptor-mediated but there is little evidence to suggest that their receptors are involved in constitutive recycling pathways (Hopkins, 1982; Bergeron, Cruz, Khan & Posner, 1985).

In the absence of ligand, effector receptors such as those for epidermal growth factor (EGF) and insulin are presumably relatively stable plasma membrane populations. The endocytic uptake of these receptors can, however, be induced by ligand binding so that, for example, a half-maximal mitogenic dose of EGF causes the internalization of up to 60 % of its receptors within 5 min (Carpenter & Cohen, 1979; Stoscheck & Carpenter, 1984). Similar kinetics have been shown for platelet-derived growth factor (PDGF) (Heldin, Wasterson & Westermark, 1985; Bowen-Pope & Ross, 1984). Internalization is followed by degradation of both the ligand and its receptor so that in the continued presence of ligand like EGF, the surface receptor population becomes reduced to a new steady state at about 20 % of the initial level.

Regulation of the uptake process

The mechanisms involved in regulating the rate of endocytic vesiculation are unknown. Rates of uptake via constitutive and ligand induced mechanisms appear, in general, to be similar (Pratten *et al.* 1980) but a number of recent reports have suggested that in some instances constitutive uptake may be actually increased by ligand binding (Schwartz, Bolognesi & Fridovich, 1984; Klausner, Harford & van Renswoude, 1984). There is also evidence that this form of uptake may be inhibited altogether during mitosis (Warren, Davoust & Cockroft, 1984). The mechanisms responsible for driving the directed movement of surface receptors are also unknown. The most thoroughly developed model accounting for membrane recycling is that put forward by Bretscher (1976). In this model movement is effected by a continuous, directed flow of membrane, which moves centripetally over the cell surface. Selected components of the flowing membrane are thought to become internalized by endocytic vesiculation, transported internally through the cell and then returned to the surface at a distant, predetermined location. This model was originally formulated to account for the extension and subsequent rearward movement of membrane seen at the leading edge of motile fibroblastic cells (Bretscher, 1976). However, it has other more general implications and can be applied to observations made on spreading epithelial cells (Bretscher, 1983, and see below) and to the directed membrane traffic seen in polarized secretory cells (Louvard, 1980).

Selectivity of membrane protein uptake

The formation of endocytic vesicles can be a selective process in which only a subset of plasma membrane components become concentrated within the invaginating membrane. The best evidence for this selectivity has been obtained for coated pits, invaginations of the plasma membrane decorated on their cytoplasmic surface by a distinctive hexagonal lattice containing the $180 \times 10^3 M_r$ non-glycosylated protein, clathrin (Goldstein, Anderson & Brown, 1979). Within these pits the selective concentration of internalizing proteins (such as the receptors for LDL and transferrin) occurs at the expense of longer-lived 'resident' proteins of the membrane (such as histocompatibility antigens) (Bretscher, 1982). Most recent interest has been focused on the role of coated pits in endocytosis because these microdomains have been shown to be involved in almost all of the constitutive uptake processes thus far examined (Bretscher, 1984; Goldstein *et al.* 1979). As yet, however, a direct role for the clathrin lattice in selecting proteins for internalization remains to be demonstrated and the possibility that some kinds of receptor-mediated endocytosis may occur via uncoated invaginations has not been excluded.

Studies on epidermoid carcinoma, A431, cells

In our recent studies we have been studying various aspects of receptor-mediated uptake by mapping the distribution of cell surface receptors for transferrin–iron and epidermal growth factor on A431 cells growing in culture (Hopkins & Trowbridge, 1983; Hopkins, 1984, 1985). By following the appearance and movement of these candidate receptor populations in the absence and presence of their exogenous ligands we have compared the pattern of behaviour of receptors that are thought to recycle constitutively (transferrin) (Watts, 1984) with those that internalize in response to ligand binding (epidermal growth factor) (Carpenter & Cohen, 1979).

MATERIALS AND METHODS

Receptors were identified using 5–12 nm gold particles complexed to receptor-specific mono-clonal antibodies. The particles were prepared by standard methods (Roth, 1983) and the antibodies, which are all IgG monoclonals, have all been thoroughly characterized (Trowbridge & Omary, 1981; Waterfield et al. 1982). The B3/25 antibody is specific for the human transferrin receptor while the EGFR1 antibody identifies the EGF receptor of A431 cells. Neither of these antibodies interferes with the binding of physiological ligand.

The cells were grown in sparse culture, rinsed free of serum and then incubated with or without the appropriate ligand before being fixed in 2 % paraformaldehyde. After quenching with bovine serum albumin (BSA)–lysine the cells were incubated with gold–antibody complexes, rinsed and fixed in 4 % glutaraldehyde. They were then dehydrated, critical-point dried, rotary-shadowed with platinum/carbon, stabilized with more carbon and then prepared as whole mounts by floating off the glass coverslip onto hydrofluoric acid. These techniques have been described in detail elsewhere (Tolson, Boothroyd & Hopkins, 1981). Control preparations were preincubated with free antibody before labelling with gold–antibody.

Correlative studies were carried out using fluorescence microscopy and transmission electron microscopy of thin plastic sections or cryosections prepared by standard methods.

RESULTS

Distribution of transferrin receptors

On fixed A431 cells incubated with gold–B3/25 particles, labelling was predominantly peripheral and heaviest at the free margins of the cells. At high resolution this label is concentrated within and around depressions of the cell surface, which varied from shallow indentations to deep cavities (Fig. 1). Thin-section studies showed that these depressions are clathrin lattice-coated micro-domains. Pre-incubation at 5 °C with free antibody reduces the labelling very significantly, demonstrating that non-specific binding is negligible (Fig. 2).

The peripheral distribution of the transferrin receptor population is strikingly similar to that described in the earlier studies of Marcus (1962) and Bretscher (1983) on the peripheral distribution of newly inserted membrane proteins on giant HeLa cells. In these studies it was suggested that this distribution identified the free cell margin as the region in which newly added membrane components are being inserted into the plasma membrane. Our earlier studies on A431 cells had shown that the recycling time for transferrin receptors in these cells was of the order of 10–15 min (Hopkins & Trowbridge, 1983) and we designed an experiment, therefore, in which a preincubation in free B3/25 at 5 °C was used to block existing surface receptors, so that on warming to 37 °C newly emerging receptors could be identified with gold–B3/25 particles.

As shown in Fig. 2 quantification of the number of particles binding with time at 37 °C showed a rapid increase over the first 15 min. These kinetics are compatible with the expected rate of appearance of new receptors. They are unlikely to correspond to the dissociation of free B3/25 because the dissociation of [^{125}I]B3/25 indicates that this occurs much more slowly (Hopkins & Trowbridge, 1983).

During the incubation with gold complexes at 37 °C, the spatial distribution of the labelling also changes. During the first 2–3 min most of the labelling is in the form of single, monodisperse particles at the cell periphery but within 5 min large, loosely associated aggregates occur. Between 5 and 10 min these aggregates move centripetally and, in addition, more closely packed groups of particles, often in ordered array, also appear (Fig. 3). These closely packed aggregates are commonly associated with the shallow pits and depressions identified as clathrin lattice-coated areas as described above. Essentially the same patterns of labelling are seen when 100 μg ml^{-1} transferrin is included during the incubations at 5 °C and 37 °C. These and other experiments described in detail elsewhere (Hopkins, 1985) suggest that in spreading A431 cells transferrin receptors appear preferentially at the leading edge of the cell as single elements. With or without ligand they are then capable of moving centripetally to form closely packed aggregates within clathrin lattice-coated domains. These domains have a well-defined distribution forming a narrow marginal band between 1 and 2 μm from the leading edge of the cell. They are frequently associated with apparently stable topographical features such as microvilli and folds, and may therefore represent relatively permanent cell surface microdomains to which the mobile receptors are recruited.

Distribution of EGF receptors

When gold particles complexed to antibodies specific for the EGF receptor are applied to prefixed cells an even distribution of monodisperse label is observed (Fig. 4). No preferred association with the cell margin, or with topographical features such as pits or microvilli is apparent. Pre-incubation with free EGFR1 antibody reduces the binding of gold–EGFR1 very significantly. If the cells are incubated with 10 ng ml^{-1} EGF at 5 °C and rinsed and then warmed to 37 °C before fixation and incubation with gold EGFR1 a rapid redistribution in receptors is apparent. Within 1 min at 37 °C discrete clusters of gold particles arranged in rings of 40–50 nm diameter appear. There are sometimes as many as 25 particles within a particle cluster and in some instances complexes of ring-like arrays forming a 'chicken-wire' arrangement occur (Fig. 4). Initially these particle clusters are not associated with any particular feature of the cell surface but within 3–5 min the cell surface immediately beneath them becomes indented (Fig. 5). Typically, these

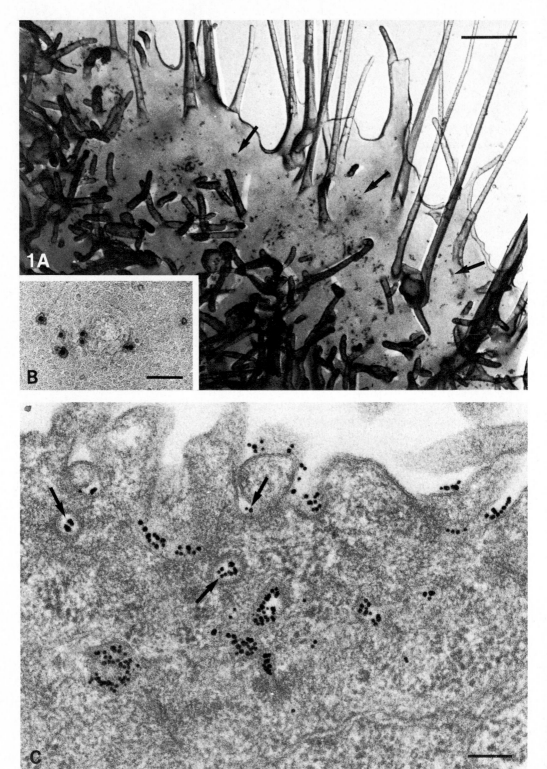

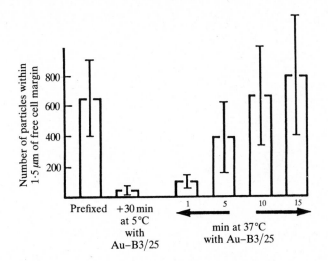

Fig. 2. Quantification of gold–anti-transferrin receptor antibody (B3/25) complexes. Data obtained as described by Hopkins (1985). Cells were preincubated for 30 min at 5 °C with $1.5\,\mu\text{g ml}^{-1}$ of B3/25 antibody, then incubated with gold–B3/25 at 37 °C.

indented pits have a circular aperture and a diameter of 40–50 nm. They also occur in cells not treated with EGF, but are then much less common. The EGF-induced pits are readily distinguished by their size and form from the larger clathrin lattice-coated depressions with which transferrin receptors become aggregated. In conventional thin sections of preparations treated with EGF and then labelled with gold–EGFR1 a high proportion of the gold particles are clearly associated with 40–50 nm diameter invaginations of the cell surface (Fig. 5). These pits often have a typical Ʊ profile and are not associated with a clathrin type lattice. They are thus similar to the 'caveolae' of fibroblasts, smooth muscle cells and endothelia and are easily distinguished from the coated pits within which transferrin receptors become concentrated. The EGF-induced redistribution of EGF receptors has also been followed by using the gold–EGFR1 procedure to label frozen ultrathin sections. In these preparations, EGF receptors have also been shown to be localized predominantly within uncoated pits before their appearance within the intracellular compartments of the endosome (Fig. 5). Together these studies demonstrate that in A431 cells EGF induces a monodisperse population of receptors to aggregate and that the aggregates that form delimit plasma membrane invaginations, which then form beneath them. Vesicles derived from these invaginations presumably transfer the EGF receptor complexes to the endosome for further processing.

Fig. 1. A. Prefixed whole mount showing distribution of transferrin receptors at the edge of A431 cell. Groups of gold particles are apparent (arrows). Bar, 50 μm. B. High-power view showing particles associated with shallow surface pit. Bar, 100 nm. C. Thin section of cell incubated with gold particles complexed with anti-transferrin receptor antibody for 5 min at 22 °C. Particles are clearly associated with clathrin lattice-coated membranes (arrows). Bar, 50 nm.

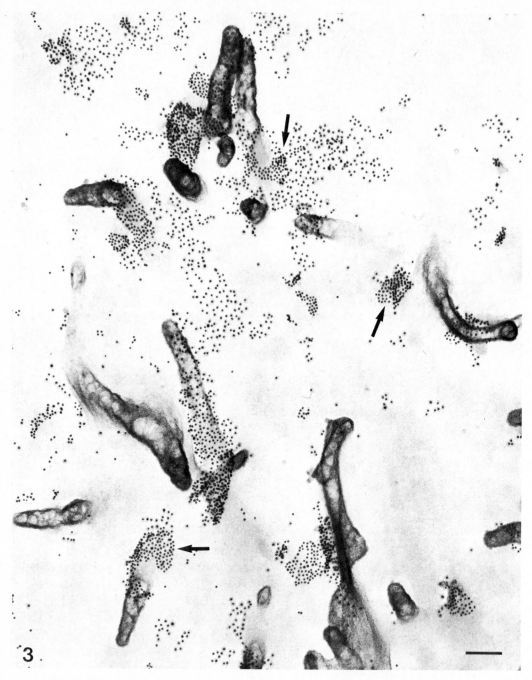

Fig. 3. Distribution of 8 nm gold–anti-transferrin receptor antibody complexes on cells incubated 30 min at 5 °C with free (1·5 μg ml^{-1}) antibody, rinsed at 5 °C and then warmed 5 min at 37 °C with gold–antibody complexes. Of the order of 50 % of the gold particles are distributed in loose aggregates, the remainder are closely packed (centre to centre, 10 nm) aggregates. The closely packed particles often display an ordered pattern (arrows) and are frequently associated with shallow pits that occur at the bases of microvilli. Whole mount preparation. Bar, 120 nm.

DISCUSSION

Previous studies on the uptake and intracellular processing of transferrin–iron and EGF suggest that their receptor populations are representative of two major kinds of endocytic uptake; constitutive and ligand-induced. Our demonstration of transferrin receptors within clathrin-coated pits even in the absence of bound ligand confirms most previous observations, which suggested that transferrin receptors recycle constitutively (Watts, 1985; Ciechanover *et al.* 1983; Bleil & Bretscher, 1982). Our observations on the emergence of newly inserted transferrin receptors also provide direct support for the view that there is a continuous centripetal flow of recycling membrane components back from the leading edge of spreading cells. The intracellular leg of this recycling pathway has not been dealt with in the present study, but it is worth noting that the cisternal elements of the peripheral endosome, which are the most likely conduit for the intracellular trafficking of internalized receptors (Hopkins & Trowbridge, 1983), have recently been shown to extend beneath the plasma membrane to the extreme margin of spreading epithelial cells (Bretscher *et al.* 1985).

In previous work the ligand-induced internalization of EGF receptors has been studied extensively in both biochemical and morphological studies. These studies have shown that an immediate consequence of EGF binding is the autophosphorylation of its receptor (Cohen, Carpenter & King, 1980; Hunter, 1984). The aggregation of the occupied receptor into clusters of between 10 and 50 components has also been shown to be an early consequence of ligand binding (Zidovetzki, Yarden, Schlessinger & Jovin, 1981) and a previous study using a ferritin–avidin, biotinylated-EGF labelling procedure identified receptor aggregates of this size on the surface of ovarian granulosa cells (Hopkins, Boothroyd & Gregory, 1981; Schrieber *et al.* 1983). At present it is not known if the processes of autophosphorylation and aggregation are related.

The induction of a transient phase of pit formation on the target cell surfaces has been described previously for both EGF and nerve growth factor (Connolly, Green & Greene, 1981, 1984). In these studies, however, the newly formed pits were identified as being coated, whereas in the present study, although some coated pits

---

Fig. 4. A. Prefixed whole mount showing distribution of EGF receptors on the surface of an A431 cell. Gold–anti-EGF–receptor complexes are predominantly monodisperse and distributed evenly over the cell surface. Whole mount. Bar, 50 μm. B. Redistribution of receptors following binding with EGF. Cells incubated at 5°C with 10 ng ml^{-1} EGF, rinsed at 5°C and then incubated 5 min at 5°C before being incubated with 8 nm gold–EGFR1 antibody complexes. Many of the receptors have become redistributed into bracelet-like clusters. Whole mount. Bar, 200 nm.

Fig. 5. Cells incubated with 10 ng ml^{-1} EGF at 5°C rinsed at 5°C then warmed 8 min at 37°C before being fixed. In A,B,D and E the cells were then incubated with 8 nm gold–EGFR1 antibody complexes. In C the fixed cells were frozen and ultrathin frozen sections prepared before incubation with 8 nm gold–EGFR1. In A,B and D the labelled cells were embedded in Epon and thin sections prepared. E. A whole mount displaying an *en face* view of the cell surface. Together these micrographs show the redistribution of occupied EGF receptors into small (40–50 nm diameter) invaginations. These invaginations lack a clathrin lattice. Bars: A–D, 200 nm; E, 40 μm.

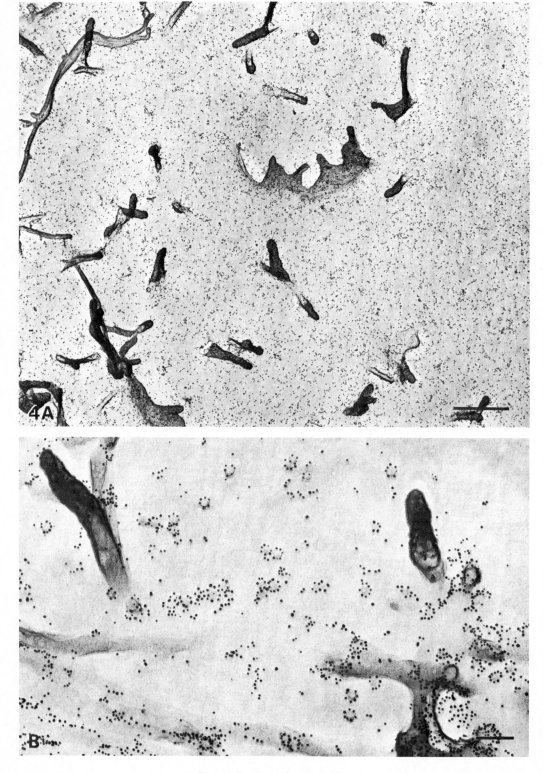

Fig. 4. For legend see p. 181

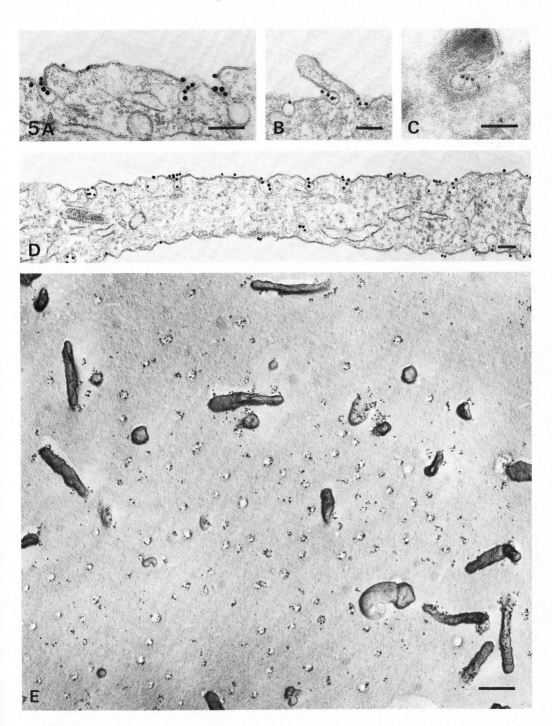

Fig. 5. For legend see p. 181

were seen to contain EGF receptors, the majority of receptor-bearing invaginations were of the uncoated variety.

The stimulation of bulk-phase endocytosis by growth factors has been reported from several systems. In most instances increased uptake occurs only some hours after growth factor binding, but in a study in which uptake in response to EGF was examined in A431 cells a stimulated uptake of the bulk phase was demonstrable within 30 s (Haigler *et al.* 1979). Using a protocol that was essentially the same as that used in the present work, it was nevertheless concluded in this study that this bulk-phase internalization was due primarily to a brief phase of EGF-stimulated ruffling and macroscopic pinocytosis and that the internalization of EGF–receptor complexes occurred predominantly via a separate micropinocytic uptake process. The site of receptor clustering before internalization was not identified in these studies but the uptake process did appear to be mediated by small (< 100 nm), smooth-surfaced vesicles.

The predominant association of internalizing EGF receptors with small uncoated cell surface pits observed in the present study has not been recorded previously. In previous work on fibroblasts, a semi-quantitative autoradiographic study showed that the majority of EGF receptors were distributed within coated pits along with LDL receptors (Carpentier *et al.* 1982). To date, with the possible exception of cholera toxin uptake (Montesano, Roth, Robert & Orci, 1982), only the transcellular pathways of endothelia have been thought to occur predominantly via smooth-surfaced pits. In future studies it will be of interest, therefore, to establish if the localization we have observed is a feature peculiar to the A431 cell or if it is a general finding for EGF receptor uptake. It is worth noting, however, that in the present study some EGF receptors were also observed within coated pits, and it is conceivable, therefore, that in previous work the association of internalizing ligand with clathrin lattice-coated pits may have been overemphasized. While the relative importance of uncoated invaginations in EGF internalization remains to be established, our observations clearly demonstrate that invaginations other than coated pits can be involved in receptor-mediated uptake. They also show that the formation of smooth-surfaced pits is inducible by physiological ligand binding.

In conclusion, therefore, our morphological studies support the view that receptor-mediated endocytosis may occur via both constitutive and ligand-induced uptake systems. They suggest, however, that the mechanisms involved in concentrating these receptors within the microdomain of the invaginating membrane may be very different. They also demonstrate that ligand-induced receptor uptake does not necessarily involve clathrin lattice-coated microdomains.

The expert technical assistance of Carole Thomas, Adele Gibson and Adrian Walsh is gratefully acknowledged. These studies were supported by grants from the Medical Research Council and the North West Cancer Research Fund.

REFERENCES

ANDERSON, R. G. W., BROWN, M. S., BEISIEGEL, U. & GOLDSTEIN, J. L. (1982). Surface distribution and recycling of the low density lipoprotein receptor as visualized with antireceptor antibodies. *J. Cell Biol.* **93**, 523–531.

ANDERSON, R. G. W. & KAPLAN, J. (1983). Receptor mediated endocytosis. *Modern Cell Biol.* **1**, 1–52.

BERGERON, J. J. M., CRUZ, J., KHAN, M. N. & POSNER, B. I. (1985). Uptake of insulin and other ligands into receptor rich endocytic components of target cells. The endosomal apparatus. *A. Rev. Physiol.* **47**, 383–403.

BLIEL, J. D. & BRETSCHER, M. S. (1982). Transferrin receptor and its recycling in HeLa cells. *EMBO J.* **1**, 351–355.

BOWEN-POPE, D. F. & ROSS, R. (1982). Platelet-derived growth factor. *J. biol. Chem.* **257**, 5161–5171.

BRETSCHER, M. S. (1976). Directed lipid flow in cell membranes. *Nature, Lond.* **260**, 21–23.

BRETSCHER, M. S. (1982). In *Membrane Recycling, CIBA Symp.* vol. 92, pp. 266–281. London: Pitman Books.

BRETSCHER, M. S. (1983). Distribution of receptors for transferrin and low density lipoprotein on the surface of giant HeLa cells. *Proc. natn. Acad. Sci. U.S.A.* **80**, 484–458.

BRETSCHER, M. S. (1984). Endocytosis: relation to capping and cell locomotion. *Science* **224**, 681–685.

BRETSCHER, M. S. (1985). *Eur. J. Cell Biol.* (in press).

BRETSCHER, M. S. & PEARSE, B. M. F. (1984). Coated pits in action. *Cell* **38**, 3–4.

BROWN, M. S. & GOLDSTEIN, J. L. (1979). Receptor mediated endocytosis: insights from the lipoprotein receptor system. *Proc. natn. Acad. Sci. U.S.A.* **76**, 3330–3337.

CARPENTER, G. & COHEN, S. (1979). Epidermal growth factor. *A. Rev. Biochem.* **48**, 193–216.

CARPENTIER, J. L., GORDEN, P., ANDERSON, R. G. W., GOLDSTEIN, J. L., BROWN, M. S., COHEN, S. & ORCI, L. (1982). Colocalisation of ^{125}I-EGF and ferritin low density lipoprotein in coated pits. *J. Cell Biol.* **95**, 73–77.

CIECHANOVER, A., SCHWARTZ, A. L., DAUTRY-VARSAT, A. & LODISH, H. F. (1983). Kinetics of internalisation and recycling of transferrin and the transferrin receptor in a human hepatoma cell line. *J. Biochem.* **258**, 9681–9689.

COHEN, S., CARPENTER, G. & KING, L. (1980). Epidermal growth factor–receptor–protein kinase interactions: copurification of receptor and epidermal growth factor enhanced phosphorylation activity. *J. biol. Chem.* **255**, 4834–4842.

CONNOLLY, J. L., GREEN, S. A. & GREENE, L. A. (1981). Pit formation and rapid changes in surface morphology of sympathetic neurones in response to nerve growth factor. *J. Cell Biol.* **90**, 176–181.

CONNOLLY, J. L., GREEN, S. A. & GREENE, L. A. (1984). Comparison of rapid changes in surface morphology and coated pit formation of PC12 cells in response to nerve growth factor, epidermal growth factor and dibutryl cyclic AMP. *J. Cell Biol.* **98**, 457–465.

GOLDSTEIN, J. L., ANDERSON, R. G. W. & BROWN, M. S. (1979). Coated pits, coated vesicles and receptor-mediated endocytosis. *Nature, Lond.* **271**, 679–685.

GONATAS, N. K., STEIBER, A., HICKEY, W. F., HERBERT, S. H. & GONATAS, J. O. (1984). Endosomes and Golgi vesicles in absorptive and fluid phase endocytosis. *J. Cell Biol.* **99**, 1379–1390.

HAIGLER, H. T., McKANNA, J. A. & COHEN, S. (1979). Rapid stimulation of pincocytosis in human carcinoma cells A431 by epidermal growth factor. *J. Cell Biol.* **83**, 82–90.

HELDIN, C. H., WASTERSON, A. & WESTERMARK, B. (1985). Platelet derived growth factor. *Mol. cell. Endocr.* **39**, 169–187.

HELENIUS, A. & MARSH, M. (1982). Endocytosis of enveloped animal viruses. In *Membrane Recycling, CIBA Fdn Symp.* vol. 92. London: Pitman.

HOPKINS, C. R. (1982). Early events in the receptor-mediated endocytosis of epidermal growth factor and alpha$_2$ macroglobulin–protease complexes. In *Membrane Recycling, CIBA Fdn Symp.* vol. 92, pp. 239–242. London: Pitman.

HOPKINS, C. R. (1984). Intracellular routing of transferrin and transferrin receptors in epidermoid carcinoma A431 cells. *Cell* **35**, 321–330.

HOPKINS, C. R. (1985). The appearance and internalisation of transferrin receptors at the margins of spreading tumour cells. *Cell* **40**, 199–208.

HOPKINS, C. R., BOOTHROYD, B. & GREGORY, H. (1981). Early events following the binding of epidermal growth factor to surface receptors on ovarian granulosa cells. *Eur. J. Cell Biol.* **24**, 259–265.

HOPKINS, C. R. & TROWBRIDGE, I. S. (1983). Internalisation and processing of transferrin and the transferrin receptor in human carcinoma A431 cells. *J. Cell Biol.* **97**, 508–521.

HUNTER, T. (1984). The epidermal growth factor receptor gene and its product. *Nature, Lond.* **311**, 414–416.

KLAUSNER, R. D., HARFORD, J. & VAN RENSWOUDE, J. (1984). Rapid internalisation of the transferrin receptor in K562 cells is triggered by ligand binding or treatment with phorbol ester. *Proc. natn. Acad. Sci. U.S.A.* **81**, 3005–3009.

LLOYD, J. B. & WILLIAMS, K. E. (1984). Non-specific adsorptive pinocytosis. *Biochem. Soc. Trans.* **12**, 527–528.

LOUVARD, D. (1980). Apical membrane aminopeptidase appears at a site of cell–cell contact in cultured kidney epithelial cells. *Proc. natn. Acad. Sci. U.S.A.* **77**, 4132–4136.

MARCUS, P. I. (1962). Dynamics of surface modification in myxovirus-infected cells. *Cold Spring Harbor Symp. quant. Biol.* **27**, 351–365.

MONTESANO, R., ROTH, J., ROBERT, A. & ORCI, L. (1982). Non-coated membrane invaginations are involved in binding and internalisation of cholera and tetanus toxins. *Nature, Lond.* **296**, 651–653.

PASTAN, I. H. & WILLINGHAM, M. C. (1981). Receptor-mediated endocytosis of hormones in cultured cells. *A. Rev. Physiol.* **43**, 239–250.

PRATTEN, M. K., WILLIAMS, K. E. & LLOYD, J. B. (1980). In *Coated Vesicles* (ed. C. J. Ockleford & A. Whyte), pp. 179–218. Cambridge University Press.

ROTH, J. (1983). The colloidal gold marker system for light and electron microscopic cytochemistry. In *Techniques in Immunocytochemistry,* vol. II, pp. 218–277. London: Academic Press.

SCHRIEBER, A. B., LIBERMAN, T. A., LAX, I., YARDEN, Y. & SCHLESSINGER, J. (1983). Biological role of epidermal growth factor-receptor clustering. *J. biol. Chem.* **258**, 846–853.

SCHWARTZ, A. L., BOLOGNESI, A. & FRIDOVICH, E. E. (1984). Recycling of the asialoglycoprotein receptor and the effect of lysosomotrophic amines on hepatoma cells. *J. Cell Biol.* **98**, 737–738.

STEINMAN, R. M., MELLMAN, I. S., MULLER, W. A. & COHN, Z. A. (1983). Endocytosis and the recycling of plasma membrane. *J. Cell Biol.* **96**, 1–27.

STEINMAN, R. M., SILVER, J. M. & COHN, Z. A. (1972). Pinocytosis in fibroblasts: quantitative studies *in vitro*. *J. Cell Biol.* **63**, 949–969.

STOSCHECK, C. M. & CARPENTER, G. (1984). Down-regulation of epidermal growth factor receptors: direct demonstration of receptor degradation in human fibroblasts. *J. Cell Biol.* **98**, 1048–1053.

TOLSON, N., BOOTHROYD, B. & HOPKINS, C. R. (1981). Cell surface labelling with gold colloid particulates: the use of avidin and staphlycoccal protein A coated gold in conjunction with biotin and fc bearing ligands. *J. Microsc.* **123**, 215–226.

TROWBRIDGE, I. S. & OMARY, M. B. (1981). Human cell surface glycoprotein related to cell proliferation is the receptor for transferrin. *Proc. natn. Acad. Sci. U.S.A.* **78**, 3039–3043.

VAN DEURS, B. & NILAUSEN, K. (1982). Pinocytosis in mouse L fibroblasts: ultrastructural evidence for direct membrane shuttle between the plasma membrane and lysosomal compartment. *J. Cell Biol.* **94**, 279–286.

WALL, D. A. & HUBBARD, A. L. (1981). The galactose specific recognition system of liver: receptor distribution. *J. Cell Biol.* **90**, 687–686.

WARREN, G., DAVOUST, J. & COCKROFT, A. (1984). Recycling of transferrin receptors in A431 cells is inhibited during mitosis. *EMBO J.* **3**, 2217–2225.

WATERFIELD, M. D., MAYES, E. L. V., STROOBANT, P., BENNET, P. L. P., YOUNG, S., GOODFELLOW, P. N., BANTING, G. S. & OZANNE, B. (1982). A monoclonal antibody to the human epidermal growth factor receptor. *J. cell Biochem.* **20**, 149–161.

WATTS, X. X. (1984).

ZIDOVETZKI, R., YARDEN, Y., SCHLESSINGER, J. & JOVIN, T. M. (1981). Rotational diffusion of epidermal growth factor complexed to cell surface receptors reflects rapid microaggregation and endocytosis of occupied receptors. *Proc. natn. Acad. Sci. U.S.A.* **78**, 6981–6985.

J. Cell Sci. Suppl. 3, 187–198 (1985)
Printed in Great Britain © The Company of Biologists Limited 1985

PHOSPHOINOSITIDES AND CELL PROLIFERATION

MICHAEL J. BERRIDGE[1], KENNETH D. BROWN[2], ROBIN F. IRVINE[2] AND JOHN P. HESLOP[1]

[1]*AFRC Unit of Insect Physiology and Pharmacology, University of Cambridge, Downing Street, Cambridge CB2 3EJ, U.K.*

[2]*AFRC Institute of Animal Physiology, Babraham, Cambridge CB2 4AT, U.K.*

SUMMARY

Certain growth factors act by stimulating the hydrolysis of inositol lipids to yield putative second messengers such as diacylglycerol (DG) and inositol trisphosphate (IP_3). One function of the former is to stimulate C-kinase, which may act by switching on a sodium/hydrogen exchanger to induce the increase in pH that appears to have a permissive effect on DNA synthesis. Studies on Swiss 3T3 cells have revealed that growth factors stimulate an increase in two separate isomers of IP_3. In addition to inositol 1,4,5-trisphosphate there was a large increase in inositol 1,3,4-trisphosphate. While the former functions to elevate intracellular calcium, which has been implicated in the control of growth of many different cell types, the function of the latter is unknown. Since the 1,3,4 isomer turns over very slowly, it may control long-term events and thus could play a role in cell growth.

There are other growth factors such as insulin and epidermal growth factor (EGF), which apparently do not work through the inositol lipids but they may initiate ionic events similar to those just described for calcium-mobilizing receptors. The bifurcating signal pathway based on IP_3/Ca^{2+} and DG/C-kinase provides an interesting framework within which to consider the mode of action of oncogenes.

INTRODUCTION

A critical period in the life of a cell occurs immediately after each mitosis when a decision must be made as to whether or not to remain within the cell cycle. During early development cells opt to remain in the cell cycle but as cell numbers increase groups of cells stop growing and enter a G_o phase during which they differentiate to perform some specific function. In some cases, such as in nerves and muscle, such cell differentiation represents a terminal decision in that the cells are incapable of returning to the cell cycle. However, there are many differentiated cells that retain the ability to return to the cell cycle if provided with an appropriate mitogenic signal usually in the form of a specific growth factor. Cell growth is carefully regulated to ensure that sufficient cells are produced during development and that cells re-enter the cell cycle at appropriate times commensurate with the requirement for new cells for body repair and other functions. This carefully orchestrated control of cell growth breaks down in cancer when individual cells break free of their normal constraints and begin to divide continuously. Such cell transformation appears to arise from a subtle alteration in some step of the normal control pathway resulting in the cell receiving an inappropriate growth stimulus delivered through the normal signal pathways. The genes responsible for these signal pathways have been referred to as proto-oncogenes, which when altered become the oncogenes responsible for cell proliferation.

The behaviour of cells in tissue culture provides a convenient model system for studying the control of cell growth in the intact organism. When first seeded in a culture dish cells will grow continuously until they become confluent and deplete the medium of growth factors, at which point they enter a stationary phase. Such quiescent cells can be induced to grow either by the addition of growth factors similar to those that are thought to be released in the intact animal or by the introduction of oncogenes through transfection or a viral vector. Such oncogenic transformation of cultured cells appear to be an excellent model system for studying the etiology of cancer because these cells, which have been transformed *in vitro*, are tumorigenic when injected back into mice. When trying to understand how cell growth is regulated, therefore, we have to consider two closely related questions. First, what are the signal pathways utilized by growth factors when they stimulate DNA synthesis? Secondly, how do oncogenes subvert this normal control pathway to lock cells in continuous bouts of cell division? The inference is that in order to find out how oncogenes work it will be necessary to understand first how growth factors act to stimulate DNA synthesis. This notion is supported by the fact that the two oncogenes *sis* and *erb*B, whose functions have been identified, have been linked with a specific growth factor and a growth factor receptor. In this article we examine a dual signal hypothesis of cell growth, which attempts to explain how many growth factors might use the inositol lipids to generate a bifurcating signal pathway ultimately responsible for stimulating DNA synthesis. This hypothesis provides an interesting framework within which to discuss how oncogenes might function.

GROWTH FACTORS AND IONS

One of the important simplifying assumptions of the dual signal hypothesis is that growth factors stimulate cell growth by means of second messenger pathways similar to those used by neurotransmitters and hormones to stimulate cellular processes such as secretion and contraction. Until recently the action of growth factors has tended to stand apart on a temporal basis in that the onset of DNA synthesis occurs after many hours whereas hormones and neurotransmitters act immediately. However, this temporal gap has been dramatically reduced by the observation that growth factors such as platelet-derived growth factor (PDGF) and fibroblast growth factor (FGF) can switch on DNA transcription within minutes (Greenberg & Ziff, 1984; Kruijer, Cooper, Hunter & Verma, 1984; Müller, Bravo, Burckhardt & Curran, 1984). However, it is important not to lose sight of the fact that growth factors do require time to act. Although they can switch on the transcription of certain genes within minutes, such short stimulations are usually not adequate to induce DNA synthesis. The growth factor must act for several hours, which presumably means that it must be capable of activating the signal pathway for a protracted period. This need for a prolonged stimulus could possibly be the basis for the synergistic interactions that exist between various growth factors. Further evidence for supposing that growth factors might use conventional messenger pathways comes from studies on salivary gland hyperplasia where DNA synthesis can be stimulated using the same neurotransmitters that stimulate amylase secretion (Guidotti, Weiss & Costa, 1972; Durham, Baserga & Butcher, 1974). Similarly, norepinephrine can stimulate DNA synthesis in hepatocytes using α_1-adrenoreceptors (Cruise, Houck & Michalopoulos, 1985).

The actions of many hormones and neurotransmitters on cellular processes such as secretion, metabolism and contraction are critically dependent upon second messengers such as cyclic AMP, inositol trisphosphate (IP_3), diacylglycerol and calcium, all of which have been implicated in the control of cell growth. The role of cyclic AMP is something of an enigma in that it can function as either a negative or a positive regulator of growth (Boynton & Whitfield, 1983). Chinese hamster ovary cells are normally inhibited by cyclic AMP, but once the cells have become infected with Rous Sarcoma virus cyclic AMP begins to promote growth (Gottesman, Roth, Vlahakis & Pastan, 1984). A possible explanation for the action of cyclic AMP is that it functions as a modulator of the calcium signal pathway, as argued previously (Berridge, 1975). In this article we will concentrate on the role of calcium, which appears to be a major ionic signal for cell proliferation. The dual signal hypothesis attempts to account for how certain growth factors use the inositol lipids as part of a bifurcating transduction mechanism in the cell membrane to deliver mitogenic signals such as calcium to the cell interior.

PHOSPHOINOSITIDES AND THE DUAL SIGNAL HYPOTHESIS

The basis of the dual signal hypothesis is that growth factors act by stimulating the hydrolysis of phosphatidylinositol 4,5-bisphosphate (PIP_2) to diacylglycerol (DG) and inositol 1,4,5-trisphosphate (IP_3) (Fig. 1). This hydrolysis of PIP_2 represents a bifurcation point, in that the two products act as second messengers to initiate two separate signal pathways (Nishizuka, 1984; Berridge, 1984a; Berridge & Irvine, 1984). The neutral diacylglycerol acts within the plane of the membrane to stimulate C-kinase (Nishizuka, 1984), which phosphorylates a specific set of proteins. The precise role of this signal pathway remains to be uncovered because as yet no function has been ascribed to any of the proteins phosphorylated by C-kinase. However, this pathway does seem to be important in controlling cell growth because it appears to be the site of action of the potent tumour-promoting phorbol esters. Castagna *et al.* (1982) showed that these phorbol esters stimulated C-kinase and subsequent studies showed that this enzyme was the cellular receptor for these tumour promotors (Kikkawa *et al.* 1983; Leach, James & Blumberg, 1983).

Just how the activation of C-kinase in the plasma membrane by DG results in the formation of a signal to convey information to the nucleus is still a mystery. One interesting possibility is that C-kinase activates the Na/H exchanger, which results in the rapid alkalinization of the cytosol that accompanies the action of many growth factors (L'Allemain, Paris & Pouyssegur, 1984; Moolenaar *et al.* 1984; Hesketh *et al.* 1985). The link between C-kinase and pH was suggested by the observation that

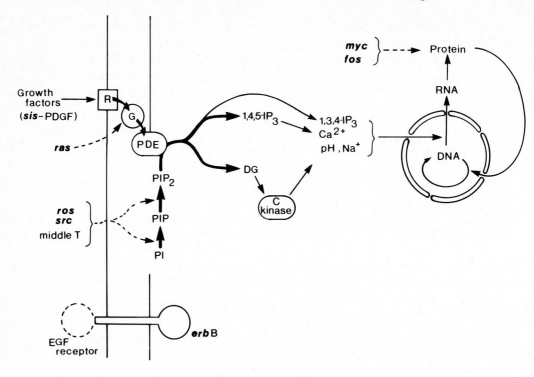

Fig. 1. Summary of the proposed role of inositol lipids in regulating cell proliferation. The signal pathway begins when specific growth factors interact with a receptor (R), which uses a G-protein (G) to activate a phosphodiesterase (PDE) to cleave PIP_2 to inositol 1,4,5-trisphosphate (1,4,5-IP_3), inositol 1,3,4-trisphosphate (1,3,4-IP_3) and diacylglycerol (DG). DG stimulates C-kinase to induce changes in pH and sodium whereas 1,4,5-IP_3 mobilizes calcium. These ionic events, perhaps operating in conjunction with 1,3,4-IP_3, may then stimulate the transcriptional and protein synthetic events that lead to DNA synthesis. The proposed sites of action of various oncogenes are included (broken arrows).

phorbol esters, which had been shown to act through C-kinase (Castagna *et al.* 1982), could activate the Na/H exchanger (Burns & Rozengurt, 1983; Rosoff, Stein & Cantley, 1984). What remains to be determined is whether the resulting increase in pH plays a role in stimulating DNA synthesis as proposed by some authors (Schuldiner & Rozengurt, 1982; L'Allemain *et al.* 1984; Moolenaar, Tsien, van der Saag & de Laat, 1983) but refuted by others (Besterman, Tyrey, Cragoe & Cuatrecasas, 1984). Despite this uncertainty, the fact that phorbol esters can stimulate early transcription of certain oncogenes (Greenberg & Ziff, 1984; Kruijer *et al.* 1984), in the same way as growth factors, indicates that the C-kinase pathway does play some role in transferring information to the cell interior but whether or not this depends upon a change in pH remains to be seen.

The other limb of the signal pathway is controlled by IP_3, which is released to the cell interior to function as a second messenger to mobilize intracellular calcium (Berridge, 1984a; Berridge & Irvine, 1984). A complication in the IP_3 story is the recent description of a 1,3,4 isomer (Irvine, Letcher, Lander & Downes, 1984). As yet the source of this isomer is unknown, but the most likely possibility is that it originates from inositol 1,3,4,5-tetrakisphosphate (1,3,4,5–IP$_4$), which has been identified in brain slices (Batty, Nahorski & Irvine, 1985) and in GH$_4$ cells, Swiss 3T3 cells and blowfly salivary gland (Heslop, Irvine, Tashjian & Berridge, 1985). There are two possible sources of 1,3,4,5-IP$_4$; it may originate either from PIP$_3$ or it may arise by phosphorylation of 1,4,5-IP$_3$ (Fig. 2). Although both 1,3,4-IP$_3$ and 1,3,4,5-IP$_4$ are potential second messengers (Irvine *et al.* 1984; Batty *et al.* 1985) no such function has been identified and we shall concentrate, therefore, on the proposed calcium mobilizing action of 1,4,5-IP$_3$ (Berridge & Irvine, 1984).

An increase in the intracellular level of calcium has been implicated in the control of growth of many different cell types (Boynton, Whitfield, Isaacs & Morton, 1974; Berridge, 1975; Metcalfe, Pozzan, Smith & Hesketh, 1980). Measurement of either calcium fluxes (Lopez-Rivas & Rozengurt, 1983) or levels of intracellular calcium with quin 2 (Moolenaar *et al.* 1984; Hesketh *et al.* 1985) indicate that many growth factors appear to act, at least in part, by mobilizing calcium from intracellular stores.

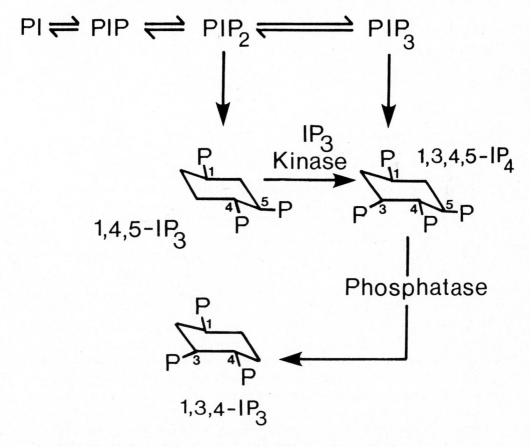

Fig. 2. The major pathways of inositol lipid metabolism illustrating the proposed mechanism for generating 1,3,4-IP$_3$ by dephosphorylation of 1,3,4,5-IP$_4$. See the text for further details.

Some of these growth factors, e.g. PDGF and vasopressin, cause a breakdown of PIP_2 to give DG (Habenicht *et al.* 1981) and IP_3 (Berridge, Heslop, Irvine & Brown, 1984). The latter has also been shown to mobilize calcium from intracellular stores in Swiss 3T3 cells (Berridge *et al.* 1984). The inositol lipid transduction mechanism thus plays an integral role in generating the calcium signal, which appears to be important in mitogenesis. However, most of the evidence linking calcium and cell proliferation is correlative in nature and there is no direct evidence to show that an increase in intracellular calcium is a *sine qua non* for the onset of DNA synthesis. Perhaps the most direct evidence implicating calcium is the observation that the early steps leading to DNA synthesis in lymphocytes can be induced by a calcium ionophore, particularly if the latter is combined with an activator of C-kinase such as a phorbol ester (Mastro & Smith, 1983; Truneh, Albert, Golstein & Schmitt-Verhulst, 1985; Kaibuchi, Takai & Nishizuka, 1985). It is relevant to point out that an increased level of calcium together with the activation of C-kinase are not sufficient to stimulate mitogenesis, which also requires receptor activation by either inteleukin-2 (Truneh *et al.* 1985) or a small amount of phytohaemoagglutinin (PHA) (Kaibuchi *et al.* 1985). Perhaps such receptor activation provides some essential messenger other than DG and calcium. It would be fascinating if this additional signal was related to one of the IP_3 isomers. The first indication that the two limbs of the bifurcating signal pathway might act synergistically with each other emerged from studies on blood platelets where near-maximal rates of serotonin secretion could be achieved by combining threshold doses of a calcium ionophore and an activator of C-kinase (Kaibuchi *et al.* 1983). The importance of the inositol lipid pathway is highlighted by the fact that such synergism has been demonstrated in many other cell types including neutrophils (Robinson, Badwey, Karnovsky & Karnovsky, 1984; Dale & Penfield, 1984), adrenal glomerulosa (Kojima, Lippes, Kojima & Rasmussen, 1983), insulin-secreting islet cells (Zawalich, Brown & Rasmussen, 1983), liver (Fain, Li, Litosch & Wallace, 1984), pancreas (de Pont & Fleuren-Jacobs, 1984), smooth muscle (Rasmussen, Forder, Kojima & Scriabine, 1984) parotid (Putney, McKinney, Aub & Leslie, 1984), parasympathetic nerve (Tanaka, Taniyama & Kusunoki, 1984), pituitary (Delbeke, Kojima, Dannies & Rasmussen, 1984), and the lymphocytes mentioned earlier. The second messenger pathways concerned with cell growth are probably very similar if not identical to those used by hormones and neurotransmitters to activate other cellular processes.

So far, attention has been focussed on those growth factors that stimulate inositol lipid breakdown and can thus activate C-kinase and mobilize intracellular calcium. However, there are other growth factors such as insulin and EGF that do not appear to act through the inositol lipids, yet they clearly have a profound effect on cell growth and it is of interest to consider whether they may function indirectly through the bifurcating signal pathway used by other growth factors or whether they have a completely independent mode of action perhaps based on their tyrosine kinase activities. EGF is a particularly interesting case because, apart from an effect on lipid labelling in A431 cells (Sawyer & Cohen, 1981; Smith *et al.* 1983), it has very little or no effect on inositol phospholipid breakdown in other proliferating cells yet it is capable of inducing changes in calcium and pH that resemble those obtained with other growth factors. Upon closer inspection, however, it is apparent that there are subtle differences in the way in which EGF brings about these ionic events, particularly concerning calcium. While the ability of other growth factors to raise intracellular calcium can occur in a calcium-free medium, the effect of EGF is totally dependent on external calcium (Hesketh *et al.* 1985). The binding of EGF to its receptors results in entry of external calcium apparently independently of PIP_2 breakdown and IP_3 formation. Similarly, EGF can stimulate an increase in pH, which again must use some mechanism independent of the C-kinase pathway (Moolenaar *et al.* 1983; Hesketh *et al.* 1985). One interesting possibility is that EGF may activate the Na/H exchanger through tyrosine phosphorylation. Such a mechanism might account for the observation that vanadate, which is particularly effective in inhibiting tyrosyl phosphatases, can stimulate an increase in intracellular pH (Cassel, Zuang & Glaser, 1984). Although EGF does not appear to stimulate inositol lipid breakdown it operates, at least in part, by activating the same second messengers operating in the bifurcating signal pathway. The mode of action of insulin is still an enigma. It certainly does not stimulate inositol lipid breakdown yet it acts synergistically with those hormones that do. For example, the concentration of bombesin necessary to stimulate DNA synthesis in Swiss 3T3 cells is greatly reduced if administered in the presence of insulin (Rozengurt & Sinnett-Smith, 1983). A possible basis for such synergism may reside in the observation that insulin can stimulate phosphatidylinositol (PI) synthesis in cells (Farese *et al.* 1984), suggesting a site of action before the bifurcation step. Alternatively, insulin could act after the bifurcation point to enhance the activity of one or other of the two signal pathways. This suggestion is based on the observation that insulin can potentiate the effect of growth factors on intracellular pH (Moolenaar *et al.* 1983) while apparently having no effect on the calcium pathway (Hesketh *et al.* 1985).

It is clear from the above discussion that we are still a long way from understanding how growth factors such as EGF and insulin contribute to the onset of cell proliferation. However, there are indications that they might fit into the framework provided by the dual signal hypothesis of cell growth. The latter also provides a framework for considering the way in which oncogenes might function to cause uncontrolled cell growth. The hypothesis is that certain oncogenes may amplify various aspects of the inositol lipid pathway so leading to an inappropriate formation of second messengers and uncontrolled cell growth (Berridge, 1984*a,b*; Sugimoto, Whitman, Cantley & Erikson, 1984; Macara, Marinetti & Balduzzi, 1984; Macara, 1985).

ONCOGENES

As the function of each oncogene is unveiled it is becoming more and more apparent that many of these can be neatly slotted into either the inositol lipid signal pathway or related pathways such as that used by EGF (Fig. 1). The first indication that oncogenes might encode proteins that function in the signal pathways used by growth factors was the discovery that the *sis* gene produced PDGF (Doolittle *et al.* 1983; Waterfield *et al.* 1983), which we now know to be a potent activator of PIP_2 hydrolysis leading to the formation of DG (Habenicht *et al.* 1981), and IP_3, calcium mobilization (Berridge *et al.* 1984), and an increase in the intracellular level of calcium (Moolenaar *et al.* 1984; Hesketh *et al.* 1985). The *erb*B gene is similar to the EGF receptor except that the external EGF binding site is missing (Downward *et al.* 1984). This truncated receptor may lead to the continuous formation of those intracellular second messengers normally associated with EGF, which might partly resemble those generated through the PI mechanism as argued earlier. Various oncogene products that are associated with the membrane have been implicated in the process of signal transduction. The *ras* gene product might function as a G protein to couple surface receptors to the phosphodiesterase (PDE) that cleaves PIP_2 to IP_3 and DG (Berridge & Irvine, 1984). By analogy with the adenylate cyclase system, the information transduction activity of the normal *ras* gene product would presumably be terminated by the hydrolysis of GTP. The absence of GTPase activity in the activated *ras* gene product (McGrath, Capon, Goeddel & Levinson, 1984; Sweet *et al.* 1984) suggests that the latter may cause continuous formation of second messengers in the absence of growth factors. The transforming gene products $pp60^{v\text{-}src}$ and $pp68^{v\text{-}ros}$ both appear to stimulate the phosphorylation of PI and can increase PI turnover *in vivo* (Macara *et al.* 1984; Sugimoto *et al.* 1984). Of particular interest is the finding that similar changes in PI metabolism can be observed in cells transformed with polyoma middle T antigen (Whitman *et al.* 1985). Since the middle T antigen is known to associate with $pp60^{c\text{-}src}$, which is the normal cellular homologue of v-*src*, Whitman *et al.* (1985) have made the intriguing suggestion that middle T might act by stimulating the PI kinase activity in association either directly or indirectly with c-*src*. Such a model may neatly explain why over-expression of c-*src* by itself is unable to transform cells whereas mutated v-*src* can (Parker, Varmus & Bishop, 1984; Shalloway, Coussens & Yacuik, 1984). The c-*src* protein may normally require some endogenous activator, which can be mimicked by middle T, whereas v-*src* may have lost this requirement for an activator and becomes constitutive with regard to enhancing PI turnover.

As described earlier, the stimulation of cells with growth factors such as PDGF results in the early transcription of the *myc* and *fos* oncogenes (Greenberg & Ziff, 1984; Kruijer *et al.* 1984; Müller *et al.* 1984). Since these genes can also be induced by phorbol esters it is conceivable that they may function further down the signal pathway to mediate the second messengers spawned by the cell surface receptors. Since *myc* and *fos* encode nuclear proteins it is conceivable that their activation may be part of the nuclear events responsible for initiating DNA synthesis.

CONCLUSION

When growth factors combine with cell surface receptors they entrain a sequence of events that gradually commits the cell to enter DNA synthesis. There is growing evidence that a signal pathway operating through the inositol lipids may provide a way of generating second messengers to convey information from the cell surface into the nucleus. The key event is the agonist-dependent hydrolysis of PIP_2 to give DG and IP_3, both of which seem to function as second messengers. While it is known that IP_3 mobilizes calcium and DG activates C-kinase, which appear to raise pH by stimulating an Na/H exchanger, just how these two signal pathways function to stimulate DNA synthesis is unknown. Whether these ionic events are themselves sufficient to initiate DNA synthesis or whether other signals are required is also a mystery. A possible solution to this problem may emerge as we begin to understand the precise function of each oncogene. At present many of the oncogene products whose functions are being revealed appear to be intimately linked with the inositol lipid signal pathway thus confirming that DG and IP_3 might be of central importance in regulating DNA synthesis.

REFERENCES

BATTY, I. R., NAHORSKI, S. R. & IRVINE, R. F. (1985). Rapid formation of inositol (1,3,4) tetraphosphate following muscarinic receptor stimulation of rat cerebral cortical slices. *Biochem. J.* (in press).

BERRIDGE, M. J. (1975). Control of cell division: a unifying hypothesis. *J. Cyclic Nucleotide Res.* **1**, 305–320.

BERRIDGE, M. J. (1984*a*). Inositol trisphosphate and diacylglycerol as second messengers. *Biochem. J.* **220**, 345–360.

BERRIDGE, M. J. (1984*b*). Oncogenes, inositol lipids and cellular proliferation. *Biotechnology* **2**, 541–546.

BERRIDGE, M. J. & IRVINE, R. F. (1984). Inositol trisphosphate, a novel second messenger in cellular signal transduction. *Nature, Lond.* **312**, 315–321.

BERRIDGE, M. J., HESLOP, J. P., IRVINE, R. F. & BROWN, K. D. (1984). Inositol trisphosphate formation and calcium mobilization in Swiss 3T3 cells in response to platelet-derived growth factor. *Biochem. J.* **222**, 195–201.

BESTERMAN, J. M., TYREY, S. J., CRAGOE, E. J. & CUATRECASAS, P. (1984). Inhibition of epidermal growth factor-induced mitogenesis by amiloride and an analog: Evidence against a requirement for Na^+/H^+ exchange. *Proc. natn. Acad. Sci. U. S. A.* **81**, 6762–6766.

BOYNTON, A. L. & WHITFIELD, J. F. (1983). The role of cyclic AMP in cell proliferation: a critical assessment of the evidence. *Adv. Cyclic Nucleotide Res.* **15**, 193–294.

BOYNTON, A. L., WHITFIELD, J. F., ISAACS, R. J. & MORTON, H. J. (1974). Control of 3T3 cell proliferation by calcium. *In Vitro* **10**, 12–17.

BURNS, C. P. & ROZENGURT, E. (1983). Serum, platelet-derived platelet growth factor, vasopressin and phorbol esters increase intracellular pH in Swiss 3T3 cells. *Biochem. biophys. Res. Commun.* **116**, 931–938.

CASSEL, D., ZUANG. Y.-X. & GLASER, L. (1984). Vanadate stimulates Na^+/H^+ exchange activity in A431 cells. *Biochem. biophys. Res. Commun.* **118**, 675–681.

CASTAGNA, M., TAKAI, Y., KAIBUCHI, K., SANO, K., KIKKAWA, U. & NISHIZUKA, Y. (1982). Direct activation of calcium-activated, phospholipid-dependent protein kinase by tumor-promoting phorbol esters. *J. biol. Chem.* **257**, 7847–7851.

CRUISE, J. L., HOUCK, K. A. & MICHALOPOULOS, G. K. (1985). Induction of DNA synthesis in cultured rat hepatocytes through stimulation of α_1, adrenoreceptor by norepinephrine. *Science* **227**, 749–751.

DALE, M. M. & PENFIELD, A. (1984). Synergism between phorbol esters and A23187 in superoxide production by neutrophils. *FEBS Lett.* **175**, 170–172.

DELBEKE, D., KOJIMA, I., DANNIES, P. S. & RASMUSSEN, H. (1984). Synergistic stimulation of prolactin release by phorbol ester, A23187 and forskolin. *Biochem. biophys. Res. Commun.* **123**, 735–741.

DE PONT, J. J. H. H. M. & FLEUREN-JACOBS, A. M. M. (1984). Synergistic effect of A23187 and a phorbol ester on amylase secretion from rabbit pancreatic acini. *FEBS Lett.* **170**, 64–68.

DOOLITTLE, R. F., HUNKAPILLER, M. W., HOOD, L. E., DEVARE, S. G., ROBBINS, K. S., AARONSON, S. A. & ANTONIADES, H. N. (1983). Simian sarcoma virus *onc* gene, v-*sis*, is derived from the gene (or genes) encoding a platelet-derived growth factor. *Science* **221**, 275–277.

DOWNWARD, J., YARDEN, Y., MAYES, E., SCRACE, G., TOTTY, N., STOCKWELL, P., ULLRICH, A., SCHLESSINGER, J. & WATERFIELD, M. D. (1984). Close similarity of epidermal growth factor receptor and v-*erb*-B oncogenes protein sequences. *Nature, Lond.* **307**, 521–527.

DURHAM, J. P., BASERGA, R. & BUTCHER, F. R. (1974). The effects of isoproterenol and its analogues on adenosine 3′,5′-monophosphate and guanosine 3′,5′-monophosphate levels in mouse parotid glands *in vivo*. Relationship to the stimulation of DNA synthesis. *Biochim. biophys. Acta* **372**, 196–217.

FAIN, J. N., LI, S-Y., LITOSCH, I. & WALLACE, M. (1984). Synergistic activation of rat hepatocyte glycogen phosphorylase by A23187 and phorbol ester. *Biochem. biophys. Res. Commun.* **119**, 88–94.

FARESE, R. V., BARNES, D. E., DAVIS, J. S., STANDAERT, M. L. & POLLET, R. J. (1984). Effect of insulin and protein synthesis inhibitors on phospholipid metabolism, diacylglycerol levels, and pyruvate dehydrogenase activity in BC 3H-1 cultured myocytes. *J. biol. Chem.* **259**, 7094–7100.

GOTTESMAN, M. M., ROTH, C., VLAHAKIS, G. & PASTAN, I. (1984). Cholera toxin treatment stimulates tumorigenicity of Rous sarcoma virus-transformed cells. *Molec. cell. Biol.* **4**, 2639–2642.

GREENBERG, M. E. & ZIFF, E. B. (1984). Stimulation of 3T3 cells induces transcription of the c-*fos* proto-oncogene. *Nature, Lond.* **311**, 433–438.

GUIDOTTI, A., WEISS, B. & COSTA, E. (1972). Adenosine 3′,5′-monophosphate concentrations and isoproterenol-induced synthesis of deoxyribonucleic acid in mouse parotid gland. *Molec. Pharmac.* **8**, 521–530.

HABENICHT, A. J. R., GLOMSET, J. A., KING, W. C., NIST, C., MITCHELL, C. D. & ROSS, R. (1981). Early changes in phosphatidylinositol and arachidonic acid metabolism in quiescent Swiss 3T3 cells stimulated to divide by platelet-derived growth factor. *J. biol. Chem.* **256**, 12 329–12 335.

HESKETH, T. R., MOORE, J. P., MORRIS, J. D. H., TAYLOR, M. V., ROGERS, J., SMITH, G. A. & METCALFE, J. C. (1985). A common sequence of calcium and pH signals in the mitogenic stimulation of eukaryotic cells. *Nature, Lond.* **313**, 481–484.

HESLOP, J. P., IRVINE, R. F., TASHJIAN, A. H. & BERRIDGE, M. J. (1985). Inositol tetrakis- and pentakisphosphates in GH₄ cells. *J. exp. Biol.* **119**, 395–402.

IRVINE, R. F. LETCHER, A. J., LANDER, D. J. & DOWNES, C. P. (1984). Inositol trisphosphates in carbachol-stimulated rat parotid glands. *Biochem. J.* **223**, 237–243.

KAIBUCHI, K., TAKAI, Y. & NISHIZUKA, Y. (1985). Protein kinase C and calcium ion in mitogenic response of macrophage-depleted human peripheral lymphocytes. *J. biol. Chem.* **260**, 1366–1369.

KAIBUCHI, K., TAKAI, Y., SAWAMURA, M., HOSHIJIMA, M., FUJIKURA, T. & NISHIZUKA, Y. (1983). Synergistic functions of protein phosphorylation and calcium mobilization in platelet activation. *J. biol. Chem.* **258**, 6701–6704.

KIKKAWA, U., TAKAI, Y., TANAKA, Y., MIYAKA, R. & NISHIZUKA, Y. (1983). Protein kinase C as a possible receptor protein for tumor-promoting phorbol esters. *J. biol. Chem.* **258**, 11 442–11 445.

KOJIMA, I., LIPPES, H., KOJIMA, K. & RASMUSSEN, H. (1983). Aldosterone secretion: effect of phorbol ester and A23187. *Biochem. biophys. Res. Commun.* **116**, 555–562.

KRUIJER, W., COOPER, J., HUNTER, T., & VERMA, I. M. (1984). Platelet-derived growth factor induces rapid but transient expression of the c-*fos* gene and protein. *Nature, Lond.* **312**, 711–716.

LEACH, K. L., JAMES, M. L. & BLUMBERG, P. M. (1983). Characterization of a specific phorbol ester aporeceptor in mouse brain cytosol. *Proc. natn. Acad. Sci. U.S.A.* **80**, 4208–4212.

LOPEZ-RIVAS, A. & ROZENGURT, E. (1983). Serum rapidly mobilizes calcium from an intracellular pool in quiescent fibroblastic cells. *Biochem. biophys. Res. Commun.* **114**, 240–247.

L'ALLEMAIN, G., PARIS, S. & POUYSSEGUR, J. (1984). Growth factor action and intracellular pH regulation in fibroblasts. *J. biol. Chem.* **259**, 5809–5815.

MACARA, I. G. (1985). Oncogenes, ions, and phospholipids. *Am. J. Physiol.* **248**, C3–C11.

MACARA, I. G., MARINETTI, G. V., & BALDUZZI, P. C. (1984). Transforming protein of avian sarcoma virus UR2 is associated with phosphatidylinositol kinase activity: Possible role in tumorigenesis. *Proc. natn. Acad. Sci. U.S.A.* (in press).

MASTRO, A. M. & SMITH, M. C. (1983). Calcium-dependent activation of lymphocytes by ionophore, A23187 and a phorbol ester tumor promotor. *J. cell. Physiol.* **116**, 51–56.

McGRATH,, J. P., CAPON, D. J., GOEDDEL, D. V. & LEVINSON, A. D. (1984). Comparative biochemical properties of normal and activated human *ras* p21 protein. *Nature, Lond.* **310**, 644–649.

METCALFE, J. C., POZZAN, T., SMITH, G. A. & HESKETH, T. R. (1980). A calcium hypothesis for the control of cell growth. *Biochem. Soc. Symp.* **45**, 1–26.

MOOLENAAR, W. H., TERTOOLEN, L. G. J. & DE LAAT, S. W. (1984). Growth factors immediately raise cytoplasmic free Ca^{2+} in human fibroblasts. *J. biol. Chem.* **259**, 8066–8069.

MOOLENAAR, W. H., TSIEN, R. Y., VAN DER SAAG, P. T. & DE LAAT, S. W. (1983). Na^+/H^+ exchange and cytoplasmic pH in the action of growth factors in human fibroblasts. *Nature, Lond.* **304**, 645–648.

MÜLLER, R., BRAVO, R., BURCKHARDT, J. & CURRAN, T. (1984). Induction of c-*fos* gene and protein by growth factors precedes activation of c-*myc*. *Nature, Lond.* **312**, 716–720.

NISHIZUKA, Y. (1984). The role of protein kinase C in cell surface signal transduction and tumor promotion. *Nature, Lond.* **308**, 693–697.

PARKER, R. C., VARMUS, H. E. & BISHOP, J. M. (1984). Expression of v-*src* and chicken c-*src* in rat cells demonstrate qualitative differences between pp60$^{v\text{-}src}$ and pp60$^{c\text{-}src}$. *Cell* **37**, 131–139.

PUTNEY, J. W., McKINNEY, J. S., AUB, D. L. & LESLIE, B. A. (1984). Phorbol ester-induced protein secretion in rat parotid gland. *Molec. Pharm.* (in press).

RASMUSSEN, H., FORDER, J., KOJIMA, I. & SCRIABINE, A. (1984). TPA-induced contraction of isolated rabbit vascular smooth muscle. *Biochem. biophys. Res. Commun.* **122**, 776–784.

ROBINSON, J. M., BADWEY, J. A., KARNOVSKY, M. L. & KARNOVSKY, M. J. (1984). Superoxide release by neutrophils: Synergistic effects of a phorbol ester and a calcium ionophore. *Biochem. biophys. Res. Commun.* **122**, 734–739.

ROSOFF, P. M., STEIN, L. F. & CANTLEY, L. C. (1984). Phorbol esters induce differentiation in a pre-B-lymphocyte cell line by enhancing Na^+/H^+ exchange. *J. biol. Chem.* **259**, 7056–7060.

ROZENGURT, E. & SINNETT-SMITH, J. (1983). Bombesin stimulation of DNA synthesis and cell division in cultures of Swiss 3T3 cells. *Proc. natn. Acad. Sci. U.S.A.* **80**, 2936–2940.

SAWYER, S. T. & COHEN, S. (1981). Enhancement of calcium uptake and phosphatidylinositol turnover by epidermal growth factor in A-431 cells. *Biochemistry* **20**, 6280–6286.

SCHULDINER, S. & ROZENGURT. E. (1982). Na^+/H^+ antiport in Swiss 3T3 cells: Mitogenic stimulation leads to cytoplasmic alkalinization. *Proc. natn. Acad. Sci. U.S.A.* **79**, 7778–7782.

SHALLOWAY, D., COUSSENS, P. M. & YACIUK, P. (1984). Overexpression of the c-*src* protein does not induce transformation of NIH 3T3 cells. *Proc. natn. Acad. Sci. U.S.A.* **81**, 7071–7075.

SMITH, K. B., LOSONCZY, I., SAHAI, A., PANNERSELVAM, M., FEHNEL, P. & SALOMON, D. S. (1983). Effect of 12-o-tetradecanoylphorbol-13-acetate (TPA) on the growth inhibitory and increased phosphatidylinositol (PI) responses induced by epidermal growth factor (EGF) in A431 cells. *J. cell. Physiol.* **117**, 91–100.

SUGIMOTO, Y., WHITMAN, M., CANTLEY, L. C. & ERIKSON, R. L. (1984). Evidence that the Rous sarcoma virus transforming gene product phosphorylates phosphatidylinositol and diacylglycerol. *Proc. natn. Acad. Sci. U. S. A.* **81**, 2117–2121.

SWEET, R. W., YOKOYAMA, S., KAMATA, T., FERAMISCO, J. R., ROSENBERG, M. & GROSS, M. (1984). The product of *ras* is a GTPase and the T24 oncogenic mutant is deficient in this activity. *Nature, Lond.* **311**, 273–275.

TANAKA, C., TANIYAMA, K. & KUSUNOKI, M. (1984). A phorbol ester and A23187 act synergistically to release acetylcholine from the guinea pig ileum. *FEBS Lett.* **175**, 165–169.

TRUNEH, A., ALBERT, F., GOLSTEIN, P. & SCHMITT-VERHULST, A-M. (1985). Early steps of lymphocyte activation bypassed by synergy between calcium ionophores and phorbol ester. *Nature, Lond.* **313**, 318–320.

WATERFIELD, M. D., SCRACE, G. T., WHITTLE, N., STROOBANT, P., JOHNSSON, A. WASTESON, A., WESTERMARK, B., HELDIN, C-H., HUANG, J. S. & DEUEL, T. F. (1983). Platelet-derived growth factor is structurally related to the putative transforming protein p28^{sis} of simian sarcoma virus. *Nature, Lond.* **304**, 35–39.

WHITMAN, M., KAPLAN, D., SCHAFFHAUSEN, B., CANTLEY, L. & ROBERTS, T. M. (1985). Phosphatidylinositol kinase activity is associated with polyoma Middle T component for transformation. *Nature, Lond.* **315**, 239–242.

ZAWALICH, W., BROWN, C. & RASMUSSEN, H. (1983). Insulin secretion: combined effects of phorbol ester and A23187. *Biochem. biophys. Res. Commun.* **117**, 448–455.

J. Cell Sci. Suppl. 3, 199–228 (1985)
Printed in Great Britain © *The Company of Biologists Limited 1985*

EARLY RESPONSE PATTERN ANALYSIS OF THE MITOGENIC PATHWAY IN LYMPHOCYTES AND FIBROBLASTS

J. C. METCALFE, T. R. HESKETH, G. A. SMITH, J. D. H. MORRIS, A. N. CORPS AND J. P. MOORE

Department of Biochemistry, University of Cambridge, Tennis Court Road, Cambridge CB2 1QW, U.K.

SUMMARY

The early biochemical responses stimulated by the action of mitogens and growth factors on mouse thymocytes and 3T3 fibroblasts are analysed as part of a systematic attempt to define the mitogenic pathways from G_0 to S phase in these cells. Although the primary response to each mitogen can be distinguished by the pattern of secondary responses they initiate, there is substantial overlap in these responses. The aim is therefore to determine whether there is early convergence on a common mitogenic pathway, defined by a sequence of responses obligatory for progression from G_0 to S phase for different mitogens and cell types. The 'dual-signal' hypothesis for the mitogenic stimulation of thymocytes is a simple version of a common mitogenic pathway. It proposes that the T-cell receptor initiates the pathway via the breakdown of phosphatidylinositol (4,5)-bisphosphate to generate a Ca signal (from the release of inositol (1,4,5)-trisphosphate) and to activate protein kinase C (from the release of diacylglycerol). The rationale for this hypothesis lies in the co-mitogenic action of the Ca^{2+}-ionophore, A23187, and the phorbol ester, 12-*o*-tetradecanoyl phorbol 13-acetate, which is assumed to activate specifically protein kinase C. However, detailed analysis of the coupling between some of the early responses, including the Ca and pH signals, phosphatidylinositol (4,5)-bisphosphate metabolism, c-*myc* gene activation and general metabolic stimulation, indicates clearly that the hypothesis is inadequate to account for the initiation of the normal mitogenic pathway in thymocytes.

INTRODUCTION

When a growth factor or mitogen interacts with its cellular receptors it is assumed that this generates a primary mitogenic signal (P), defined as the first intracellular biochemical response that results directly from the mitogen–receptor interaction. The primary signal initiates the transition from the quiescent state (G_0) to G_1 and commits the cell to metabolic activation by triggering an extensive network of secondary responses that result ultimately in DNA synthesis in S phase. We assume that within this network there is a sequence of specific secondary responses ($S_1 \ldots S_x$) that is obligatory for progression through G_1 and the subsequent commitment to S phase. An obligatory secondary response is defined by the criterion that specific inhibition of the response aborts the subsequent G_1 to S transition. These two components, P and the sequence of responses $S_1 \ldots S_x$, define the mitogenic pathway from G_0 as far as S phase in normal eukaryotic cells (Fig. 1). The general question that concerns us is whether the various mitogens that act on different types of cell operate through distinct mitogenic pathways, or whether there is a common

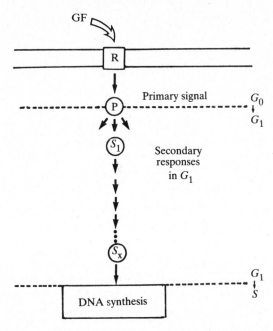

Fig. 1. The mitogenic pathway from G_0 to S. A growth factor or mitogen interacts with its receptor, R, in this instance on the cell surface, to activate the primary mitogenic signal P to initiate the G_0 to G_1 transition. This triggers a network of secondary responses containing a sequence of obligatory responses $S_1 \ldots S_x$, illustrated as a linear progression as the simplest possibility.

sequence of obligatory responses for different mitogens and cell types that can usefully be defined as a common mitogenic pathway underlying the phenotypic variation in responses in different cell types.

This rather formal statement of the problem serves to define the terms used here in a comparative analysis of early responses to mitogens and of subsequent DNA synthesis in lymphocytes and fibroblasts. Our approach assumes that by defining some of the obligatory responses in G_1, and the causal relationships between them through the use of specific inhibitors, it will be possible to compare the mitogenic pathways, at least in broad outline, for a variety of mitogens acting on two very different types of cell. Interest in the biochemical mechanisms controlling the progression from G_0 to S phase in normal cells has intensified as the proteins encoded by several oncogenes have been identified and shown to be related either to the transduction of the primary signal or to secondary responses in G_1 (reviewed by Berridge, 1984). A detailed description of the mitogenic pathway(s) from G_0 to S phase in normal cells will probably be necessary to understand how control of the pathway is subverted by specific oncogene products.

The simplest version of a common mitogenic pathway would be one in which the different mitogens and growth factors that normally act on cells *in vivo* (i.e. physiological mitogens) all caused the same primary signal. It is, however, clear from data summarized here, and from previous studies, that the primary mitogenic signal must be different for various mitogens acting on the same type of cell because the patterns of secondary responses generated by the different mitogens can be clearly distinguished. This is a simple example of the use of early response pattern analysis, which can also be applied to obtain detailed information about the relationship between the mitogenic pathways activated by different mitogens, as illustrated below. If the primary signals for different mitogen receptors are distinct, the concept of a common mitogenic pathway will be useful only if there is convergence of the different pathways on an early secondary response from which the subsequent commitment to S phase is driven. A key question, therefore, is whether there is a common early response that is obligatory for mitogenic stimulation.

Some of the secondary responses common to lymphocytes and fibroblasts are summarized in Fig. 2. Among the earliest responses that can be detected, in some instances within 10 s of the addition of mitogens, are ionic signals (increases in the free cytoplasmic Ca^{2+} concentration ($[Ca]_i$) and cytoplasmic pH (pH_i) (Tsien, Pozzan & Rink, 1982; Hesketh *et al.* 1983*b*, 1985; Moolenaar, Tsien, van der Saag & de Laat, 1983; Morris *et al.* 1984). Some mitogens that cause these ionic signals also stimulate the simultaneous breakdown of phosphatidylinositol (4,5)-bisphosphate (PtdInsP$_2$) to inositol (1,4,5)-trisphosphate (InsP$_3$) (Moore *et al.* 1984; Taylor *et al.*

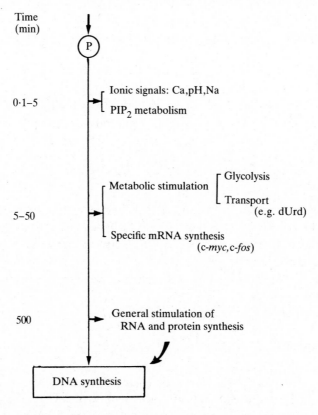

Fig. 2. Secondary responses in lymphocytes and fibroblasts. The time-scales of the secondary responses that are analysed are only approximate.

1984; Berridge, Heslop, Irvine & Brown, 1984). At a later stage, approximately 5- to 10-fold longer, there is a general metabolic stimulation of the cells marked by an increase in glycolysis and in the uptake of metabolites such as uridine (reviewed by Hume & Weidemann, 1980). At about the same time mRNA is transcribed from two proto-oncogenes, c-*fos* and c-*myc* (Kelly, Cochran, Stiles & Leder, 1983; Greenberg & Ziff, 1984; Moore, Todd, Hesketh & Metcalfe, 1985). This precedes by about another order of magnitude a general increase in RNA and protein synthesis (Hume & Weidemann, 1980). It is clear that these biosynthetic responses late in G_1 are obligatory (by the criterion of specific block) in both lymphocytes and fibroblasts for progression to S phase. The biochemical mechanisms for the initiation of RNA and protein synthesis are thought to be the same in all eukaryotic cells, so that mitogenic pathways are presumed to be highly convergent for different cells and different mitogens, at least late in G_1. While it is very likely that there are many other specific responses in G_1 common to both lymphocytes and fibroblasts (e.g. phosphorylation of the S_6 ribosomal protein etc.) many of these responses remain to be defined in lymphocytes.

To resolve whether there is a common mitogenic pathway in lymphocytes and fibroblasts it is therefore necessary to determine whether any early response common to the cells is obligatory for subsequent DNA synthesis. No clear causal relationships have yet been established between any of the early secondary responses and the general stimulation of RNA and protein synthesis in lymphocytes and fibroblasts later in G_1. It is only for sea urchin eggs that any early response has been shown to be obligatory for all of the subsequent events in the fertilization pathway that have been examined. When the sea urchin egg is fertilized, there is a transient Ca signal, complete in about 3 min, followed by a sustained increase in pH_i. The general view is that one, or both, of these coupled ionic signals is necessary for all of the subsequent responses up to and including DNA synthesis, which is initiated after about 40 min. The transient Ca signal can be by-passed by raising pH_i directly with NH_3, which results in the stimulation of many of the normal metabolic responses and DNA synthesis (Whitaker & Steinhardt, 1982).

Although the activation of sea urchin eggs differs substantially from the activation of somatic cells, notably in that enhanced RNA and protein synthesis are not obligatory for DNA synthesis after fertilization, the ionic signals in the sea urchin egg provide a useful working hypothesis: is the ionic 'kick-start' to the fertilization pathway a general mechanism for somatic eukaryotic cells, or is it a peculiarity of the egg system?

EARLY RESPONSE PATTERN ANALYSIS IN LYMPHOCYTES

The Ca and pH signals

T and B lymphocytes of several species show a polyclonal mitogenic response to appropriate antibodies directed against the antigen receptors on the cell surface. B lymphocytes are stimulated by anti-immunoglobulin antibodies (Nash & Ling, 1976), whereas T cells are stimulated by several monoclonal antibodies to components of the T-cell receptor and other surface structures such as the T_{11} antigen (Beverly & Callard, 1981; Weiss, Daley, Hodgdon & Reinherz, 1984a). A rapid increase in $[Ca]_i$ occurs in both types of cell within a few seconds of addition of the mitogenic antibodies (Pozzan, Arslan, Tsien & Rink, 1982; O'Flynn, Linch & Tatham, 1984; Weiss, Imboden, Shobach & Stobo, 1984b), but no corresponding pH_i studies have been reported. No mitogenic antibodies for mouse T cells (thymocytes) have been described, but various lectins that act as polyclonal mitogens (e.g. concanavalin A (ConA), phytohaemagglutinin (PHA), etc.) bind to and cross-link components of the T-cell receptor through their carbohydrate moieties and thus mimic the action of specific antibodies (Weiss, Imboden, Shobach & Stobo, 1984b; Samelson, Harford, Schwartz & Klausner, 1985). Various studies have shown that receptor cross-linking is obligatory for the mitogenic action of antibodies on T or B cells. The early responses that have been examined so far in thymocytes stimulated with mitogenic antibodies are indistinguishable from those stimulated by lectins, which is consistent with activation of the cells through the same receptor. However, actions of the lectins are distinguishable from those of the mitogenic antibodies in that the lectins inhibit DNA synthesis at supra-optimal concentrations whereas the antibodies do not. Two mechanisms have been proposed for the inhibitory effect of supraoptimal lectin concentrations. Edelman and co-workers showed that the inhibition occurs very late in G_1 and suggested that the supraoptimal concentrations of lectins bind to proteins on the cell surface, other than the mitogen receptors, that blocked essential surface-modulating activity controlled by the cytoskeleton (McClain & Edelman, 1976). We have shown that supra-optimal lectin concentrations cause rapid capping of the mitogen receptors, thus removing the receptors from the cell surface prematurely before commitment to S phase has occurred (Pozzan, Corps, Hesketh & Metcalfe, 1981). These mechanisms are not mutually exclusive. However, the self-inhibitory effect of the lectins on DNA synthesis complicates correlation with early responses that are not inhibited at supramitogenic lectin concentrations. Thus, although most of the analysis described here relates to ConA as a T-cell polyclonal mitogen, direct comparison with the mitogenic antibodies will be essential. For example, an immediate prediction, based on the assumption of a common mitogen receptor for the mitogenic antibodies and lectins, is that the antibodies will generate a pH_i response similar to that induced by the lectins.

The most extensive data for the ionic signals in lymphocytes have been obtained for mitogens that act on mouse thymocytes. We have compared the ionic responses to ConA and to two 'opportunistic' co-mitogens, the phorbol ester 12-*o*-tetradecanoyl phorbol 13-acetate (TPA) and the calcium ionophore A23187. The Ca signal in response to ConA in cells that have been allowed to become quiescent for more than about 8 h after isolation by incubation at 37°C in culture medium consists of two distinguishable components (Hesketh *et al.* 1985). A rapid, transient increase in $[Ca]_i$ is observed either in normal medium or in the absence of extracellular Ca^{2+}, and is therefore attributed to Ca^{2+} release from an intracellular pool (Fig. 3). There is also a sustained increase in $[Ca]_i$ to 150–200 nM from approximately 100 nM in

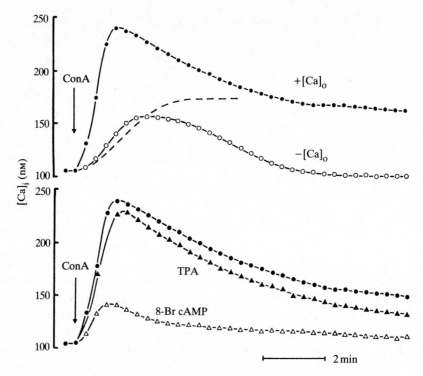

Fig. 3. The [Ca]$_i$ response to ConA in quiescent thymocytes. The cells were loaded with the fluorescent indicator quin 2 as described by Hesketh *et al.* (1985) and assays were performed at 37°C. Upper diagram: cells were treated with ConA (1·0 µg ml^{-1}) in normal medium ([Ca]$_o$ = 0·43 mM) (●———●) or in medium at low [Ca]$_o$ = 120 nM (○———○). The broken curve indicates the response in freshly isolated thymocytes, which contain a proportion of metabolically active cells (see text). Lower diagram: cells were treated with ConA (1·0 µg ml^{-1}) in normal medium (●———●) or in the presence of 5 nM-8-Br cAMP (△———△) or 10 nM-TPA (▲———▲).

unstimulated cells (Hesketh *et al.* 1983*b*, 1985). This signal declines back to 100 nM with the same time course as cap formation by ConA on the cell surface over approximately 24 h (Hesketh, Bavetta, Smith & Metcalfe, 1983*b*). It appears, therefore, that the persistent component of the Ca signal requires a continuous interaction of the mitogen with its receptors. This is confirmed by the observation that removal of ConA from its receptors by α-methyl mannose immediately reverses the Ca signal.

In freshly isolated cells the transient component of the Ca signal is greatly diminished, whereas the persistent signal is very similar to that in cells allowed to become quiescent (Hesketh *et al.* 1985). The freshly isolated cells are metabolically active (e.g. they have a high rate of lactate production) and contain a small population of larger cells in *S* phase (Reeves, 1977). The data suggest strongly that the transient release of Ca^{2+} from the intracellular pool occurs only in the quiescent cells in G_0, whereas the persistent Ca signal in response to ConA may also occur in activated cells in the cell cycle. The mechanism by which the persistent Ca signal is generated remains to be established. It is dependent on Ca^{2+} in the medium and presumably requires either a persistent stimulation of Ca^{2+} influx or an inhibition of active Ca^{2+} efflux across the plasma membrane.

Agents that inhibit the Ca signal specifically are essential to establish whether the signal is obligatory for subsequent DNA synthesis, but unfortunately no specific reagents for blocking the signal have been identified. Removal of Ca^{2+} from the medium blocks the persistent Ca signal and eventually abolishes the transient signal by depleting the cells of Ca^{2+} (Hesketh *et al.* 1985). However, the viability of the cells also decreases in Ca^{2+}-free medium and it is clear that Ca^{2+} depletion has extensive effects on the cells in addition to the effects on the Ca signal.

Agents that elevate intracellular cyclic AMP, or membrane-permeant cyclic AMP analogues such as 8-bromo cyclic AMP (8-Br cAMP), antagonize both the transient and persistent components of the Ca signal (Hesketh *et al.* 1985) (Fig. 3), and block subsequent DNA synthesis in response to ConA (Wang, Sheppard & Foker, 1976). It is very unlikely, however, that the activation of cyclic AMP-dependent protein kinases results in specific block of the Ca signal. It is of interest that the endogenous cyclic AMP concentration is very high in thymocytes immediately after isolation compared with the level in quiescent cells (Moore, Smith, Hesketh & Metcalfe, 1983), and the Ca signal in response to ConA within 30–60 min of isolation is small or undetectable. The persistent Ca signal that is characteristic of freshly isolated cells develops with a time-course similar to that of the decline in the cyclic AMP concentration to the level in quiescent cells (i.e. after about 1–1·5 h; J. P. Moore, unpublished data). Whether the early block on the Ca signal is due solely to the very high cyclic AMP content of freshly prepared thymocytes has not been established, but the observation is consistent with evidence that endogenous cyclic AMP antagonizes the Ca signal. As the cyclic AMP level declines and the $[Ca]_i$ response increases, the T cells become refractory to agents that elevate cyclic AMP (e.g. prostaglandin E_1) and show no significant response after 2–3 h (J. P. Moore, unpublished data). It has recently been shown that in cultured hepatocytes there is a progressive increase in β-adrenergic responses mediated by cyclic AMP coinciding with a decline in α-adrenergic responses mediated by $[Ca]_i$. It was proposed that this was due to a decline in the activity of a G protein (N_i) which activates the effector system for the $[Ca]_i$ response but also has a reciprocal inactivating effect on adenylate cyclase (Itoh, Okajima & Ui, 1984). It is possible that in thymocytes the reverse process occurs in which a G protein progressively inactivates adenylate cyclase, while activating the $[Ca]_i$ response. The effector system for the transient component of the Ca signal in thymocytes is probably coupled to the activation of polyphospho-inositide phosphodiesterase by the release of $Ins(1,4,5)P_3$ (discussed below), and although the mechanism by which the enzyme is activated has not been established, preliminary evidence suggests that polyphosphoinositide phosphodiesterase is coupled functionally to the T-cell receptor through G proteins, as in mast cells and platelets (Haslam & Davidson, 1984; Cockcroft & Gomperts, 1985).

The pH_i increase in response to ConA is slower than the Ca signal and is fully developed after 4–5 min (Fig. 4), but the two responses are not directly coupled.

Thus, removal of Ca from the medium to abolish the Ca signal did not block the increase in pH_i in response to ConA. TPA (10 nM) generated a pH_i increase of 0·25–0·30 unit without any significant effect on $[Ca]_i$, whereas A23187 at mitogenic concentrations (25–50 nM) increased pH_i by 0·12–0·18 unit. Unlike the pH_i responses to ConA and TPA, the response to mitogenic concentrations of A23187 was dependent on extracellular Ca^{2+} ($[Ca]_o$) and is directly coupled to the substantial increase in $[Ca]_i$ to 500–750 nM. All three mitogens therefore cause increases in pH_i and for each an extracellular Na^+ concentration greater than 5 mM is required for the maximal response, suggesting that the pH_i increase is generated by stimulation of a Na^+/H^+ exchanger (Hesketh *et al.* 1985). The removal of ConA from the cell surface by α-methyl mannose does not immediately affect the pH_i response, in contrast to the rapid reversal of the Ca signal, whereas removal of Ca^{2+} from the medium by EGTA immediately reverses the pH_i response to A23187 (J. P. Moore, unpublished data).

PtdInsP₂ metabolism

Although the Ca signal occurs very rapidly after the addition of ConA, it is a secondary response rather than the primary signal since some of the later secondary responses, including the pH_i increase, are generated when the Ca signal is abolished by prolonged incubation at low $[Ca]_o$ (Hesketh *et al.* 1985). The mechanisms by which the ionic signals are coupled to the primary response to ConA must therefore allow the signals to be generated independently of each other and we have assumed as

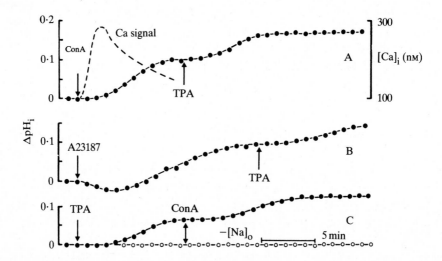

Fig. 4. pH_i responses in quiescent thymocytes. The cells were loaded with the fluorescent indicator quene 1 as described by Hesketh *et al.* (1985) and assays were performed at 37 °C. A. Comparison of the time-courses of the pH_i and $[Ca]_i$ responses to ConA. The additional pH_i increase to a subsequent addition of 10 nM-TPA is also shown. B. pH_i responses to sequential additions of A23187 (100 nM) and 10 nM-TPA. C. Effect of $[Na]_o$ 125 mM (●——●), <0·1 mM (○——○) on the sequential pH_i responses to 10 nM-TPA and ConA (1·0 μg ml⁻¹).

a working hypothesis that the $[Ca]_i$ and pH_i responses are generated by the breakdown in $PtdInsP_2$, which we have shown to be stimulated by ConA in T cells (Moore *et al.* 1984). In this 'dual signal' hypothesis, derived from the work of Nishizuka, Berridge and others (Nishizuka, 1984; Berridge, 1984; Berridge & Irvine, 1984), the release of $Ins(1,4,5)P_3$ from $PtdInsP_2$ is assumed to cause the release of Ca^{2+} from the intracellular pool (presumably the endoplasmic reticulum) and to account for the transient component of the Ca signal in thymocytes. Whether the other isomer of inositol trisphosphate, $Ins(1,3,4)P_3$, which has recently been described (Irvine, Letcher, Lander & Downes, 1984), is responsible for the sustained $[Ca]_i$ increase, for example by inhibiting the plasma membrane Ca^{2+} pump or stimulating Ca^{2+} entry from the medium into the cells, remains to be determined. (It has also been suggested that $PtdInsP_2$ may regulate the plasma membrane Ca^{2+}-ATPase activity directly; Thiyagarajah & Lim (1984).) The other product of $PtdInsP_2$ breakdown is diacylglycerol, and this is widely assumed to act as an endogenous activator of protein kinase C (PK-C) (Kishimoto *et al.* 1980). This would account for the increase in pH_i in T cells in response to ConA, by analogy with the effect of TPA as an exogenous PK-C activator (Castagna *et al.* 1982).

An important corollary of this hypothesis, central to the analysis of the mitogenic pathways in T cells, is that it provides a direct explanation for the co-mitogenic action of A23187 with TPA. In this model, the opportunistic mitogens by-pass the physiological pathway acting through $PtdInsP_2$ breakdown, by increasing $[Ca]_i$ and activating PK-C directly as their respective primary responses, which are assumed to be obligatory secondary responses for mitogenic stimulation by ConA. This would, of course, represent a very early convergence of the physiological and opportunistic mitogenic pathways. Attractive though this is, however, our conclusion from analysis of the responses to the three mitogens is that the secondary responses to ConA cannot be derived solely from the Ca signal it generates together with any activation of PK-C it may cause. The dual-signal hypothesis for thymocytes is considered now in more detail (Fig. 5), to illustrate how this conclusion has been reached from an analysis of the pattern of early responses.

All three mitogens stimulate the synthesis of PtdIns, which can be detected as enhanced [^{3}H]inositol incorporation after 30–60 min (Moore, Smith, Hesketh & Metcalfe, 1982), and stimulate a net increase in PtdIns phosphorylation to PtdInsP and $PtdInsP_2$, which is maximal within 10 min (Taylor *et al.* 1984). However, only ConA also stimulates the breakdown of $PtdInsP_2$ to release $InsP_3$ (Fig. 6). This response occurs faster than the stimulation of net $PtdInsP_2$ synthesis (Fig. 7) and coincides closely in time course with Ca^{2+} release, although analysis of the $Ins(1,4,5)P_3$ and $Ins(1,3,4)P_3$ isomers released as a function of time should provide a more critical comparison of this correlation (Irvine *et al.* 1984*b*). The $InsP_3$ response to ConA is substantially inhibited by 8-Br cAMP, which is consistent with the effect of cyclic AMP on the transient Ca signal (Taylor *et al.* 1984; Hesketh *et al.* 1985). From these and other data it is entirely plausible that $InsP_3$ is responsible for the release of intracellular Ca^{2+} in thymocytes. This remains to be demonstrated directly in the permeabilized cells, although the response has been shown in permeabilized

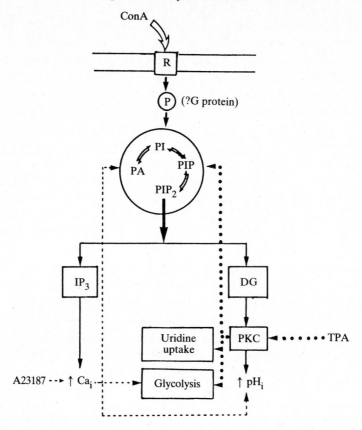

Fig. 5. The dual-signal hypothesis for the mitogenic pathway in thymocytes. The diagram illustrates the main features of the hypothesis for the mitogenic action of ConA (⟶) TPA (···▷) and A23187 (---▷) summarized in the text. InsP$_3$ generated by the breakdown of PtdInsP$_2$ in response to ConA releases intracellular Ca to raise [Ca]$_i$, and the co-product diacyl glycerol activates PK-C to increase pH$_i$. The diagram also indicates that TPA and A23187 activate the phosphatidic acid to PtdInsP$_2$ cycle but not the breakdown of PtdInsP$_2$ to InsP$_3$ and diacyl glycerol. ConA, TPA and A23187 stimulate glycolysis, but only ConA and TPA stimulate uridine uptake. A23187 activates the increase in pH$_i$ via the [Ca]$_i$ response without activating PK-C. The primary signals from A23187 and from TPA converge on the mitogenic pathway for ConA at a very early stage in this model.

fibroblasts (Irvine, Brown & Berridge, 1984). The regeneration of PtdInsP$_2$ in response to ConA also allows persistent responses to be generated by InsP$_3$ release from PtdInsP$_2$.

What is much less certain is whether the activation of PK-C by ConA is sufficient to account for early secondary responses that are common to both ConA and TPA. These include the stimulation of PtdIns synthesis and phosphorylation, glycolysis and uridine uptake, and of c-*myc* gene activation. There are two mechanisms by which ConA might activate PK-C in the dual-signal hypothesis (Fig. 5): through diacylglycerol or through the increase in [Ca]$_i$, since the isolated enzyme is co-activated by Ca^{2+} with lipids (Takai *et al.* 1979). However, detailed analysis of the early responses to A23187 suggests clearly that a rise in [Ca]$_i$ does not activate PK-C. For example, the uptake of uridine into the cells is stimulated by TPA but not by A23187 (A. N. Corps, unpublished data). The uridine response to TPA is not affected by A23187 and therefore a rise in [Ca]$_i$ does not block the uridine response when PK-C is activated. We conclude that the pHi and other early responses to A23187 must be coupled to the [Ca]$_i$ increase by a pathway that does not involve

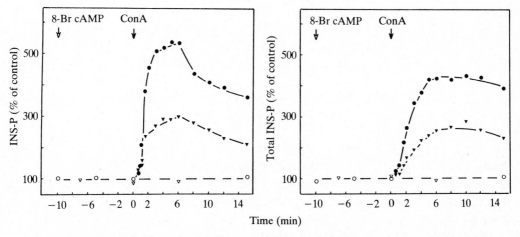

Fig. 6. Release of inositol phosphates in response to ConA. Thymocytes were labelled for 18 h with myo-[2-^{3}H]inositol and incubated for 10 min at 37°C with (∇, $\blacktriangledown$) or without ($\bigcirc$, $\bullet$) 8-Br cAMP before addition of ConA (1 μg ml^{-1}). Left, release of InsP$_3$; right, release of total inositol phosphates (InsP$_3$+InsP$_2$+InsP).

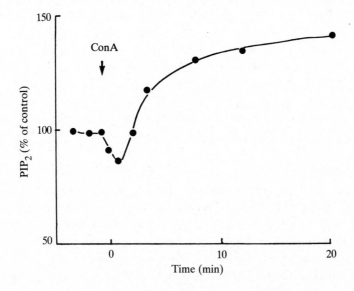

Fig. 7. Effect of ConA on PtdInsP$_2$. The initial decrease in PtdInsP$_2$ is attributed to the rapid breakdown of the lipid in response to ConA that precedes the stimulation of net PtdInsP$_2$ synthesis.

PK-C activation. It also follows that ConA cannot activate PK-C solely through the Ca signal it generates.

Similar analysis of the early metabolic responses suggests that ConA does not cause significant activation of PK-C, for example through released diacylglycerol. ConA stimulates the uridine response, but the response is blocked by prolonged depletion of extracellular Ca^{2+} (Fig. 8). If PK-C activation by ConA depends upon extracellular Ca^{2+}, then other responses common to ConA and TPA that depend on PK-C activation should also be dependent on $[Ca]_o$ for ConA. In contrast to this, the stimulation of glycolysis, assayed as lactate production, is independent of $[Ca]_o$ for both ConA and TPA, and the response to the two mitogens together is approximately additive, even at TPA concentrations that cause the maximal response to TPA alone (Fig. 8). This demonstrates that the stimulation of glycolysis by ConA is very unlikely to depend significantly on PK-C activation. Taken together with similar indirect analyses of other responses (e.g. PtdIns synthesis), any activation of PK-C by ConA is estimated to be less than 10 % of the maximal activation achieved by TPA. We have been unable to detect an increase in diacylglycerol in mouse thymocytes stimulated by ConA, although there is a substantial amount of the lipid in quiescent cells, which may obscure the release from $PtdInsP_2$ if this is in a small specific pool. It remains to be demonstrated, however, that a transient increase in diacylglycerol can cause sustained activation of PK-C, and it is therefore necessary to develop a direct assay for PK-C activation in thymocytes by identifying a unique protein substrate for the enzyme, as found in fibroblasts (Rozengurt, Rodriguez-Pena & Smith, 1983*a*).

The most significant general conclusion from these studies is that when the Ca signal and any PK-C activation generated by ConA are mimicked by appropriate combinations of A23187 and TPA, the early responses to the opportunistic mitogens are small compared with the responses to ConA. We conclude that the lectin must generate an unidentified signal, in addition to the Ca signal and any PK-C activation, to account for both the early responses and for subsequent mitogenic stimulation. The same conclusion was reached recently for another mitogenic lectin, PHA, based on an analysis of mitogenic stimulation of T cells. PHA was required in addition to A23187 with TPA for progression to DNA synthesis when the T cells were depleted of macrophages (Kaibuchi, Takai & Nishizuka, 1985).

c-myc *gene activation*

The c-*myc* and c-*fos* proto-oncogenes are the cellular counterparts of the transforming genes of the avian myelocytomatosis and FBJ murine osteosarcoma viruses (Roussel *et al.* 1979; Curran & Teich, 1982). It has been reported recently that mitogens activate both the c-*myc* and c-*fos* genes within 1 h in various cells in G_0 (Kelly *et al.* 1983; Campisi *et al.* 1984; Greenberg & Ziff, 1984; Muller, Bravo, Burckhardt & Curran, 1984; Kruijer, Cooper, Hunter & Verma, 1984). The amounts of c-*myc* mRNA and protein remain elevated in proliferating normal cells and are not thought to be regulated by the cell cycle, other than by entry into G_0 (Thompson, Challoner, Neiman & Groudine, 1985; Hann, Thompson & Eisenman,

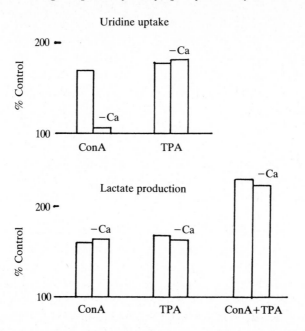

Fig. 8. Effect of $[Ca]_o$ on the stimulation of uridine uptake and glycolysis by ConA and TPA in quiescent fibroblasts. Uridine uptake was assayed as $[^3H]$uridine incorporation into RNA and glycolysis was assayed as lactate production; 2 h after the addition of $1 \cdot 0 \, \mu g \, ml^{-1}$ of ConA or 10 nM-TPA to thymocytes in normal medium ($[Ca]_o = 0 \cdot 43$ mM) or with added EGTA ($[Ca]_o = 120$ nM) at 37°C.

1985). The c-*myc* and c-*fos* proteins are located in the nucleus, but their functions have not been defined (Abrams, Rohrschneider & Eisenman, 1982; Curran, Miller, Zokas & Verma, 1984). Nevertheless, these specific gene activations establish an early link between the primary signal and nuclear activation and are promising candidates for obligatory secondary responses early in G_1.

In quiescent fibroblasts the c-*fos* gene is induced more rapidly than c-*myc* (within 10–20 min) in response to TPA and to some of the growth factors that act on these cells (e.g. platelet-derived growth factor; PDGF), but the expression is transient (Greenberg & Ziff, 1984; Muller *et al.* 1984; Kruijer *et al.* 1984). In T and B lymphocytes the c-*myc* gene has been shown to be activated by ConA and lipopolysaccharide, respectively (Kelly *et al.* 1983; Moore *et al.* 1985). The two key questions that concern us are whether the genes are activated by ionic signals in the normal mitogenic pathway, and whether the expression of these genes is obligatory for subsequent DNA synthesis.

We have found that each of the mitogens, ConA, TPA and A23187, activated the c-*myc* gene in mouse thymocytes within 15–30 min and the amount of c-*myc* mRNA in the cells increased for at least 4 h (Fig. 9). No c-*myc* mRNA could be detected in unstimulated thymocytes, and the increase in c-*myc* mRNA in response to ConA is estimated to be at least 10-fold, consistent with the previous report of Kelly *et al.* (1983). If the amount of c-*myc* mRNA in cells stimulated with an optimal mitogenic concentration of ConA (approximately $0.80\,\mu\mathrm{g\,ml}^{-1}$; see Fig. 10A) for 2 h is normalized as 100 %, the relative amounts in cells treated under the same conditions with optimal co-mitogenic concentrations of either TPA (10 nM) or A23187 (25–50 nM) were 280+57 % and 187+37 % (S.E.M.; $n = 9$). Thus, although neither TPA nor A23187 is mitogenic by itself, each caused an increase in c-*myc* mRNA comparable with that stimulated by ConA. Optimal co-mitogenic concentrations of TPA with A23187 caused larger increases in DNA synthesis than ConA alone (Fig. 10B) and were synergistic in stimulating c-*myc* mRNA by 850+186 % ($n = 6$) (Fig. 11). Taken together, the data show that while mitogenic stimulation by the three mitogens is always associated with activation of the c-*myc* gene, this activation is not sufficient to cause commitment to DNA synthesis, which must also depend on and be modulated by other responses.

Activation of the c-*fos* gene was transient and clearly preceded the increase in c-*myc* mRNA as found previously in fibroblasts. An increase in c-*fos* mRNA was stimulated by A23187 within 7·5 min and the amount of mRNA increased by at least 100-fold within 20 min before declining over 3 h. The maximal amount of c-*fos* mRNA was estimated to be at least 30-fold greater than that of c-*myc* in the cells. The c-*fos* gene was also activated by ConA and TPA with transient time-courses similar to that shown for A23187. It is assumed that each of the mitogens causes expression of the c-*myc* and c-*fos* genes as the proteins, although this has not been demonstrated in thymocytes (but see Persson *et al.* 1984).

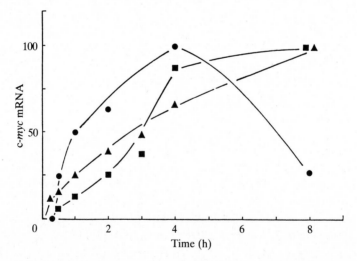

Fig. 9. Activation of the c-*myc* gene by mitogens in thymocytes. Quiescent cells were incubated with ConA (■, $0.8\,\mu\mathrm{g\,ml}^{-1}$); TPA (▲, 10 nM) or A23187 (●, 50 nM) before the RNA was isolated, fractionated on agarose gels and the c-*myc* mRNA assayed as described by Moore *et al.* (1985). Data shown are the relative intensities of the c-*myc* mRNA bands determined by scanning densitometry, normalized to 100 for the maximal response to each mitogen over the time indicated (8 h). N.B., in the text, the amount of c-*myc* mRNA stimulated by TPA and/or A23187 is compared with the response to ConA at a fixed time (2 h) in the same experiment: the data are the means of several such experiments.

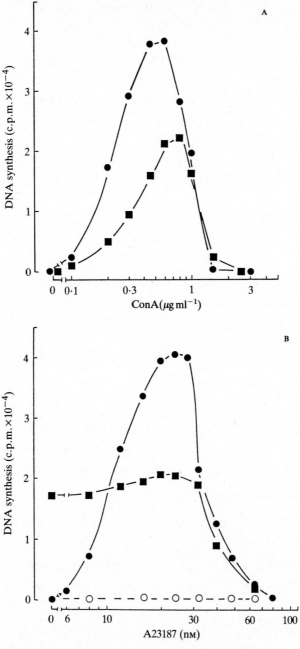

Fig. 10. Mitogenic stimulation of thymocytes. Stimulation was assayed by [³H]-thymidine incorporation into DNA at 42–48 h after addition of mitogens as described by Moore *et al.* (1982). A. Mitogenic stimulation by ConA in the presence (●———●) or absence (■———■) of 10 nM-TPA. B. Stimulation by A23187 either alone (○----○) or with 0·8 μg ml⁻¹ ConA (■———■) or with 10 nM-TPA (●———●).

Table 1. *Ionic and cyclic nucleotide modulation of* c-myc *mRNA in thymocytes*

	Relative amount of c-*myc* mRNA			
Mitogen	$-Ca^{2+}$	$-Na^{+}$	+5 mM-8-Br cAMP	+5 mM-8-Br cGMP
ConA	53 ± 12 (6)	141 ± 31 (6)	11 ± 4 (3)	73 (2)
TPA	112 ± 28 (4)	156 ± 15 (4)	41 (2)	n.d.
A23187	<5 (4)	<5 (2)	n.d.	n.d.

The cells were incubated in a simplified salts solution with or without 5 mM-8-Br cAMP or 5 mM-8-Br cGMP. The low-Ca^{2+} medium was adjusted to 120 nM by addition of EGTA. The Na^{+}-free medium contained 130 mM-choline chloride instead of NaCl. The cells were incubated for 2 h with or without mitogen at 37°C in air before assay of c-*myc* (Moore *et al.* 1985). The data are expressed relative to the response to each mitogen in simplified salts solution (100%). n.d., not determined.

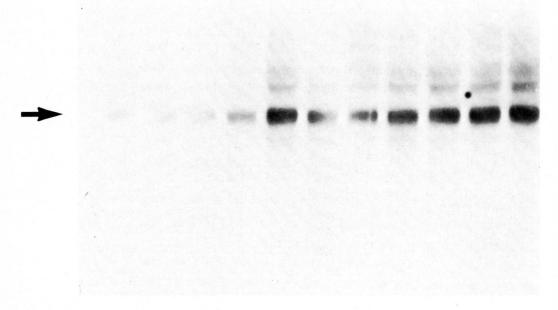

[A23187] 0 30 50 80   0 15 30 40 50 60 80 100
nM

+ 10nM–TPA

Fig. 11. Northern blot analysis of c-*myc* activation in cells stimulated for 2 h with the concentrations of A23187 indicated with or without 10 nM-TPA. The major c-*myc* band is arrowed.

The effects of modulating the Ca and pH signals on the expression of the c-*myc* gene were examined separately. The pH$_i$ response to each of the three mitogens is abolished by reduction of [Na]$_o$ to less than 1 mM. However, replacing NaCl in the medium with choline chloride did not block the increase in c-*myc* mRNA stimulated by either ConA or TPA although the response to A23187 was blocked by the removal of Na^+ (Table 1). We conclude, therefore, that the pH_i increase is not necessary for the activation of the c-*myc* gene in the normal mitogenic pathway.

The activation of the c-*myc* gene by mitogenic concentrations of A23187, which raise $[Ca]_i$ from 100 nM in resting cells to approximately 500–750 nM, was abolished completely by addition of EGTA to reduce $[Ca]_o$ to 120 nM (Table 1). Under these conditions A23187 causes only a small, transient increase in $[Ca]_i$ that is attributable to the release of Ca^{2+} from intracellular stores. The failure of A23187 to activate the c-*myc* gene in the absence of extracellular Ca^{2+} is not due to any inhibitory effect of the ionophore under these conditions, since the combination of TPA with A23187 in the presence of EGTA stimulated a large increase in c-*myc* mRNA, comparable with that induced by TPA alone. The activation of the c-*myc* gene by the ionophore is therefore directly correlated with the increase in $[Ca]_i$. In marked contrast to A23187, the increase in c-*myc* mRNA in mouse thymocytes stimulated by TPA occurs by a mechanism independent of $[Ca]_o$ (Table 1) or of any increase in $[Ca]_i$.

ConA activates the c-*myc* gene at low $[Ca]_o$ (120 nM), although to a reduced extent (approximately 50%, see Table 1), and a $[Ca]_o$ greater than approximately 100 μM was necessary for maximal stimulation of the c-*myc* mRNA increase. We have noted earlier that ConA causes only a transient increase in $[Ca]_i$ at low $[Ca]_o$ and the data clearly imply that activation of the c-*myc* gene in response to ConA is not solely a consequence of the increased $[Ca]_i$. There may be a contribution from the Ca signal in normal medium, by analogy with the $[Ca]_o$-dependent activation by A23187, but as emphasized earlier, the removal of Ca^{2+} from the medium may inhibit the activation of the c-*myc* gene by ConA through mechanisms other than the decrease in the $[Ca]_i$ response.

Agents that elevate cyclic AMP (e.g. prostaglandin E_1), or 8-Br cAMP, inhibit substantially the Ca signal in response to ConA. In contrast, 8-Br cGMP has no effect. Neither cyclic nucleotide analogue (5 mM) increased c-*myc* mRNA levels by itself, but 8-Br cAMP was a potent inhibitor of the response to ConA, whereas 8-Br cGMP was relatively ineffective (Table 1). However, the inhibition of c-*myc* expression by 8-Br cAMP cannot be attributed specifically to its effect on the $[Ca]_i$ response to ConA since 8-Br cAMP also antagonized the activation of the c-*myc* gene by TPA (Table 1), which is $[Ca]_i$-independent. The data do not therefore establish a causal relationship between the Ca signal and c-*myc* activation in response to ConA. However, it may be noted that 8-Br cAMP has consistent effects on the early responses to ConA (Ca signal, $InsP_3$ and c-*myc* expression) and on subsequent DNA synthesis, which are all substantially inhibited, whereas 8-Br cGMP has little effect.

We conclude that expression of the c-*myc* gene as mRNA can occur without any increase in pH_i in thymocytes. The gene can be activated by at least two distinct pathways: by A23187 through elevation of $[Ca]_i$, independently of PK-C activation; or by TPA through PK-C, independent of $[Ca]_i$. The response to ConA is, at most, only partially dependent on the increase in $[Ca]_i$, and it remains to be demonstrated

Ca signal

pH$_i$ increase

PI synthesis

PIP$_2$ synthesis

IP$_3$ release

c-*myc* activation

Uridine uptake

Glycolysis

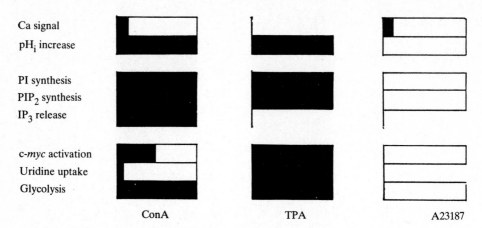

ConA   TPA   A23187

Fig. 12. Early response pattern analysis in thymocytes. Open bars indicate the normalized response in standard medium ([Ca]$_o$ = 0·43 mM) and filled bars are the relative response in low-Ca medium ([Ca]$_o$ = 120 nM).

by direct assay whether any activation of PK-C by ConA is a significant component of the [Ca]$_i$-independent activation of the c-*myc* gene by this mitogen.

The ionic dependence of the early responses

The effects of [Na]$_o$ and [Ca]$_o$ have been determined for all of the early responses examined. None of the responses shown in Fig. 12 were found to depend on [Na]$_o$ except for the pH$_i$ signal, although depolarizing media with Na$^+$ replaced by K$^+$ caused greatly enhanced glycolysis in quiescent cells. Low [Na]$_o$ inhibited responses to A23187 (e.g. c-*myc*, see Table 1) but this may be due to toxic effects of the ionophore under these conditions. We conclude that none of the secondary responses to ConA or TPA shown in Fig. 12 depends on the pH$_i$ signal.

Data for the dependence of early responses on [Ca]$_o$ are summarized in simplified form in Fig. 12, where the relative responses in normal medium ([Ca]$_o$ = 0·43 mM) and in low [Ca]$_o$ (120 nM) are compared. The main conclusions from the pattern of early responses to each mitogen and the effects of [Ca]$_o$ are summarized.

(1) The responses in normal medium confirm that the primary signals from each mitogen must be different since there are qualitative differences in the pattern of secondary responses.

(2) Neither TPA nor A23187 cross-activate the primary response to each other or to ConA. Thus neither of the opportunistic mitogens causes the full repertoire of responses to ConA, nor do they abolish responses to ConA that they do not activate themselves.

(3) All of the responses to TPA are independent of [Ca]$_o$, consistent with activation of PK-C independent of [Ca]$_i$ as the primary response to this mitogen.

(4) All of the responses to A23187 are abolished at low [Ca]$_o$, although there is a residual transient [Ca]$_i$ increase from Ca^{2+} in the intracellular pool. This is

consistent with the $[Ca]_i$ increase in normal medium acting as the primary response to A23187.

(5) The responses to ConA show varied dependence on $[Ca]_o$ confirming that the $[Ca]_i$ increase cannot be the primary response to ConA. The mechanisms by which the $[Ca]_o$-dependent and $[Ca]_o$-independent responses are generated remain to be established, but they cannot be assumed to be derived solely from the $[Ca]_i$ response and activation of PK-C, respectively.

Taken together with the more detailed analyses presented earlier, this summary illustrates the information that can be derived from a comparative analysis of the early responses to the mitogens and the effect of ionic perturbations on them. It provides some insight into the mechanisms through which the responses may be coupled, and evidence for extensive but incomplete convergence of the early secondary responses to mitogens that activate different primary signals.

Are the early ionic responses obligatory for subsequent DNA synthesis?

It was noted earlier that it is difficult to establish whether early responses are obligatory for the mitogenic pathway because completely specific inhibitors of the various responses are not generally available. Mitogenic stimulation by any co-mitogenic combination of the three T-cell mitogens is preceded by an early pH_i increase. Although this response is not obligatory for any of the other early responses examined, it is possible that the pH_i increase may be necessary for progression through the later stages of G_1. Alternatively, the pH_i response may fall entirely within the permissive pH_i range for the mitogenic pathway to proceed from G_0 to S phase, and may therefore be a consequential response rather than obligatory. Many agents that inhibit Na^+/H^+ exchange (e.g. amiloride) are not specific and their inhibitory effects on DNA synthesis do not therefore have diagnostic value in determining the role of the pH_i response (Besterman, Tyrey, Cragoe & Cuatrecasas, 1984; Davis & Czech, 1985). However, more specific analogues of amiloride have been reported that block Na^+/H^+ exchange in fibroblasts, without inhibiting DNA synthesis (Besterman *et al.* 1984).

Mitogenic stimulation by the T-cell mitogens is preceded by an early Ca signal, although it may be noted that optimal co-mitogenic combinations of ConA with TPA (Fig. 10A) generate only a very small early Ca signal. The partial dependence of c-*myc* activation on $[Ca]_o$ in response to ConA is at present the most suggestive evidence that a $[Ca]_i$ increase may normally be required for progression through G_1 in the pathway activated by the T-cell receptor. The stimulated uptake of uridine into the cells, although almost entirely dependent on $[Ca]_o$, is not an obligatory response since progression to DNA synthesis will occur in media without uridine (A. N. Corps, unpublished data).

The inability of A23187 to cause mitogenic stimulation by itself in mouse thymocytes clearly indicates that the early generation of both $[Ca]_i$ and pH_i responses in the cells is not a sufficient stimulus for these cells to reach S phase. The co-mitogenic action of A23187 with TPA is consistent with a mitogenic pathway activated by the two primary signals from the combined mitogens. A23187 with TPA activates all of the early responses that have been reported for ConA, except for the breakdown of PtdInsP$_2$ to release InsP$_3$ (Taylor *et al.* 1984). This additional response to ConA is consistent with the inference drawn from the early response pattern analysis that there is an unidentified signal derived from the primary response to ConA that is an obligatory component of the mitogenic pathway for ConA. Whether that signal is also activated by A23187 with TPA as a secondary response to their primary signals is of key interest in defining the convergence of the mitogenic pathways. However, the recent observations from Nishizuka's laboratory suggest that the unidentified signal from the lectin is not activated by TPA with A23187. The requirement for PHA (assumed to act through the T-cell receptor) in addition to TPA and A23187 to cause mitogenic stimulation of mouse thymocytes depleted of accessory cells strongly suggests that PHA (or ConA) generates an independent obligatory response that is not generated by TPA with A23187 (Kaibuchi *et al.* 1985). Although this inference is clear, the point remains to be demonstrated unambiguously, since the obligatory responses to the mitogens might conceivably differ, depending on the presence or absence of accessory cells (mono-cytes and macrophages). It should also be noted that although the primary signal for ConA is clearly shown by the degradation of PtdInsP$_2$ to be distinct from the responses to TPA with A23187, there is no evidence to indicate whether that particular response is related to the unidentified mitogenic signal from ConA.

   In human and pig T lymphocytes, A23187 is able to cause mitogenic stimulation by itself (Maino, Green & Crumpton, 1974; Luckasen, White & Kersey, 1974). This raises the unresolved question as to whether the coupling between the mitogenic pathways activated in the T cells by A23187 or TPA is a function of T-cell species, or whether it is the requirement for activation of the accessory cells that is species-dependent. There is no evidence at present to suggest that the requirement for interleukin-2 (Gillis & Mizel, 1981) and the expression of its receptors on T cells (Robb, Munck & Smith, 1981) can be by-passed in cell preparations depleted of accessory cells if the T cells are to proceed to S phase. It is clear however that analysis of the later stages in G_1 in T cells will be facilitated by the use of pure T-cell preparations.

   There are at least two mechanisms by which the transient component of the $[Ca]_i$ response may be involved in cell activation. The rise in $[Ca]_i$ may modulate the activity of Ca^{2+}-sensitive enzymes (e.g. via calmodulin). Although this may trigger subsequent responses, the requirement for persistent interaction of ConA with the T cells suggests that the transient component of the $[Ca]_i$ increase may be incidental to the release of Ca^{2+} from the endoplasmic reticulum to allow this organelle to function in the activated cells, possibly to allow the synthesis of membrane proteins. If, for example, the synthesis of the receptors for interleukin-2 was inhibited in endo-plasmic reticulum loaded with Ca^{2+}, it would be expected that the Ca^{2+} concen-tration inside the endoplasmic reticulum would have to remain low throughout G_1 until expression of the interleukin-2 receptor was complete. This may in turn require continuous activation of the T-cell receptor to give sustained release of InsP$_3$ isomers and thereby maintain the endoplasmic reticulum at a low Ca^{2+} content. Whether the persistent $[Ca]_i$ increase in ConA-stimulated cells, which declines over 24 h back to the level in quiescent cells, is obligatory for progression through G_1 is unclear. There are indications that the cells become independent of extracellular Ca^{2+} after the interleukin-2 receptor has been expressed (Weiss *et al.* 1984*a*), and it is possible to speculate that both the expulsion of Ca^{2+} from the endoplasmic reticulum to give the transient $[Ca]_i$ response, and the persistent increase in $[Ca]_i$, are necessary to transit the early Ca^{2+}-sensitive phase of G_1.

This hypothesis clearly predicts that no cell could progress to S phase without clearing the Ca^{2+} load from the endoplasmic reticulum and maintaining it in the low Ca^{2+} state for an appropriate period to permit essential membrane protein synthesis. The fibroblast system can provide a critical test of this hypothesis.

COMPARISON BETWEEN EARLY RESPONSES IN 3T3 FIBROBLASTS AND THYMOCYTES

Mitogens acting on 3T3 fibroblasts

A wide range of agents act as mitogens on 3T3 fibroblasts, many of which have been identified and their secondary responses characterized by the work of Rozengurt and colleagues (reviewed by Rozengurt *et al.* 1983*b*). Here we analyse the relationship between mitogenic stimulation and early responses to seven mitogens that each generate distinct primary signals judged by their patterns of secondary responses (Table 2). Three of the mitogens, platelet-derived growth factor (PDGF), epidermal growth factor (EGF) and insulin, have receptors with intrinsic tyrosine kinase activity that is stimulated by binding the growth factor (Cohen, Carpenter & King, 1980; Ushiro & Cohen, 1980; Ek, Westermark, Wasteson & Heldin, 1982; Cooper *et al.* 1982; Kasuga *et al.* 1982; van Obberghen *et al.* 1983). Nevertheless, their patterns of secondary responses are quite distinct and it remains to be demonstrated formally that activation of the tyrosine kinases is responsible for any or all of the secondary responses. Agents that elevate cyclic AMP or mimic its action are co-mitogenic for 3T3 fibroblasts (Pruss & Herschman, 1979; Rozengurt, Legg, Strang & Courtney-Luck, 1979), presumably through the activation of cyclic AMP-dependent kinases, whereas two of the other mitogens, vasopressin (VP) and prostaglandin $F_{2\alpha}$ ($PGF_{2\alpha}$) generate unidentified primary responses. TPA acts as an opportunistic mitogen on fibroblasts (Dicker & Rozengurt, 1978), but the mitogenic activity of A23187 on these cells is elusive. The Ca^{2+} ionophore generates many of the early secondary responses observed with other mitogens but rarely stimulates significant DNA synthesis as a co-mitogen acting on early-passage fibroblasts. However, in cells that have been passaged for several weeks in culture, A23187 is frequently a potent co-mitogen with insulin. We do not understand the cellular basis of this variability and further analysis of A23187 responses in relation to DNA synthesis has been omitted.

Substantial stimulation of DNA synthesis in quiescent fibroblasts usually requires the simultaneous action of two mitogens or growth factors on the cells. We find that all co-mitogenic combinations that give a synergistic effect on subsequent DNA

Table 2. *The pattern of early responses to some of the mitogens acting on 3T3 fibroblasts*

Mitogen	Early response								
	Tyrosine kinase	PK-C	PK-A	$[Ca]_i$	pH_i	Uridine	Glycolysis	c-myc	c-fos
PDGF	+ (1)	+ (15)	+ (17)	+ (10)	+ (11)	N.D.	N.D.	+ (6), (12)	+ (12)
EGF	+ (1)	− (15)	− (13)	+ (8)	+ (5)	+ (14)	+ (2)	− (6)/(+) (12)	(+) (12)
Insulin	N.D.	− (15)	− (13)	− (8)	(+) (5)	+ (16)	+ (2)	− (6)	N.D.
VP	N.D.	+ (15)	− (13)	+ (8)	+ (5)	+ (9)	+ (9)	N.D.	N.D.
PGF$_{2\alpha}$	N.D.	N.D.	N.D.	+ (8)	+ (5)	− (9)	+ (9)	N.D.	N.D.
[cAMP] increase or 8-Br cAMP	N.D.	− (15)	+	− (5)	(+) (5)	− (9)	+ (9)	N.D.	N.D.
TPA	N.D.	+ (15)	− (13)	− (8)	+ (5)	+ (4)	+ (3)	+ (6)	+ (7)

(+) denotes a response less than 50 % of the maximal response to other mitogens.

(1) Cooper et al. (1982); (2) Diamond, Legg, Schneider & Rozengurt (1978); (3) Diamond, O'Brien & Baird (1980); (4) Dicker & Rozengurt (1979); (5) Hesketh et al. (1985); (6) Kelly et al. (1983); (7) Kruijer et al. (1984); (8) Morris et al. (1984); (9) Morris (1984); (10) Moolenaar, Tertolen & de Laat (1984); (11) Moolenaar et al. (1983); (12) Muller et al. (1984); (13) Rozengurt et al. (1981); (14) Rozengurt, Mierzejewski & Wigglesworth (1978); (15) Rozengurt et al. (1983a); (16) Rozengurt, Stroobant, Waterfield, Deuel & Keehan (1983b).

Table 3. *Sequential [Ca]ᵢ and [pH]ᵢ responses to combinations of mitogens and subsequent DNA synthesis*

Mitogen combination A+B	$[Ca]_i$ response A+B; B+A		pH_i response A+B; B+A		DNA synthesis
PDGF+EGF	++	++	++	++	−
+insulin	+−	−+	+(+)	(+)+	+
+VP	+−	+−	++	+(+)	−
+PGF$_{2\alpha}$	+−	++	++	++	−
+8-Br cAMP	+−	−+	+−	(+)−	−
+TPA	+−	−+	++	++	−
EGF+insulin	+−	−+	+(+)	(+)+	+
+VP	++	++	++	++	+
+PGF$_{2\alpha}$	++	++	++	++	−
+8-Br cAMP	+−	−+	+(+)	(+)+	+
+TPA	+−	−−	++	++	+
Insulin+VP	−+	+−	(+)+	+(+)	+
+PGF$_{2\alpha}$	−+	+−	(+)+	+(+)	+
+8-Br cAMP	−−	−−	(+)(+)	(+)(+)	+
+TPA	−−	−−	(+)+	+(+)	+
VP+PGF$_{2\alpha}$	++	++	++	++	−
+8-Br cAMP	+−	−+	+(+)	(+)+	−
+TPA	+−	−+	++	+−	−
PGF$_{2\alpha}$+8-Br cAMP	+−	−+	+(+)	(+)+	−
+TPA	+−	−+	++	++	−
8-Br cAMP+TPA	−−	−−	(+)+	+(+)	+

To assay the sequential ionic signals, the mitogens were added sequentially at 4 to 10-min intervals (A+B or B+A denotes sequence). A sequence of ++ for the $[Ca]_i$ or pH responses implies that well-defined responses were observed for both mitogens (it does not imply that the response to the second mitogen was strictly independent of the response to the first mitogen). (+) denotes the small pH_i responses to insulin or 8-Br cAMP (see text). For DNA synthesis, + denotes that [^{3}H]thymidine incorporation in response to the combination of mitogens was at least fivefold greater than the response to mitogens separately and is referred to as synergistic combination in the text.

synthesis initiate the mitogenic pathway from the time that both agents are present: delaying the addition of either agent causes a corresponding delay in DNA synthesis. This observation is not consistent with the proposal that mitogens are either 'competence' factors that initiate the mitogenic pathway or 'progression' factors that drive the cells through the later stages of G_1. The only exceptions to the requirement for two co-mitogens for DNA synthesis are PDGF and bombesin, which have been reported to cause significant DNA synthesis by themselves (Rozengurt *et al.* 1983; Rozengurt & Sinnett-Smith, 1983). In our hands, mitogenic stimulation by these agents is variable and less than 30% of the maximal stimulation achieved with co-mitogenic mixtures of EGF with insulin. Furthermore, the response to either mitogen is enhanced synergistically by the co-addition of insulin. The co-mitogenic effects of the mitogens are summarized in Table 3 and discussed in relation to the ionic signals and other responses below.

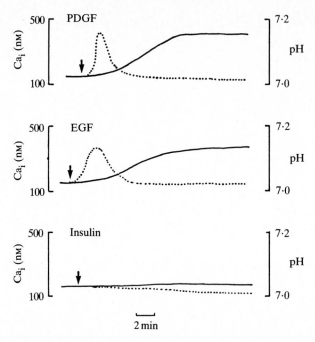

Fig. 13. Ionic signals from growth factors acting on 3T3 fibroblasts. The cells were loaded with quin 2 or BCECF, and $[Ca]_i$ and pH_i were assayed as described by Hesketh *et al.* (1985). The time-courses are compared for the Ca signal ($\cdots\cdots$) and the pH_i response (——).

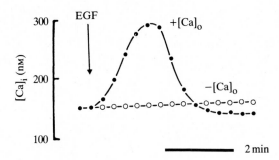

Fig. 14. Effect of $[Ca]_o$ on the $[Ca]_i$ response to EGF in 3T3 fibroblasts.

Ionic signals and PtdInsP₂ metabolism

The Ca and pH responses for the three growth factors PDGF, EGF and insulin are shown in Fig. 13. Both PDGF and EGF generate a transient Ca signal followed by a sustained increase in pH_i, whereas the responses to insulin are marginal, with no increase in $[Ca]_i$ and any increase in pH_i limited to less than 0·05. The primary response from the insulin receptor is therefore clearly distinguished from the primary responses to PDGF or EGF. Furthermore, although the ionic responses to PDGF or EGF are similar, the mechanisms by which they are generated are quite distinct: the EGF response is entirely dependent on $[Ca]_o$ (Fig. 14), whereas the response to

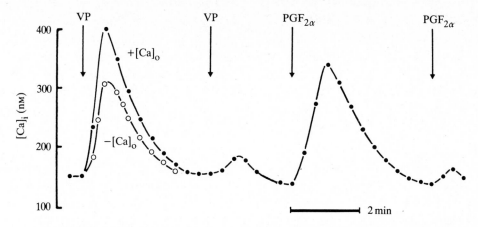

Fig. 15. Sequential Ca signals in response to VP and $PGF_{2\alpha}$. The cells were treated with successive additions of VP ($10\,ng\,ml^{-1}$) and then successive additions of $PGF_{2\alpha}$ ($100\,ng\,ml^{-1}$) as indicated. Also shown is the effect of low Ca medium ($[Ca]_o = 120\,nM$).

PDGF is $[Ca]_o$-independent. The two growth factors may also differ in their effects on $PtdInsP_2$ metabolism in that EGF does not cause $PtdInsP_2$ breakdown (J. D. H. Morris and J. P. Moore, unpublished data) but PDGF causes an increase in inositol phosphates (Berridge *et al.* 1984). Of the other mitogens in Table 3 only VP and $PGF_{2\alpha}$ increase inositol phosphates and generate both Ca and pH_i responses. TPA causes a substantial pH_i increase of approximately 0·20 without a prior Ca signal, similar to its action on thymocytes, and 8-Br cyclic AMP stimulates only a marginal increase in pH_i. A23187 generates both a Ca signal and a slower pH_i response and both signals are dependent on $[Ca]_o$ as in thymocytes.

An interesting feature of the ionic signals in response to the sequential addition of mitogens is the interactions between the mitogens that they imply. The data in Table 3 show that PDGF blocks the subsequent $[Ca]_i$ response to VP and $PGF_{2\alpha}$, but not to EGF. VP blocks only the subsequent $[Ca]_i$ response to PDGF (i.e. there is a reciprocal blocking mechanism), whereas $PGF_{2\alpha}$ or EGF do not affect the subsequent $[Ca]_i$ responses to any of the other three mitogens which give Ca signals.

The data suggest that if VP and $PGF_{2\alpha}$ both release intracellular Ca^{2+} via $InsP_3$, then neither mitogen depletes the Ca^{2+} pool sufficiently to inhibit the response to the other (Fig. 15). The inability of either VP or PDGF to block the subsequent $[Ca]_i$ response to EGF is also of interest. Both VP and PDGF activate PK-C assayed indirectly by the phosphorylation in intact cells of an 80 kDa polypeptide (Rozengurt *et al.* 1983a), and TPA blocks the $[Ca]_i$ response to EGF. This suggests that the activation of PK-C by VP or PDGF is small compared with that achieved by TPA. This is also indicated by the additional increases in pH_i to TPA when added after VP or PDGF: if PK-C were activated fully by either mitogen there would be no additional pH_i response to TPA. In fact, only a small part of the pH_i response to PDGF alone can be due to activation of PK-C, since an additional pH_i increase is stimulated by PDGF after the response to TPA. Uncoupling of $PtdInsP_2$ breakdown from PK-C activation is implied by the responses to PGF_2. Activation of PK-C by TPA stimulates an increase in uridine uptake (Dicker & Rozengurt, 1979), but $PGF_{2\alpha}$ neither causes this uridine response (Jimenez de Asua *et al.* 1982) nor blocks the uridine response to TPA or VP (J. D. H. Morris, unpublished data). The implication is that any activation of PK-C by $PGF_{2\alpha}$ is below the threshold detectable by the indirect uridine uptake assay.

Ionic signals and DNA synthesis

The data in Table 3 compare systematically the ionic signals and DNA synthesis in response to all of the pair combinations of the seven mitogens. Of the 21 combinations, 10 stimulate DNA synthesis synergistically to an extent significantly greater than the sum of the responses to the ligands separately, including all six combinations with insulin, which appears to be the most generally effective co-mitogen. (Single mitogens usually give less than 10% of the [^{3}H]thymidine incorporation obtained with optimal combinations of mitogens such as EGF+insulin.) Of the 10 synergistic mitogenic combinations, six stimulate both Ca and pH_i responses, and the other four a pH_i response only. For one of these combinations (insulin + 8-Br cAMP) the total pH_i increase was small (<0·08) and less than that for the other synergistic combinations (0·20+0·03). The mitogenic combinations that give a pH_i increase only as an early ionic response can provide a critical test for the hypothesis that it is necessary to clear Ca^{2+} from the endoplasmic reticulum for progression to S phase. This Ca^{2+} release need not necessarily occur in an early burst, and assays of the releasable Ca^{2+} load in the endoplasmic reticulum throughout G_1 will be required to resolve this point.

All of the 11 mitogenic combinations that do not cause synergistic stimulation of DNA synthesis generate both ionic responses, clearly indicating that these signals do not constitute a sufficient stimulus for progression of a substantial proportion of the cells to S phase. A further point is that neither EGF nor insulin (together, the most potent co-mitogenic combination for 3T3 cells) activates c-*myc* and c-*fos* expression substantially (Kelly *et al.* 1983; Greenberg & Ziff, 1984; Kruijer *et al.* 1984; Muller *et al.* 1984). The effect of these mitogens in combination on the activation of the c-*myc* and c-*fos* genes through G_1 should define limits to which their expression may be necessary for subsequent DNA synthesis.

This work was supported by grants from the SERC and MRC to J.C.M., and from the MRC to J.P.M. We thank Dr Enrique Rozengurt for early passage 3T3 fibroblasts, Dr Georgina Nemecek for highly purified PDGF, Dr Robin Irvine for phosphorylated phosphatidylinositols and inositol (1,4,5)-trisphosphate and Dr John Todd for preparation of c-*myc* and v-*fos* probes.

REFERENCES

ABRAMS, H. D., ROHRSCHNEIDER, L. R. & EISENMAN, R. N. (1982). Nuclear location of the putative transforming protein of Avian Myelocytomatosis Virus. *Cell* **29**, 427–439.

BERRIDGE, M. J. (1984). Oncogenes, inositol lipids and cellular proliferation. *Biotechnology* **7**, 541–546.

BERRIDGE, M. J. & IRVINE, R. F. (1984). Inositol trisphosphate, a novel second messenger in cellular signal transduction. *Nature, Lond.* **312**, 315–321.

BERRIDGE, M. J., HESLOP, J. P., IRVINE, R. F. & BROWN, K. D. (1984). Inositol trisphosphate formation and calcium mobilisation in Swiss 3T3 cells in response to platelet-derived growth factor. *Biochem. J.* **222**, 195–201.

BESTERMAN, J. M., TYREY, S. J., CRAGOE, E. J. & CUATRECASAS, P. (1984). Inhibition of epidermal growth factor-induced mitogenesis by amiloride and an analog: Evidence against a requirement for Na^+/H^+ exchange. *Proc. natn. Acad. Sci. U.S.A.* **81**, 6762–6766.

BEVERLEY, P. C. L. & CALLARD, R. E. (1981). Distinctive functional characteristics of human T lymphocytes defined by E rosetting or a monoclonal anti-T cell antibody. *Eur. J. Immun.* **11**, 329–334.

CAMPISI, J., GRAY, H. E., PARDEE, A. B., DEAN, M. & SONENSHEIN, G. E. (1984). Cell cycle control of c-*myc* but not c-*ras* expression is lost following chemical transformation. *Cell* **36**, 241–247.

CASTAGNA, M., TAKAI, Y., KAIBUCHI, K., SANO, K., KIKKAWA, U. & NISHIZUKA, Y. (1982). Direct activation of calcium activated, phospholipid dependent protein kinase by tumour promoting phorbol esters. *J. biol. Chem.* **257**, 7847–7851.

COCKCROFT, S. & GOMPERTS, B. D. (1985). Role of guanine nucleotide binding protein in the activation of polyphosphoinositide phosphodiesterase. *Nature, Lond.* **314**, 534–536.

COHEN, S., CARPENTER, G. & KING, L. (1980). Epidermal growth factor–receptor–protein kinase interactions. *J. biol. Chem.* **255**, 4834–4842.

COOPER, J. A., BOWEN-POPE, D. F., RAINES, E., ROSS, R. & HUNTER, T. (1982). Similar effects of platelet-derived growth factor on the phosphorylation of tyrosine in cellular proteins. *Cell* **31**, 263–273.

CURRAN, T., MILLER, A. D., ZOKAS, L. & VERMA, I. M. (1984). Viral and cellular fos proteins: A comparative analysis. *Cell* **36**, 259–268.

CURRAN, T. & TEICH, N. M. (1982). Candidate product of the FBJ murine osteosarcoma virus oncogene: Characterisation of a 55,000-Dalton phosphoprotein. *J. Virol.* **42**, 114–122.

DAVIS, R. J. & CZECH, M. P. (1985). Amiloride directly inhibits growth factor receptor tyrosine kinase. *J. biol. Chem.* **260**, 2543–2551.

DIAMOND, I., LEGG, A., SCHNEIDER, J. A. & ROZENGURT, E. (1978). Glycolysis in quiescent cultures of 3T3 cells. *J. biol. Chem.* **253**, 866–871.

DIAMOND, L., O'BRIEN, T. G. & BAIRD, W. M. (1980). Tumour promotors and the mechanism of tumour promotion. *Adv. Cancer Res.* **32**, 1–80.

DICKER, P. & ROZENGURT, E. (1978). Stimulation of DNA synthesis by tumour promoter and pure mitogenic factors. *Nature, Lond.* **276**, 723–726.

DICKER, P. & ROZENGURT, E. (1979). Synergistic stimulation of early events and DNA synthesis by phorbol esters, polypeptides, growth factors, and retinoids in cultured fibroblasts. *J. supramolec. Struct.* **11**, 79–93.

EK, B., WESTERMARK, B., WASTESON, A. & HELDIN, C-H. (1982). Stimulation of tyrosine-specific phosphorylation by platelet-derived growth factor. *Nature, Lond.* **295**, 419–420.

GILLIS, S. & MIZEL, S. B. (1981). T-cell lymphoma model for the anlaysis of interleukin 1-mediated T-cell activation. *Proc. natn. Acad. Sci. U.S.A.* **78**, 1133–1137.

GREENBERG, M. E. & ZIFF, E. B. (1984). Stimulation of 3T3 cells induces transcription of the c-*fos* proto-oncogene. *Nature, Lond.* **311**, 433–437.

HANN, S. R., THOMPSON, C. B. & EISENMAN, R. N. (1985). C-*myc* oncogene protein synthesis is independent of the cell cycle in human and avian cells. *Nature, Lond.* **314**, 366–369.

HASLAM, R. J. & DAVIDSON, M. M. L. (1984). Guanine nucleotides decrease the free Ca^{++} required for secretion of serotonin from permeabilized blood platelets. Evidence of a role for a GTP-binding protein in platelet activation. *FEBS Lett.* **174**, 90–95.

HESKETH, T. R., BAVETTA, S., SMITH, G. A. & METCALFE, J. C. (1983a). Duration of the calcium signal in the mitogenic stimulation of thymocytes. *Biochem. J.* **214**, 575–579.

HESKETH, T. R., MOORE, J. P., MORRIS, J. D. H., TAYLOR, M. V., ROGERS, J., SMITH, G. A. & METCALFE, J. C. (1985). A common sequence of calcium and pH signals in the mitogenic stimulation of eukaryotic cells. *Nature, Lond.* **313**, 481–484.

HESKETH, T. R., SMITH, G. A., MOORE, J. P., TAYLOR, M. V. & METCALFE, J. C. (1983b). Free cytoplasmic calcium concentration and the mitogenic stimulation of lymphocytes. *J. biol. Chem.* **258**, 4876–4882.

HUME, D. A. & WEIDEMANN, M. J. (1980). *Mitogenic Lymphocyte Transformation, Res. Monographs Immun.*, vol. 2. Amsterdam: Elsevier/North-Holland.

ITOH, H., OKAJIMA, F. & UI, M. (1984). Conversion of adrenergic mechanism from an α- to a β-type during primary culture of rat hepatocytes. *J. biol. Chem.* **259**, 15 464–15 473.

IRVINE, R. F., BROWN, K. D. & BERRIDGE, M. J. (1984a). Specificity of inositol trisphosphate-induced calcium release from permeabilized Swiss-mouse 3T3 cells. *Biochem. J.* **221**, 269–272.

IRVINE, R. F., LETCHER, A. J., LANDER, D. J. & DOWNES, C. P. (1984b). Inositol trisphosphates in carbachol-stimulated rat parotid glands. *Biochem. J.* **223**, 237–243.

JIMINEZ DE ASUA, L., OTTO, A. M., ODILE-ULRICH, O., MARTIN-PEREZ, J. & THOMAS, G. (1982). *Prostaglandins and Cancer*. pp. 309–331. New York: Alan R. Liss Inc.

KAIBUCHI, K., TAKAI, Y. & NISHIZUKA, Y. (1985). Protein kinase C and calcium ion in mitogenic response of macrophage-depleted human peripheral lymphocytes. *J. biol. Chem.* **260**, 1366–1369.

KASUGA, M., ZICK, Y., BLITHE, D. L., CRETTAZ, M. & KAHN, R. C. (1982). Insulin stimulates tyrosine phosphorylation of the insulin receptor in a cell-free system. *Nature, Lond.* **298**, 667–669.

KELLY, K., COCHRAN, B. H., STILES, C. D. & LEDER, P. (1983). Cell specific regulation of the c-*myc* gene by lymphocyte mitogens and platelet-derived growth factor. *Cell* **35**, 603–610.

KISHIMOTO, A., TAKAI, Y., MORI, T., KIKKAWA, U. & NISHIZUKA, Y. (1980). Activation of calcium and phospholipid-dependent protein kinase by diacylglycerol, its possible relation to PI turnover. *J. biol. Chem.* **255**, 2273–2276.

KRUIJER, W., COOPER, J. A., HUNTER, T. & VERMA, I. M. (1984). Platelet-derived growth factor induces rapid but transient expression of the c-*fos* gene and protein. *Nature, Lond.* **312**, 711–716.

LUCKASEN, J. R., WHITE, J. G. & KERSEY, J. H. (1974). Mitogenic properties of a calcium ionophore, A23187. *Proc. natn. Acad. Sci. U.S.A.* **71**, 5088–5090.

MAINO, V. C., GREEN, M. N. & CRUMPTON, M. J. (1974). The role of calcium ions in initiating transformation of lymphocytes. *Nature, Lond.* **251**, 324–327.

McCLAIN, D. A. & EDELMAN, G. M. (1976). Analysis of the stimulation–inhibition paradox exhibited by lymphocytes exposed to concanavalin A. *J. exp. Med.* **144**, 1494–1508.

MOOLENAAR, W. H., TERTOOLEN, L. G. J. & DE LAAT, S. W. (1984). Growth factors immediately raise cytoplasmic free Ca^{2+} in human fibroblasts. *J. biol. Chem.* **259**, 8066–8069.

MOOLENAAR, W. H., TSIEN, R. Y., VAN DER SAAG, P. T. & DE LAAT, S. W. (1983). Na^+/H^+ exchange and cytoplasmic pH in the action of growth factors in human fibroblasts. *Nature, Lond.* **304**, 645–648.

MOORE, J. P., JOHANNSSON, A., HESKETH, T. R., SMITH, G. A. & METCALFE, J. C. (1984). Calcium signals and phospholipid methylation in eukaryotic cells. *Biochem. J.* **221**, 675–684.

MOORE, J. P., SMITH, G. A., HESKETH, T. R. & METCALFE, J. C. (1982). Early increases in phospholipid methylation are not necessary for the mitogenic stimulation of lymphocytes. *J. biol. Chem.* **257**, 8183–8189.

MOORE, J. P., SMITH, G. A., HESKETH, T. R. & METCALFE, J. C. (1983). Large effects of preparative techniques on lymphocyte cyclic AMP content. *Biochem. J.* **216**, 207–213.

MOORE, J. P., TODD, J., HESKETH, T. R. & METCALFE, J. C. (1985). C-*myc* gene activation, ionic signals and DNA synthesis in thymocytes. *J. biol. Chem.* (in press).

MORRIS, J. D. H. (1984). Biochemical events in the mitogenic stimulation of 3T3 fibroblasts. Ph. D thesis, University of Cambridge.

MORRIS, J. D. H., METCALFE, J. C., SMITH, G. A., HESKETH, T. R. & TAYLOR. M. V. (1984). Some mitogens cause rapid increases in free calcium in fibroblasts. *FEBS Lett.* **169**, 189–193.

MULLER, R., BRAVO, R., BURCKHARDT, J. & CURRAN, T. (1984). Induction of c-*fos* gene and protein by growth factors precedes activation of c-*myc*. *Nature, Lond.* **312**, 716–720.

NASH, A. A. & LING, N. R. (1976). Persistence of anti-immunoglobulin on the lymphocyte membrane. *Nature, Lond.* **264**, 255–256.

NISHIZUKA, Y. (1984). The role of protein kinase C in cell surface signal transduction and tumour promotion. *Nature, Lond.* **308**, 693–698.

O'FLYNN, K., LINCH, D. C. & TATHAM, P. E. R. (1984). The effect of mitogenic lectins and monoclonal antibodies on intracellular free calcium in human T-lymphocytes. *Biochem. J.* **219**, 661–666.

PERSSON, H., HENNIGHAVREN, I., TAUB, R., DE GRADO, W. & LEDER, P. (1984). Antibodies to human c-*myc* oncogene product: Evidence of an evolutionarily conserved protein induced during cell proliferation. *Science* **225**, 687–693.

POZZAN, T., ARSLAN, P., TSIEN, R. Y. & RINK, T. J. (1982). Anti-immunoglobin, cytoplasmic free calcium, and capping in B lymphocytes. *J. Cell Biol.* **94**, 335–340.

POZZAN, T., CORPS, A. N., HESKETH, T. R. & METCALFE, J. C. (1981). Mitogenic stimulation and the redistribution of concanavalin A receptors on lymphocytes. *Expl Cell Res.* **134**, 399–408.

PRUSS, R. M. & HERSCHMAN, H. R. (1979). Cholera toxin stimulates division of 3T3 cells. *J. cell. Physiol.* **98**, 469–474.

REEVES, J. P. (1977). 3-*O*-Methylglucose transport by rat thymocyte subpopulations. *J. cell. Physiol.* **92**, 309–319.

ROBB, R. J., MUNCK, A. & SMITH, K. A. (1981). T cell growth factor receptors, quantitation specificity and biological relevance. *J. exp. Med.* **154**, 1455–1474.

ROUSSEL, M., SAULE, S., LAGROU, C., ROMMENS, C., BEUG, H., GRAF, T. & STEHELIN, D. (1979). Three new types of viral oncogene of cellular origin specific for haematopoietic cell transformation. *Nature, Lond.* **281**, 452–455.

ROZENGURT, E., LEGG, A., STRANG, G. & COURTNEY-LUCK, N. (1981). Cyclic AMP: A mitogenic signal for Swiss 3T3 cells. *Proc. natn. Acad. Sci. U.S.A.* **78**, 4392–4396.

ROZENGURT, E., MIERZEJEWSKI, K. & WIGGLESWORTH, N. (1978). Uridine transport and phosphorylation in mouse cells in culture: Effect of growth-promoting factors, cell-cycle transit and oncogenic transformations. *J. cell. Physiol.* **97**, 241–252.

ROZENGURT, E., RODRIGUEZ-PENA, M. & SMITH, K. A. (1983a). Phorbol esters, phospholipase C, and growth factors rapidly stimulate the phosphorylation of a M_r 80,000 protein in intact quiescent 3T3 cells. *Proc. natn. Acad. Sci. U.S.A.* **80**, 7244–7248.

ROZENGURT, E. & SINNET-SMITH, J. (1983). Bombesin stimulation of DNA synthesis and cell division in cultures of Swiss 3T3 cells. *Proc. natn. Acad. Sci. U.S.A.* **80**, 2936–2940.

ROZENGURT, E., STROOBANT, P., WATERFIELD, M. D., DEUEL, T. F. & KEEHAN, M. (1983b). Platelet-derived growth factor elicits cyclic AMP accumulation in Swiss 3T3 cells. Role of prostaglandin production. *Cell* **34**, 265–272.

SAMELSON, L. E., HARFORD, J., SCHWARTZ, R. H. & KLAUSNER, R. D. (1985). A 20-kDa protein associated with the murine T-cell antigen receptor is phosphorylated in response to activation by antigen or concanavalin A. *Proc. natn. Acad. Sci. U.S.A.* **82**, 1969–1973.

TAKAI, Y., KISHIMOTO, A., IWASA, Y., KAWAHARA, Y., MORI, T. & NISHIZUKA, Y. (1979). Calcium-dependent activation of a multifunctional protein kinase by membrane phospholipids. *J. biol. Chem.* **254**, 3692–3695.

TAYLOR, M. V., METCALFE, J. C., HESKETH, T. R., SMITH, G. A. & MOORE, J. P. (1984). Mitogens increase phosphorylation of phosphoinositides in thymocytes. *Nature, Lond.* **312**, 462–465.

THIYAGARAJAH, P. & LIM, S. C. (1984). Phosphatidylinositol 4,5-bisphosphate stimulates paratoid endoplasmic reticulum ($Ca^{++} + Mg^{++}$)-ATPase. *Biochem. Int.* **9**, 625–630.

THOMPSON, C. B., CHALLONER, P. B., NEIMAN, P. E. & GROUDINE, M. (1985). Levels of c-*myc* oncogene mRNA are invariant throughout the cell cycle. *Nature, Lond.* **314**, 363–366.

TSIEN, R. Y., POZZAN, T. & RINK, T. J. (1982). T-cell mitogens cause early changes in cytoplasmic free Ca^{2+} and membrane potential in lymphocytes. *Nature, Lond.* **295**, 68–71.

USHIRO, H. & COHEN, S. (1980). Identification of phosphotyrosine as a product of epidermal growth factor-activated protein kinase in A-431 cell membranes. *J. biol. Chem.* **255**, 8363–8365.

VAN OBBERGHEN, E., ROSSI, B., KOWALSKI, A., GAZZANO, H. & PONZIO, G. (1983). Receptor-mediated phosphorylation of the hepatic insulin receptor: evidence that the M_r 95,000 receptor subunit is its own kinase. *Proc. natn. Acad. Sci. U.S.A.* **80**, 945–949.

WANG, T., SHEPPARD, J. R. & FOKER, J. E. (1976). Rise and fall of cyclic AMP required for onset of lymphocyte DNA synthesis. *Science* **201**, 155–157.

WEISS, A., IMBODEN, J., SHOBACH, D. & STOBO, J. (1984b). Role of T3 surface molecules in human T-cell activation: T3-dependent activation results in an increase in cytoplasmic free calcium. *Proc. natn. Acad. Sci. U.S.A.* **81**, 4169.

WEISS, M. J., DALEY, J. F., HODGDON, J. C. & REINHERZ, E. L. (1984a). Calcium dependency of antigen-specific (T_3-T_1) and alternative (T_{11}) pathways of human T-cell activation. *Proc. natn. Acad. Sci. U.S.A.* **81**, 6836–6840.

WHITAKER, M. J. & STEINHARDT, R. A. (1982). Ionic regulation of egg activation. *Q. Rev. Biophys.* **15**, 593–666.

J. Cell Sci. Suppl. 3, 229–242 (1985)
Printed in Great Britain © The Company of Biologists Limited 1985

SYNERGISTIC SIGNALS IN MITOGENESIS: ROLE OF ION FLUXES, CYCLIC NUCLEOTIDES AND PROTEIN KINASE C IN SWISS 3T3 CELLS

ENRIQUE ROZENGURT* AND STANLEY A. MENDOZA†

Imperial Cancer Research Fund, PO Box 123, Lincoln's Inn Fields, London WC2A 3PX, U.K.

SUMMARY

A fundamental feature in the action of most mitogenic agents when added to quiescent cells in serum-free medium is that they exhibit striking synergistic effects when applied in specific combinations. A tenable hypothesis of growth control must provide a cogent explanation for the molecular mechanisms underlying this complex pattern of synergistic effects. To gain an understanding of the mechanisms by which these synergistic effects arise, we studied the initial cellular responses associated with the interaction of mitogenic factors and hormones with the cell, including changes in cation fluxes, cyclic nucleotides and cellular phosphoproteins. In this paper, some of our recent results on the early signals and responses elicited by multiple growth-promoting agents in quiescent cultures of Swiss 3T3 cells will be summarized. On the basis of the emerging information, we propose a framework that integrates early events and synergistic effects in a unified hypothesis of growth control.

INTRODUCTION

Quiescent cultures of the mouse 3T3 cell line, which has provided a useful model system for many studies on growth control, can be stimulated to reinitiate DNA synthesis and cell division by a variety of exogenous agents added to serum-free medium (Rozengurt, 1980, 1983). The mitogenic effectiveness of a variety of growth-promoting agents in Swiss 3T3 cells is summarized in Table 1. The striking feature is that only platelet-derived growth factor (PDGF) and related factors (Dicker, Pohjanpelto, Pettican & Rozengurt, 1981; Lopez-Rivas, Stroobant, Waterfield & Rozengurt, 1984) and the peptides of the bombesin family (Rozengurt & Sinnett-Smith, 1983) can induce DNA synthesis when added in the absence of other growth factors. In contrast, the remaining array of agents only stimulate initiation of DNA synthesis in Swiss 3T3 cells when added in specific combinations (see Rozengurt, 1980, 1983, 1985, for references). The pattern of these striking and specific synergistic interactions among defined growth-promoting molecules has critical mechanistic implications which must be explained by any hypothesis of growth control.

In an effort to gain an understanding of the mechanism by which these synergistic effects arise, our attention has been focused on the initial cellular responses

---

*To whom correspondence should be addressed.

† Permanent address: Department of Pediatrics, School of Medicine, University of California, San Diego, La Jolla, CA 92093, U.S.A.

Table 1. *Synergistic effects among mitogenic agents added to quiescent cultures of Swiss 3T3 cells maintained in serum-free medium*

	PDGF/FDGF	Bombesin	Vasopressin	Phorbol esters, teleocidin	Diacylglycerol (OAG)	Insulin	EGF	Cholera toxin	PGE$_1$	NECA	cAMP analogues	Anti-microtubule agents
PDGF/FDGF		++++	+++	+++	+++	++++	++++	+++	+++	+++	+++	++++
Bombesin			++	++	++	++++	+++	++	++	++	++	+++
Vasopressin				−	−	+++	++	++	++	++	++	−
Phorbol esters teleocidin					−	+++	++	++	++	++	++	−
Diacylglycerol (OAG)						+++	++	++	++	++	++	−
Insulin							+++	+++	+++	+++	+++	−
EGF								+	+	+	+	−
Cholera toxin									−	−	−	−
PGE$_1$										−	−	−
NECA											−	−
cAMP analogues												−
Antimicrotubule												

The original data can be obtained from references given in the text and in recent reviews (Rozengurt, 1980, 1983, 1984, 1985; Rozengurt *et al.* 1985). ++++, +++, ++, +, −, represent 80–100%, 60–80%, 20–40%, 5–20% and <2% of the maximal response ($[^3H]$thymidine incorporation into acid-precipitable material) achieved. In some cases, a factor causes a shift in the dose-response of another factor but does not alter the maximal response; for clarity these situations are not described in the Table. They can be found in the original publications.

associated with the interaction of mitogenic factors and hormones with the cell, in the expectation that the early events will provide useful clues to primary regulatory mechanisms. Some of our recent studies on the early signals and cellular responses elicited by growth factors in quiescent cultures of Swiss 3T3 cells will be briefly described. Subsequently, a framework that integrates these early events and the synergistic effects among mitogens in a unified hypothesis of growth control will be discussed.

IONIC RESPONSES ELICITED BY GROWTH FACTORS IN QUIESCENT CELLS

Monovalent ion fluxes

One of the earliest responses elicited by the addition of serum and growth factors to quiescent cultures of 3T3 fibroblasts is an increase in the activity of the ouabain-sensitive Na^+/K^+ pump (Rozengurt & Heppel, 1975). The activity of the Na^+/K^+ pump in intact fibroblasts is limited and regulated by cytosolic Na^+ (Smith & Rozengurt, 1978; Mendoza, Wigglesworth, Pohjanpelto & Rozengurt, 1980). Since serum and growth factors stimulate the entry of Na^+ into quiescent cells (Rozengurt, 1981a), it has been suggested that one of the initial events that occurs in fibroblastic cells that have been stimulated to proliferate is an increase in the rate of Na^+ influx into the cells with a subsequent stimulation of Na^+/K^+ pump activity.

Because the translocation of Na^+ across the plasma membrane of 3T3 cells is mediated, at least in part, by an amiloride-sensitive Na^+/H^+ antiport system, the stimulation of Na^+ entry by mitogenic agents leads to an increase in intracellular pH (Schuldiner & Rozengurt, 1982; Burns & Rozengurt, 1983, 1984; Lopez-Rivas *et al*. 1984). The fact that mitogenic stimulation leads to cytoplasmic alkalinization has been substantiated using different combinations of growth factors, cell types and techniques (see Rozengurt & Mendoza, 1986, for review). The ability of growth factors to induce cytoplasmic alkalinization suggests that the activation of Na^+/H^+ exchange is a primary effect of the mitogens rather than a secondary mechanism for the extrusion of protons resulting from a growth factor-induced acceleration of cellular metabolism. It is plausible that the stimulation of a proliferative response in quiescent cells depends on maintaining intracellular pH (Mendoza & Rozengurt, unpublished) and K^+ concentration (Lopez-Rivas, Adelberg & Rozengurt, 1982; Burns & Rozengurt, 1984) above critical threshold levels. As discussed recently (Rozengurt & Mendoza, 1986), these threshold concentrations may play a permissive and, or, a triggering role in mitogenesis.

Divalent cation fluxes

Addition of serum to quiescent cultures of Swiss 3T3 cells and other fibroblast cell lines induces a marked increase in the rate of Ca^{2+} efflux from radioactively labelled cells (Lopez-Rivas & Rozengurt, 1983). This is one of the earliest events (15 s) that takes place in quiescent fibroblasts after stimulation with serum. Changes in Ca^{2+} distribution are not restricted to serum-stimulated cells since vasopressin stimulates the efflux of $^{45}Ca^{2+}$ from $^{45}Ca^{2+}$-loaded cells (Lopez-Rivas & Rozengurt, 1984). Likewise, homogeneous preparations of PDGF cause a marked and dose-dependent (half-maximal effect at 6×10^{-10}M) stimulation of $^{45}Ca^{2+}$ efflux from quiescent 3T3 cells (Lopez-Rivas & Rozengurt, unpublished results). Since the stimulation of $^{45}Ca^{2+}$ efflux can be elicited in the absence of extracellular Ca^{2+}, it seems that serum, vasopressin and PDGF release this cation from an intracellular store(s). Indeed, vasopressin caused a rapid 50% decrease in the total Ca^{2+} content of the cells (Lopez-Rivas & Rozengurt, 1984). This release would be likely to increase the concentration of cytosolic Ca^{2+} [Ca_i^{2+}] which, in turn, leads to Ca^{2+} efflux mediated by the plasma membrane Ca^{2+}-ATPase. This interpretation was confirmed by the finding that vasopressin, PDGF and bombesin caused a rapid two- to three-fold increase in [Ca_i^{2+}] measured by changes in the fluorescence of quin-2. The increases in [Ca_i^{2+}] were brief, with [Ca_i^{2+}] falling to or near basal levels in 3–5 min (Fig. 1). This Ca^{2+} mobilization may be mediated by inositol 1,4,5-triphosphate (IP_3), which has been implicated as a second messenger in the action of ligands that induce receptor-mediated inositol lipid turnover and Ca^{2+} release (Berridge & Irvine, 1984). Interestingly, neither insulin nor EGF induces Ca^{2+} mobilization or increases [Ca_i^{2+}] in 3T3 cells (Lopez-Rivas & Rozengurt, 1983; Fig. 1).

ACTIVATION OF PROTEIN KINASE C IN INTACT CELLS

Ca^{2+}-sensitive, phospholipid-dependent protein kinase (protein kinase C), which is stimulated by unsaturated diacylglycerol and serves as a major receptor for the tumour promoters of the phorbol ester family (see Nishizuka, 1984, for a review), may play an important role in signalling a variety of cellular responses including cell growth. Accordingly, it is of importance to determine which mitogenic agents lead to activation of protein kinase C in intact, quiescent cells. Recently, we reported that a rapid increase in the phosphorylation of a $M_r = 80\,000$ cellular protein (termed 80k) reflects the activation of protein kinase C in intact cells (see Rozengurt, Rodriguez-Pena & Sinnett-Smith, 1985, for a review). For example, addition of biologically active phorbol esters stimulates a rapid (15 s) phosphorylation of this protein (Rozengurt, Rodriguez-Pena & Smith, 1983c). Further, phospholipid breakdown induced by exogenous phospholipase C, which generates diacylglycerol, causes a rapid enhancement of 80k phosphorylation (Rozengurt et al. 1983c). In addition, the synthetic diacylglycerol 1-oleoyl-2-acetyl-glycerol (OAG) stimulates the phosphorylation of the same 80k phosphoprotein in quiescent 3T3 cells (Rozengurt, Rodriguez-Pena, Coombs & Sinnett-Smith, 1984; Rozengurt et al. 1985). Finally, prolonged pretreatment of the cells with phorbol ester, which leads to a marked decrease in the number of specific phorobol ester binding sites (Collins & Rozengurt, 1982a,b, 1984) and to disappearance of protein kinase C activity measured in cell-free preparations (Rodriguez-Pena & Rozengurt, 1984; Rozengurt et al. 1985), prevents the increase in 80k phosphorylation elicited by all these diverse agents: namely, phorbol esters, phospholipase C and OAG (Rozengurt et al. 1983c, 1984; Rodriguez-Pena & Rozengurt, 1985). Although the 80k phosphoprotein has not been

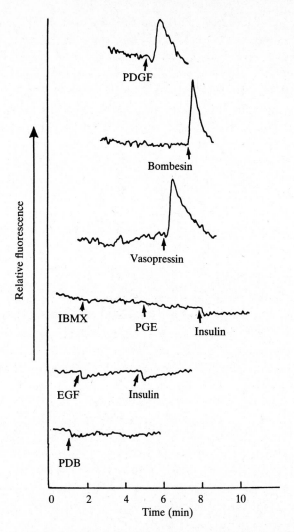

Fig. 1. For these studies, Swiss 3T3 cells were grown on Cytodex 2 beads suspended in Dulbecco's modified Eagle's medium (DMEM) containing 10% foetal bovine serum (FBS) and constantly stirred at 37°C. After 6 days, the medium was changed to DMEM containing 1% FBS. Twenty-four hours later, beads were washed with DMEM and then incubated for 45 min in this medium containing 15 μM-quin-2 acetoxymethylester. They were then washed three times with a solution containing 140 mM-NaCl, 5 mM-KCl, 0·9 mM-MgCl$_2$, 1·8 mM-CaCl$_2$, 25 mM-glucose, amino acids at the same concentration as in DMEM, 20 mM-Hepes and sufficient Tris to bring the pH to 7·2. After washing, beads containing about 2·5 mg of cell protein were suspended and stirred at 37°C in a 10 mm cuvette. Fluorescence was followed in a Perkin-Elmer LS-5 fluorimeter (excitation wavelength, 339 nm; emission wavelength, 492 nm). At the times indicated by the arrows, vasopressin (20 ng ml^{-1}), bombesin (10 ng ml^{-1}), PDGF (1·25 μg ml^{-1}), phorbol dibutyrate (200 ng ml^{-1}), insulin (10 μg ml^{-1}), EGF (15 ng ml^{-1}), PGE$_1$ (250 ng ml^{-1}) or methylisobutyl-xanthine (IBMX) (50 μM) was added. Control (Ca$_i$$^{2+}$) was 158±8 nM ($n = 55$).

identified, the detection of changes in its phosphorylation provides a useful approach to determine which mitogenic agents activate protein kinase C in intact cells.

In the course of studies designed to determine which extracellular agents activate protein kinase C in intact fibroblastic cells we found that addition of PDGF (Rozengurt *et al.* 1983*c*; Rodriguez-Pena & Rozengurt, 1985) or of mitogenic peptides such as vasopressin and bombesin (Zachary & Rozengurt, unpublished data) causes a potent and extremely rapid increase in the phosphorylation of the 80k cellular protein. Hence, protein kinase C might not only mediate the multiple biological actions of phorbol esters but it may play a fundamental role in effecting the proliferative response elicited by serum, and certain growth factors and mitogenic hormones in their target cells. Substantial evidence for this hypothesis has come from recent studies demonstrating that the synthetic diacylglycerol OAG, which stimulates protein kinase C in intact cells, is a potent mitogen for Swiss 3T3 cells acting as a phorbol ester agonist (Rozengurt *et al.* 1984).

Protein kinase C and ion fluxes

In view of the possibility that protein kinase C may play a role in the control of the proliferative response, it was important to define whether activation of protein kinase C elicits monovalent ionic fluxes in quiescent 3T3 cells. Recently, Vara, Schneider & Rozengurt (1985) reported that addition of OAG or PBt$_2$ to Swiss 3T3 cells rapidly enhances amiloride-sensitive Na$^+$/H$^+$ antiport activity leading to stimulation of the Na$^+$/K$^+$ pump. Previously, Dicker & Rozengurt (1981*a*) showed that the biologically active phorbol esters PBt$_2$ and TPA stimulated Na$^+$ entry and Na$^+$/K$^+$ pump in 3T3 cells; the half-maximal concentration of PBt$_2$ needed to elicit this early effect was virtually identical to the K_d of [^{3}H]PBt$_2$ for its high-affinity receptor in these cells (Collins & Rozengurt, 1982*a*). In addition, the activators of protein kinase C, e.g. PBt$_2$ and OAG, increase pH$_i$ (Burns & Rozengurt, 1983; Vara *et al.* 1985). In contrast, phorbol esters fail to stimulate ^{45}Ca^{2+} efflux from quiescent 3T3 cells preloaded with this isotope (unpublished results) or to increase (Ca$_i^{2+}$) as judged by changes in the fluorescence of quin-2 (Fig. 1).

Prolonged pretreatment with PBt$_2$ markedly reduces the stimulation of ^{86}Rb$^+$ or ^{22}Na$^+$ uptake by subsequent addition of either PBt$_2$ or OAG. This loss of ionic responses to OAG and PBt$_2$ seen in 3T3 cells with a greatly reduced number of high-affinity phorbol ester receptors and activity of protein kinase C (see above) implicates this phosphotransferase system in the stimulation of monvalent cation fluxes. These findings strongly suggest that activation of protein kinase C leads, either directly or indirectly, to increased activity of the Na$^+$/H$^+$ antiport system, which in turn promotes Na$^+$ influx, increases pH$_i$ and stimulates the Na$^+$/K$^+$ pump activity. In this manner, protein kinase C may represent an important molecular link in the sequence of events triggered by the binding of growth-promoting factors to their respective receptors. However, since the activity of the Na$^+$/H$^+$ antiport is also enhanced by some mitogens that do not activate protein kinase C in 3T3 cells (e.g. EGF + insulin), it is likely that these ionic fluxes may be regulated by mechanisms not involving protein kinase C (Vara & Rozengurt, 1985).

Protein kinase C and transmodulation of EGF receptor

A set of structurally unrelated ligands including phorbol esters, vasopressin, PDGF and FDGF inhibit the binding of $[^{125}I]EGF$ to specific surface receptors in Swiss 3T3 cells and other cell lines (Rozengurt & Collins, 1983). A feature shared by all the inhibitory ligands is that the modulation of EGF binding is rapid in onset and results from a decrease in the apparent affinity of the EGF receptor population for EGF (Rozengurt, Brown & Pettican, 1981*a*; Rozengurt, Collins, Brown & Pettican, 1982; Collins, Sinett-Smith & Rozengurt, 1983). Since the various ligands that inhibit EGF binding interact with sites that are distinct from EGF receptors, the decrease in the affinity of the EGF receptors occurs through an indirect mechanism termed 'transmodulation' (Rozengurt & Collins, 1983). Although the significance of transmodulation as an early response in mitogenesis remains unclear, it is likely that the decreases in apparent affinity of the EGF receptor induced by various agents could occur by a common mechanism (Rozengurt *et al.* 1982; Collins & Rozengurt, 1983; Rozengurt & Collins, 1983).

Considerable evidence implicates protein kinase C in the transmodulation of the EGF receptor affinity. Recent studies showed that OAG causes a rapid and striking decrease in the apparent affinity of this receptor without changing the total number of sites (Sinnett-Smith & Rozengurt, 1985). Further, the transmodulation induced by OAG or PBt_2 is blocked by greatly reducing protein kinase C by prior treatment of the cells with phorbol esters (Collins & Rozengurt, 1982*a*, 1984; Sinnett-Smith & Rozengurt, 1985). Interestingly, protein kinase C has recently been shown to phosphorylate the EGF receptor of human epidermal carcinoma A431 cells at specific sites (Hunter, Ling & Cooper, 1984). The possibility that the interconversion of EGF receptors from a high-affinity state to a low-affinity one induced in 3T3 cells by phorbol esters, OAG, vasopressin, PDGF and FDGF, results from the covalent modification of the EGF receptor catalysed by protein kinase C, is attractive and warrants further experimental work.

CYCLIC NUCLEOTIDES AND INITIATION OF DNA SYNTHESIS

The role of cyclic nucleotides, cyclic AMP (cAMP) and cyclic GMP, in the control of the proliferative response of quiescent fibroblastic cells has been the subject of a large and controversial amount of literature (Rozengurt, 1981*b*). Recently, we found that increased cellular concentrations of cAMP promoted by cholera toxin (Rozengurt, Legg, Strang & Courtenay-Luck, 1981*b*), adenosine agonists (Rozengurt, 1982*a*), cAMP derivatives (Rozengurt, 1982*b*), prostaglandin E_1 (Rozengurt, Collins & Keehan, 1983*b*) or forskolin act synergistically with other growth-promoting agents to stimulate DNA synthesis in quiescent cultures of 3T3 cells (Table 1; Rozengurt, 1985, for references).

Since a sustained increase in the cellular level of cAMP constitutes a growth-promoting signal for Swiss 3T3 cells, it was important to evaluate whether physiological growth factors added to serum-free medium could alter cAMP metabolism in 3T3 cells. Interestingly, PDGF induced a striking accumulation of cAMP in 3T3 cells incubated in the presence of inhibitors of cyclic nucleotide degradation (Rozengurt *et al.* 1983*a*). In contrast, other growth-promoting factors including EGF, vasopressin, phorbol esters, OAG or insulin failed to increase the level of cAMP (Rozengurt *et al.* 1983*a*; unpublished results). This accumulation of cAMP elicited by PDGF was mediated by increased synthesis of E-type prostaglandins, which in turn stimulated cAMP synthesis through their own receptor (Rozengurt *et al.* 1983*b*). These findings suggest that cAMP may be one of the signals utilized by PDGF to stimulate initiation of cell proliferation in Swiss 3T3 cells.

Cyclic AMP and other early responses

Increased cellular level of cAMP stimulates the Na^+/K^+ pump mediated uptake of $^{86}Rb^+$ into Swiss 3T3 (Paris & Rozengurt, 1982). In contrast to the stimulation of the Na/K^+ pump within 1–2 min after the addition of Na^+ flux modulators (serum, PDGF, vasopressin, phorbol esters), the stimulation of ouabain-sensitive $^{86}Rb^+$ uptake by cAMP-elevating agents reached a maximal effect after hours of incubation. Further, increased cAMP failed to augment Na^+ influx into 3T3 cells whereas, under identical conditions, serum markedly increased Na^+ entry into 3T3 cells (Paris & Rozengurt, 1982; Rozengurt & Courtenay-Luck, 1982). These findings suggest that the time-dependent stimulation of Na^+/K^+ pump activity caused by increased cAMP levels contrasts mechanistically with the rapid control of pump activity by other growth factors, which is primarily mediated by increased Na^+ entry into the cells.

In other studies, we found that a rapid increase in cAMP does not activate protein kinase C, stimulate Ca^{2+} mobilization (Fig. 1) or induce transmodulation of EGF receptor affinity (unpublished results). We suggest that cAMP, presumably acting through cAMP-dependent protein kinase, activates a pathway leading to mitogenesis that is clearly separate from that utilized by growth factors and mitogenic factors that enhance Na^+ fluxes, transmodulate EGF receptor and activate protein kinase C. The effect of cAMP on pH_i requires further experimental work. A summary of the early responses elicited by each individual growth-promoting factor is presented in Table 2.

SYNERGISTIC EFFECTS AND EARLY SIGNALS: A UNIFIED FRAMEWORK

As mentioned previously a salient feature in the action of most mitogenic agents when added to quiescent cells in serum-free medium is that they exhibit striking synergistic effects when applied in specific combinations. Indeed, a tenable hypothesis of growth control must provide a cogent explanation for the mechanism(s) underlying this complex pattern of synergistic effects. Inspection of Tables 1 and 2 shows that a group of mitogenic agents, such as the tumour promoters phorbol esters and teleocidin, the synthetic diacylglycerol OAG and the neurohypophyseal hormone vasopressin and its related peptides, elicit a common set of early events: namely, they activate protein kinase C, enhance monovalent ion fluxes and transmodulate the EGF receptor but do not alter the basal level of cAMP. Addition of any

Table 2. *Early response elicited by individual growth promoting factors in Swiss 3T3 cells*

	Na⁺ influx/ increase in pH$_i$	Stimulation Na⁺/K⁺ pump	Ca²⁺ mobilization	EGF receptor transmodulation	80k phosphorylation	Arachidonic acid release	Elevation of cAMP
PDGF/FDGF	+/+	+	+	+	+	+	+
Bombesin	+/+	+	+	+	+	+	+
Vasopressin	+/+	+	+	+	+	−	−
Phorbol esters	+/+	+	−	+	+	−	−
Diacylglycerol	+/+	+	−	+	+	−	−
Insulin	+/+	+	−	−	−	−	−
EGF	−/+	+	−	−	−	−	−
Cholera toxin	−/ND	+	−	−	−	−	+
PGE$_1$	−/ND	+	−	−	−	−	+
NECA	−/ND	+	−	−	−	−	+
cAMP analogues	−/ND	+	−	−	−	+	+
Colchicine	−/−	−	−	−	−	−	−

The responses to each factor are shown. The magnitude of these responses vary but are not indicated. The original data can be obtained from references in the respective sections in the text and from recent reviews (Rozengurt, 1985; Rozengurt & Mendoza, 1986; Rozengurt *et al.* 1985). ND, not determined.

of these agents individually to quiescent 3T3 cells fails to induce a significant mitogenic response. Further, combinations of this class of agents, e.g. vasopressin and phorbol esters (Dicker & Rozengurt, 1980; Collins & Rozengurt, 1984), teleocidin and phorbol esters (Collins & Rozengurt, 1982b), teleocidin and vasopressin (Collins & Rozengurt, 1982b), diacylglycerol and vasopressin (Rozengurt et al. 1984) or even teleocidin, phorbol esters and vasopressin (Collins & Rozengurt, 1982b) and diacylglycerol, phorbol esters and vasopressin (Rozengurt et al. 1984) also failed to induce DNA synthesis. Agents that increase intracellular cyclic AMP, such as PGE_1 (Rozengurt et al. 1983b), the adenosine analogue 5'-N-ethylcarboxamide adenosine (Rozengurt, 1982a), cholera toxin (Rozengurt et al. 1981b) and cyclic AMP derivatives (Rozengurt, 1982b), produce a totally different pattern of early events. These agents do not activate protein kinase C, stimulate Na^+ flux or transmodulate EGF receptors. Furthermore, they fail to stimulate DNA synthesis when added singly or in combination. We suggest that agents sharing a common signalling system fail to act synergistically to stimulate initiation of DNA synthesis.

The critical point is that the agents mentioned above become potent mitogens when added to quiescent 3T3 cells in combinations that elicit the generation of both types of signals and thereby activate cAMP-dependent protein kinase and protein kinase C simultaneously. For example, combinations such as phorbol esters and cholera toxin (Rozengurt et al. 1981b), teleocidin and cholera toxin (Collins & Rozengurt, 1982b), vasopressin and butcAMP (Rozengurt, 1982b), vasopressin and cholera toxin (Collins & Rozengurt, 1983), diacylglycerol and PGE_1 (unpublished result) are mitogenic for Swiss 3T3 cells. Insulin, which can synergize with both types of extracellular factors at supramaximal concentrations, does not act in an identical way to either group of agents. In fact, this hormone does not activate protein kinase C (Rozengurt et al. 1983c), induce Ca^{2+} mobilization (Lopez-Rivas & Rozengurt, 1983; Fig. 1, this paper) or increase the level of cAMP in intact 3T3 cells (Rozengurt et al. 1981b). Any of these synergistic effects can be further enhanced by disruption of the microtubule network, which acts at a later point in G_1 (Friedkin & Rozengurt, 1981; Wang & Rozengurt, 1983). As proposed recently (Rozengurt, 1985), synergistic effects between extracellular factors appear to result from the generation of separate intracellular signals, which act in concert to elicit the complete array of metabolic processes required for a proliferative response. In this manner, complex synergistic effects and early cellular responses can be readily predicted.

In contrast to many mitogenic ligands, PDGF and FDGF stimulate DNA synthesis in the absence of any synergistic factor (Table 1). This has been verified with homogeneous preparations of PDGF (Lopez-Rivas et al. 1984) and poses important questions concerning the model of synergistic signals. Recent findings indicate that PDGF elicits the generation of the early signals that synergistically lead to initiation of DNA synthesis. As indicated in Table 2, PDGF activates protein kinase C, as judged by the increase in the phosphorylation of the 80k phosphoprotein in intact 3T3 cells (Rozengurt et al. 1983a; Rodriguez-Pena & Rozengurt, 1985). The activation of this phosphotransferase system may contribute to the marked transmodulation of EGF receptor affinity (Collins & Rozengurt, 1983) and to the stimulation of Na^+ influx, enhancement of pH_i and increase in Na^+/K^+ pump activity caused by PDGF (Lopez-Rivas *et al.* 1984). PDGF also elicits mobilization of Ca^{2+} from intracellular stores (Fig. 1), an effect that could be mediated by IP_3, a water-soluble product that is released by inositol lipid breakdown catalysed by phospholipase C activation (Berridge & Irvine, 1984). An additional striking response elicited by PDGF is a large release of arachidonic acid, which is converted into stable derivatives such as E-type prostaglandins that, in turn, bind to their own receptor to stimulate cAMP synthesis (Rozengurt *et al.* 1983a,b). In this manner, PDGF stimulates all the early responses discussed in the preceding sections, which is in line with its potency as a complete mitogen (see Table 1).

Recently, we found that the regulatory tetradecapeptide bombesin is a potent mitogen for Swiss 3T3 cells (Rozengurt & Sinnett-Smith, 1983). At low (nanomolar) concentrations, bombesin and its analogues stimulate the initiation of DNA synthesis in a significant fraction (25–40 %) of the 3T3 cell population. This effect is elicited in serum-free medium and in the absence of any added factors. Thus, like PDGF, bombesin provides an interesting model peptide to test further the interpretation of the data summarized in Tables 1 and 2. Our current results show that bombesin binds to a specific receptor and stimulates ion fluxes, activates protein kinase C, transmodulates EGF receptor and alters cAMP metabolism (Zachary & Rozengurt, 1985; Rozengurt & Sinnett-Smith; Mendoza, Schneider & Rozengurt, unpublished data). The possibility that neuropeptides may play a physiological role in the control of target cell growth (e.g. in a trophic manner) deserves further consideration.

The integration of early signals and multiple synergistic effects in a unified framework, as proposed above, has important implications. So, this hypothesis leads to the conclusion that the signals that elicit cell growth are the same as those used by a variety of hormones and neurotransmitters to evoke short-term cellular responses. It is reasonable to question whether the proposition that cells use the same molecular signals for ostensibly different purposes is tenable, in particular since the decision to grow and divide is of paramount importance in the life cycle of a cell. A key feature in the action of most mitogenic signals is that they have to occupy their receptors for

Table 3. *Ca^{2+} mobilization, activation of protein kinase C and, or, elevation of intracellular cAMP are not required for the mitogenic responses elicited by insulin in combination with PBt$_2$, PGE$_1$ or EGF*

Mitogenic combination	Monovalent ion fluxes	Ca^{2+} mobilization	Activation of protein kinase C	Elevation of cAMP	DNA synthesis
Insulin + PBt$_2$	+	−	+	−	+++
Insulin + PGE$_1$	+	−	−	+	+++
Insulin + EGF	+	−	−	−	+++

In contrast, we have not observed stimulation of DNA synthesis by any combination of growth-promoting agents without an increase in monovalent ion flux.

hours before they stimulate increased DNA synthesis in the cell population (Rozengurt, Legg & Pettican, 1979; Dicker & Rozengurt, 1980; 1981b; Rozengurt, 1982a). For example, a large (100-fold) but transient (15 min) increase in the cellular levels of cAMP is not sufficient to act as a mitogenic signal for quiescent 3T3 cells; cAMP concentration must remain elevated for several hours before it acts as a mitogenic stimulus (Rozengurt, 1982a,b). Likewise, a transient exposure to PBt$_2$ or to vasopressin is not sufficient to stimulate mitogenesis (Dicker & Rozengurt, 1981b). When time is taken into consideration, it can be envisaged that the same molecular signals that elicit short-term responses can recruit more functional units if they continue to operate. In this manner, the long-recognized link between cellular function and growth becomes a logical consequence of the use of common signals.

It should be pointed out that there are many aspects of the signalling of fibroblast cell proliferation that remain poorly understood. It is not known whether the tyrosine-directed protein kinase activity associated with the receptors for EGF, PDGF, IGF and insulin plays a role in the elicitation of the early responses and signals that contribute to cell proliferation. In addition, there is only fragmentary knowledge of the mechanism by which such mitogenic signals are translated into the cell nucleus to initiate the program of cell growth. For example, Ca^{2+} mobilization, activation of protein kinase C and elevation of cAMP are not required for eliciting mitogenesis in the presence of insulin (Table 3). Nevertheless, the multiple control of the initiation of DNA synthesis by identifiable intracellular signals (i.e. ion fluxes, diacylglycerol, cAMP and cytoskeletal organization) provides a flexible model for understanding the organization and strategy of the mechanisms whereby extra-cellular agents may regulate animal cell proliferation.

The authors greatly appreciate the expert technical aasistance of Mr James Sinnett-Smith in performing the measurements of cytosolic Ca^{2+} concentration. The manuscript was written during the tenure of an American Cancer Society Eleanor Roosevelt International Cancer Fellowship awarded by the International Union Against Cancer to S.A.M.

REFERENCES

BERRIDGE, M. J. & IRVINE, R. F. (1984). Inositol triphosphate, a novel second messenger in cellular signal transduction. *Nature, Lond.* **312**, 315–321.

BURNS, C. P. & ROZENGURT, E. (1983). Serum, platelet-derived growth factor, vasopressin and phorbol esters increase intracellular pH in Swiss 3T3 cells. *Biochem. biophys. Res. Commun.* **116**, 931–938.

BURNS, C. P. & ROZENGURT, E. (1984). Extracellular Na$^+$ and initiation of DNA synthesis: roles of intracellular pH and K$^+$. *J. Cell Biol.* **98**, 1082–1089.

COLLINS, M. K. L. & ROZENGURT, E. (1982a). Binding of phorbol esters to high-affinity sites on murine fibroblastic cells elicits a mitogenic response. *J. cell. Physiol.* **112**, 42–50.

COLLINS, M. K. L. & ROZENGURT, E. (1982b). Stimulation of DNA synthesis in murine fibroblasts by the tumor promoter teleocidin: Relationship to phorbol esters and vasopressin. *Biochem. biophys. Res. Commun.* **104**, 1159–1166.

COLLINS, M. K. L. & ROZENGURT, E. (1983). Vasopressin induces selective desensitization of its mitogenic response in Swiss 3T3 cells. *Proc. natn. Acad. Sci. U.S.A.* **80**, 1924–1928.

COLLINS, M. K. L. & ROZENGURT, E. (1984). Homologous and heterologous mitogenic desensitization of Swiss 3T3 cells to phorbol esters and vasopressin: Role of receptor and postreceptor steps. *J. cell. Physiol.* **118**, 133–142.

COLLINS, M. K. L., SINNETT-SMITH, J. W. & ROZENGURT, E. (1983). Platelet-derived growth factor treatment decreases the affinity of the epidermal growth factor receptors of Swiss 3T3 cells. *J. biol. Chem.* **258**, 11689–11693.

DICKER, P. & ROZENGURT, E. (1980). Phorbol esters and vasopressin stimulation DNA synthesis by a common mechanism. *Nature, Lond.* **287**, 607–612.

DICKER, P. ROZENGURT, E. (1981*a*). Phorbol ester stimulation of Na influx and Na–K pump activity in Swiss 3T3 cells. *Biochem. biophys. Res. Commun.* **100**, 433–441.

DICKER, P. & ROZENGURT, E. (1981*b*). Stimulation of DNA synthesis by transient exposure of cell cultures to TPA or polypeptide mitogens: Induction of competence or incomplete removal? *J. cell. Physiol.* **109**, 99–109.

DICKER, P., POHJANPELTO, P., PETTICAN, P. & ROZENGURT, E. (1981). Similarities between fibroblast-derived growth factor and platelet-derived growth factor. *Expl Cell Res.* **135**, 221–227.

FRIEDKIN, M. & ROZENGURT, E. (1981). The role of cytoplasmic microtubules in the regulation of the activity of peptide growth factors. In *Advances in Enzyme Regulation*, vol. 19 (ed. G. Weber), pp. 39–59. Oxford: Pergamon Press.

HUNTER, T., LING, N. & COOPER, J. A. (1984). Protein kinase C phosphorylation of the EGF receptor at a threonine residue close to the cytoplasmic face of the plasma membrane. *Nature, Lond.* **311**, 480–483.

LOPEZ-RIVAS, A., ADELBERG, E. A. & ROZENGURT, E. (1982). Intracellular K^+ and the mitogenic response of 3T3 cells to peptide factors in serum-free medium. *Proc. natn. Acad. Sci. U.S.A.* **79**, 6275–6279.

LOPEZ-RIVAS, A. & ROZENGURT, E. (1983). Serum rapidly mobilizes calcium from an intracellular pool in quiescent fibroblastic cells. *Biochem. biophys. Res. Commun.* **114**, 240–247.

LOPEZ-RIVAS, A. & ROZENGURT, E. (1984). Vasopressin rapidly stimulates Ca^{2+} efflux from an intracellular pool in quiescent Swiss 3T3 cells. *Am. J. Physiol.* **247**, C156–C162.

LOPEZ-RIVAS, A., STROOBANT, P., WATERFIELD, M. D. & ROZENGURT, E. (1984). Ionic responses rapidly elicited by porcine platelet-derived growth factor in Swiss 3T3 cells. *EMBO J.* **3**, 939–944.

MENDOZA, S. A., WIGGLESWORTH, M. M., POHJANPELTO, P. & ROZENGURT, E. (1980). Na entry and Na–K pump activity in murine, hamster and human cells. Effect of monensin, serum, platelet extract and viral transformation. *J. cell. Physiol.* **103**, 17–27.

NISHIZUKA, Y. (1984). The role of protein kinase C in cell surface signal transduction and tumour promotion. *Nature, Lond.* **308**, 693–698.

PARIS, S. & ROZENGURT, E. (1982). Cyclic AMP stimulation of Na–K pump activity in quiescent Swiss 3T3 cells. *J. cell. Physiol.* **112**, 273–280.

RODRIGUEZ-PENA, A. & ROZENGURT, E. (1984). Disappearance of Ca^{2+}-sensitive, phospholipid-dependent protein kinase in phorbol ester treated 3T3 cells. *Biochem. biophys. Res. Commun.* **120**, 1053–1059.

RODRIGUEZ-PENA, A. & ROZENGURT, E. (1985). Serum, like phorbol esters, rapidly activates protein kinase C in intact quiescent fibroblasts. *EMBO J.* **4**, 71–76.

ROZENGURT, E. (1980). Stimulation of DNA synthesis in quiescent cultured cells: Exogenous agents, internal signals and early events. *Curr. Top. cell. Reguln* **17**, 59–88.

ROZENGURT, E. (1981*a*). Stimulation of Na influx pump activity and DNA synthesis in quiescent cultured cells. *Adv. Enzyme Reguln* **19**, 61–85.

ROZENGURT, E. (1981*b*). Cyclic AMP: A growth-promoting signal for mouse 3T3 cells. *Adv. Cyclic Nucleotide Res.* **14**, 429–442.

ROZENGURT, E. (1982*a*). Adenosine receptor activation in quiescent Swiss 3T3 cells: Enhancement of cAMP levels, DNA synthesis and cell division. *Expl Cell Res.* **139**, 71–78.

ROZENGURT, E. (1982*b*). Synergistic stimulation of DNA synthesis by cyclic AMP derivations and growth factors in mouse 3T3 cells. *J. cell. Physiol.* **112**, 343–250.

ROZENGURT, E. (1983). Growth factors, cell proliferation and cancer: An overview. *Molec. Biol. Med.* **1**, 169–181.

ROZENGURT, E. (1984). Role of ion fluxes and cyclic nucleotides in signalling mitogenesis. in 3T3 cells. In *Hormones and Cell Regulation*, vol. 8 (ed. J. E. Dumont & J. Nunez), pp. 17–36. Elsevier Science Publications.

ROZENGURT, E. (1985). The mitogenic response of cultured 3T3 cells: Integration of early signals and synergistic effect in a unified framework. *Molec. Aspects Cell Reguln* **4** (in press).

ROZENGURT, E., BROWN, K. D. & PETTICAN, P. (1981a). Vasopressin inhibition of epidermal growth factor binding to cultured mouse cells. *J. biol. Chem.* **256**, 716–722.

ROZENGURT, E. & COLLINS, M. (1983). Molecular aspects of growth factor action: receptors and intracellular signals. *J. Path.* **141**, 309–331.

ROZENGURT, E., COLLINS, M., BROWN, K. D. & PETTICAN, P. (1982). Inhibition of epidermal growth factor binding to mouse cultured cells by firbroblast-derived growth factor. *J. biol. Chem.* **257**, 3680–3686.

ROZENGURT, E., COLLINS, M. K. L. & KEEHAN, M. (1983b). Mitogenic effect of prostaglandin E in Swiss 3T3 cells: Role of cyclic AMP. *J. cell. Physiol.* **116**, 379–384.

ROZENGURT, E. & COURTENAY-LUCK, N. (1982). Signalling mitogenesis in 3T3 cells: Role of monovalent ion fluxes and cyclic nucleotides. *Biosci. Rep.* **2**, 589–595.

ROZENGURT, E. & HEPPEL, L. A. (1975). Serum rapidly stimulates ouabain-sensitive ^{86}Rb uptake in quiescent 3T3 cells. *Proc. natn. Acad. Sci. U.S.A.* **72**, 4492–4495.

ROZENGURT, E., LEGG, A. & PETTICAN, P. (1979). Vasopressin stimulation of mouse 3T3 cell growth. *Proc. natn. Acad. Sci. U.S.A.* **76**, 1284–1287.

ROZENGURT, E., LEGG, A., STRANG, G. & COURTENAY-LUCK, N. (1981b). Cyclic AMP: A mitogenic signal for Swiss 3T3 cells. *Proc. natn. Acad. Sci. U.S.A.* **78**, 4392–4396.

ROZENGURT, E. & MENDOZA, S. A. (1986). Early stimulation of Na^+/H^+ antiport, Na^+/K^+ pump activity and Ca^{2+} fluxes in fibroblast mitogenesis. In *Curr. Topics in Memb. and Transport* (ed. L. Mandel & D. Benos). New York: Academic Press (in press).

ROZENGURT, E., RODRIGUEZ-PENA, A., COOMBS, M. & SINNETT-SMITH, J. (1984). Diacylglycerol stimulates DNA synthesis and cell division in mouse 3T3 cells. Role of Ca^{2+}-sensitive phospholipid-dependent protein kinase. *Proc. natn. Acad. Sci. U.S.A.* **81**, 5748–5752.

ROZENGURT, E., RODRIGUEZ-PENA, A. & SINNETT-SMITH, J. (1985). Signalling mitogenesis in 3T3 cells: role of Ca^{2+}-sensitive, phospholipid-dependent protein kinase. *Proc. Ciba Symp.* **19**, (in press).

ROZENGURT, E., RODRIGUEZ-PENA, M. & SMITH, K. A. (1983c). Phorbol esters, phospholipase C and growth factors rapidly stimulate the phosphorylation of a M_r 80 000 protein in intact quiescent 3T3 cells. *Proc. natn. Acad. Sci. U.S.A.* **80**, 7244–7248.

ROZENGURT, E. & SINNETT-SMITH, J. (1983). Bombesin stimulation of DNA synthesis and cell division in cultures of Swiss 3T3 cells. *Proc. natn. Acad. Sci. U.S.A.* **80**, 2936–2940.

ROZENGURT, E., STROOBANT, P., WATERFIELD, M. D., DEUEL, T. D. & KEEHAN, M. (1983a). Platelet derived growth factor elicits cyclic AMP accumulation in Swiss 3T3 cells: Role of prostaglandin synthesis. *Cell* **34**, 265–272.

SCHULDINER, S. & ROZENGURT, E. (1982). Na^+/H^+ antiport in Swiss 3T3 cells: mitogenic stimulation leads to cytoplasmic alkalinization. *Proc. natn. Acad. Sci. U.S.A.* **79**, 7778–7782.

SINNETT-SMITH, J. W. & ROZENGURT, E. (1985). Diacylglycerol treatment rapidly decreases the affinity of the epidermal growth factor receptors of Swiss 3T3 cells. *J. cell. Physiol.* **124**, 81–86.

SMITH, J. B. & ROZENGURT, E. (1978). Serum stimulates the Na^+/K^+ pump in quiescent fibroblasts by increasing Na^+ entry. *Proc. natn. Acad. Sci. U.S.A.* **75**, 5560–5564.

VARA, F., SCHNEIDER, J. A. & ROZENGURT, E. (1985). Ionic responses rapidly elicited by activation of protein kinase C in quiescent Swiss 3T3 cells. *Proc. natn. Acad. Sci. U.S.A.* **82**, 2384–2388.

VARA, F. & ROZENGURT, E. (1985). Stimulation of Na^+/H^+ antiport activity by epidermal growth factor and insulin occurs without activation of protein kinase C. *Biochem. biophys. Res. Commun.* **130**, 646–653.

WANG, Z.-W. & ROZENGURT, E. (1983). Interplay of cAMP and microtubules in modulating the initiation of DNA synthesis in 3T3 cells. *J. Cell Biol.* **96**, 1743–1750.

ZACHARY, I. & ROZENGURT, E. (1985). High affinity receptors for peptides of the bombesin family in Swiss 3T3 cells. *Proc. natn. Acad. Sci. U.S.A.* (in press).

The Company of Biologists Limited, founded in 1925, is a 'Company Limited by Guarantee' having tax-exempt charitable status. There is a Board of Directors consisting of about 20 professional biologists, two of them appointed annually by the Society for Experimental Biology, who receive no salary or fees for their services. The Company's main function is to own and produce *The Journal of Experimental Biology,* the *Journal of Cell Science*, and the *Journal of Embryology and Experimental Morphology*, and to appoint the Editors of these journals. These are part-time appointments held by established professional biologists of some eminence, and once they have been appointed the Company exercises no control over editorial policy.

The Company is precluded by its charitable status from making a commercial profit on its operations, and its aim is to produce high-quality journals at the lowest possible price. Any surplus on publishing not required for the journals' reserves is transferred to an Educational Trust Fund, which makes substantial grants in aid of societies concerned with the fields of interest covered by the Company's journals. Grants are also made to individuals, mostly research students and junior research workers, for travel and expenses in connection with their research.

The Company's independence of commercial publishers enables them to choose the most effective form of publishing to give papers accepted the widest possible circulation in journals of high quality and prestige. Planned changes in production and distribution of the journals should result in significant increases in the speed of publication, and it is hoped to reduce the time between the acceptance of a paper and its publication to no more than 13 weeks in the near future.

Other projects of benefit to biology are being developed.

The Company of Biologists Limited
Department of Zoology, Downing Street, Cambridge CB2 3EJ

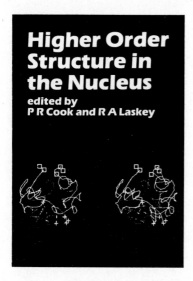

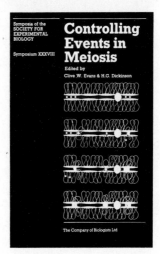